NURSING HOME MENU PLANNING- FOOD PURCHASING, MANAGEMENT

BROTHER HERMAN E. ZACCARELLI, C. S. C.
International Director
International Food Research and Educational Center
North Easton, Mass.

MRS. JOSEPHINE MAGGIORE, R. D.
Director, Nursing Home Consultant Division
International Food Research and Educational Center
North Easton, Mass.

Published by
INSTITUTIONS/VOLUME FEEDING MAGAZINE
5 S. Wabash Ave., Chicago, Ill. 60603

JULE WILKINSON, Editor

Distributed by:
Cahners Books, 89 Franklin St., Boston, Mass. 02110

Second printing

Library of Congress Catalog Card Number: 73-182087
ISBN 0-8436-0541-3

Printed in the United States of America

Dedication

The International Food Research Center is now 12 years old. In this span of time it has become well known as a leading Center for food service education and research. Equally important, the Center has fostered a variety of service programs among the elderly.

The success of a far-flung enterprise depends upon the faith and the support of many. This book is dedicated to two priests of the Congregation of Holy Cross. They not only stood by the authors in the early days of the Center but have continued over the years to give tirelessly of their time and exceptional talent in behalf of the Center. This book is dedicated to:

Reverend Richard Sullivan, C.S.C.

and

Reverend George DePrizio, C.S.C.

Table of Contents

Foreword

The aged person in our health care facilities looks forward to meals as the event of the day and it is important for the foodservice director to do everything possible to make meals attractive and nutritious.

This manual, co-authored by Brother Herman E. Zaccarelli, C.S.C., Director of the Food Research and Educational Center, North Easton, Mass. and Mrs. Josephine Maggiore, R.D., of the staff of the Food Research Center, is designed for the purpose of guiding the foodservice director in the effective discharge of his responsibility: to provide appealing, nutritional meals in an attractive environment that will encourage, protect and promote the health and well being of the patients.

The material in this manual is presented as a source of reference and an aid in the day-to-day administration of the foodservice facility. The manual brings the artistry of the kitchen together with the modern techniques of creative management.

Features of the book are 1095 menus plus special menus for holidays; basic planning for nursing home menus; use of leftover foods; planning for nutrition and the proper feeding of aged persons. The steps to be taken in setting up a system for food purchases, an organization chart for the dietary department, a listing of qualifications and requirements for positions in foodservice are among the many subjects of prime importance to the nursing home administrator.

Of special interest will be menus and diets for the sick, with emphasis on diabetic diets, sodium restricted diets, low fat diets, liquid diets, high carbohydrates, high proteins and special allergy diets and recipes for menu items required for such diets.

The foodservice administrator today must be constantly alert to all the factors of environment and patient care as well as changes in emphasis dictated by government and other external influences. With this in mind, this manual, the first of its kind, attempts to provide the basic tools to enable the foodservice administrator to perform his tasks effectively.

2

About the Authors

Brother Herman E. Zaccarelli, C. S. C., International Director, International Food Research and Educational Center, North Easton, Mass. has been closely associated with the food service industry throughout his career. He draws on his varied experience both as an operator and consultant as he directs the research, educational seminars and publications currently provided by the Center for operators of church-related food facilities in this country and throughout the world.

Mrs. Josephine Maggiore, R. D., Director of the Nursing Home Consultant Division of the International Food Research and Educational Center, a member of the American Dietetic Assn., has served as a hospital dietitian, a director of school lunch operations and as consultant to nursing homes. Her on-the-job experience in providing food for the aged makes her menus easy to implement. Mrs. Maggiore has also learned what menu items and combinations—within practical limits—will meet with the greatest acceptance from the elderly.

How to Use This Book

The MENU PLANNER BOOK may be used each
year.. . . . .
as the MENUS start with the. . . . .
first Sunday of the year.

Any MENUS needed before the first Sunday
of the year may be selected from the section
in this book titled. . . . .   Extra Monday
                                          Extra Tuesday
                                          Extra Wednesday
                                          Extra Thursday
                                          Extra Friday
                                          Extra Saturday

Holiday menus may be selected from
the section titled. . . HOLIDAYS.

CODES

Beverage(s) . . . . typed in this
manner means . . . . .Coffee
                                          Tea
                                          Milk
                                        Sanka
                                         Water

Beverage(s)*. . . . . typed in this
manner means . . . . Milk
                                            or
                       Selected Fruit Juices

served at 8:30 P.M.

Recipes for many of the dishes listed in the menus on pp. 90-306 have been cross-referenced to **THE PROFESSIONAL CHEF** and **THE PROFESSIONAL CHEF'S BAKING RECIPES**, both books published by INSTITUTIONS/VOLUME FEEDING MAGAZINE, 5 S. Wabash, Chicago, Ill. 60603. The appearance of one chef's hat 🍳 indicates a recipe in **THE PROFESSIONAL CHEF**; two chef's hats 🍳🍳 indicate a recipe in **THE PROFESSIONAL CHEF'S BAKING RECIPES**. The figure in parentheses after a designated recipe notes the page on which the recipe appears.

Introduction

One of the purposes of this book is to give you a chance to read in print the things you have learned as an intern in a well managed kitchen. Experience may be the best teacher but it is not reliable where food is concerned. Discipline, common sense, understanding and a real desire to create a sense of well being can combine to produce results equal to, and often better than, the wealth of "experience" said to be earned by years in a kitchen.

The Art of Cooking, and it is an Art, as well as a profession, is by no means the easiest job in the world, but it can be one of the most rewarding. Perhaps you will be surprised to read that:

80% of kitchen and dining room employees can work on any food service project successfully, provided it is well organized with competent supervisors on hand constantly.

17% of the people engaged in "commercial," or large scale, cooking can exercise independent judgment and only

3% are actually capable of creating a planned project and carrying it through successfully without direction or assistance.

It is no wonder a self-reliant Food Supervisor, Head Cook or Dietitian is often somewhat arbitrary, and always very proud of the work being accomplished. This "elite" 3% "live" their work and are on the lookout continually for ways to improve their abilities. Their success is due to their self-motivation habits, which may have been developed early in life, perhaps in days spent as "Mother's Helper."

The qualities that the successful Head Cook, Food Supervisor or Dietitian share can best be summed up as follows:

1. INITIATIVE. . . .this is both a necessity and an asset.

2. ENTHUSIASM. ."internal equipment" that a cook must have to turn a disadvantage into an advantage.

3. IMAGINATION. mistakes will occur, deliveries stop, problems multiply, but another way can be found.

4. SINCERITY. . . on the part of the supervisor builds confidence in each employee.

5. ACTION. . . . . do it now - there is no substitute for action.

To help a Kitchen and Dining Room run smoothly—to overcome the daily upsets occurring from unexpected major or minor "disasters," these few precautions can save the day, even when important help fail to show.

1. Insist on proper equipment.
2. Insist on using recipes and following them exactly.
3. Rely on recipes that have been tested and used in your kitchen. When a recipe is added and used for the first time, make it an event in the kitchen. (You'll have more interested employees.)
4. Employees easily recognize enthusiasm and confidence in a supervisor. They are quick to respond to experience and common sense. As the Chef at the Waldorf Astoria Hotel in New York, says, "You're no cook, no matter how many degrees you hold, unless you know how food is supposed to LOOK as well as TASTE!!!!"

Feeding Aged Persons

Those who are feeding groups of aged persons must be sure that older people receive all of the nutrients needed to ensure them optimum health and efficiency.

It is important for the Food Service Director to check the nutritional adequacy of the menu. Does it follow the "Basic Four" pattern?

Consulting with the patient and finding out his likes and dislikes and what he prefers is extremely important. It is wise to see that the staff follows through with the suggestions you have made on individual patients.

Communication between the physicians, nurses, nurses' aides and dietary personnel is most important. Feeding the patient should be a team effort.

In addition to nutrient content, a Food Service Director must also be concerned with the aged person's frequent need for chopped, ground or pureed foods.

The recommended daily allowances of nutrients required by the aged are estimates. For example, 55-75 year old men require 2400 calories and 65 grams of protein. Females require 1700 calories and 55 grams of protein.

We must remember to season the food properly and to be sure that it is served in an attractive manner.

Your staff must be taught to treat the aged in your institution with patience and with an attitude that shows they really care about the patient's wants and needs. We must learn to coordinate our impressions of their dietary needs with their wants.

THE RECOMMENDED DIETARY ALLOWANCE
Regardless of the consistency of the food provided for the patient, i. e. pureed, ground, soft or regular, certain nutrients are still required.

The Recommended Dietary Allowance should be used as a guide to planning menus for geriatric patients and also as a guide for the nutritional assessment of the patient. The Recommended Dietary Allowance establishes nutrient requirements for both male and female. Some of the recommendations are as follows:

	Male	Female
Age (years)	55-75 +	55-75 +
Weight (lb.)	154	128
Height (in.)	67	62
Calories	2400	1700
Protein (g.)	65	55
Vitamin A (IU)	5000	5000
Ascorbic Acid (mg.)	60	55
Niacin (mg. equiv.)	14	13
Riboflavin (mg.)	1.7	1.5
Thiamin (mg.)	1.2	1.0
Calcium (g.)	0.8	0.8
Iron (mg.)	10	10

A menu pattern should be developed which meets the Recommended Dietary allowance for males and females aged 55-75+. It is especially important to provide these nutrients.

(See pages 10-11 for meal pattern with nutrient composition for geriatric patient in an institution.)

The meal pattern should be tailor-made for the majority of the patients in the home, but the nutrient composition should be at least two-thirds of the Recommended Dietary Allowance. Some homes offer their main meal at noon and perhaps serve more meat, while other homes offer their main meal at night. Make your menu pattern to suit your individual needs but be sure it includes the necessary nutrients.

MEAL PATTERN WITH NUTRIENT COMPOSITION

Meal Pattern	Calories	Protein g	Vit. A IU
BREAKFAST			
Orange juice (4 oz)	85		
Enr. whole wheat toast (2 slices)	124	4	
Butter/margarine (2 tsp.)	72		330
Oatmeal (1C)	148	5.4	
Whole milk (4 oz.)	81	4.3	180
LUNCH Cooked meat (2 1/2 oz.)	230	22	
Vegetable (1/2 C) (Peas)	68	5	600
Enr. bread (1 sl.)	62	2	
Butter/margarine (1 tsp.)	36		165
Fruit (1/2 C)	45		
Milk (4 oz.)	81	4.3	180
DINNER Cooked meat (2 1/2 oz.)	230	22	
Vegetable (1/2 C)	20	1	320
Potato (1/2 C)	65	1.9	
Bread (1 sl.)	62	2	
Butter/margarine (1 tsp.)	36		165
Cake (3x3x1/2 in.)	148	1.8	
Milk (4 oz.)	81	4.3	180
TOTAL	1674	80.00	2120

FOR GERIATRIC PATIENT IN AN INSTITUTION

Ascorbic Acid mg	Niacin mg	Ribo-flavin mg	Thia-mine mg	Calcium g	Iron mg
56					
	.10	.08	.12	.04	1.2
	.4	.05	.22	.02	1.7
	.1	.21	.04	.15	.05
	5.0	.15	.10	.06	1.50
13	1.7	.09	.27		1.90
	.05	.04	.06	.02	.6
	.9	.05	.01		.5
	.1	.21	.04	.15	.05
	5.0	.15	.10	.06	1.50
4	.3	.04	.03		1.3
16	1.2	.04	.09		.5
	.05	.04	.06	.02	.6
	.1	.04	.08	.02	.2
	.1	.20	.04	.15	.05
89	15.00	1.4	.88	.09	11.65

Dietary Department

PURPOSE:

The primary purpose of this department is to furnish the patients and staff with wholesome, nourishing and attractive meals to sustain the nutritional needs of the guests residing there, as well as to add to their contentment and happiness.

SCOPE:

This department covers all food service areas: kitchen, storerooms and dishwashing areas. All activities connected with food production or service come within this department.

RESPONSIBILITIES:

1. The person in charge of food production and food service shall be the Food Service Director.

2. The Food Service Director shall be responsible for the direction of food managment and for the purchasing of foods and related supplies.

3. The Food Service Director shall work in close harmony with the Administrator and the Dietary Consultant.

ORGANIZATION CHART FOR DIETARY DEPARTMENT

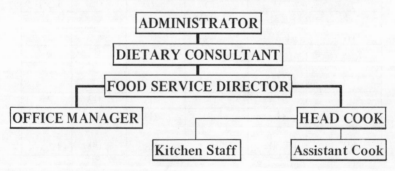

ORGANIZATION OF A DIETARY DEPARTMENT

Staffing the Dietary Department is one of the management functions of the Food Service Director. Staffing means to hire, train, evaluate, promote, discipline and appropriately compensate the employees of your department. Before you can undertake this task, you must clarify the kinds of employees you need in your department and how many. The following are tools that will enable you to specify the kind of workers necessary to fill the various jobs in your food service department.

Job Analysis

Definition: The procedure used in collecting information about one specific job.

Objectives: 1. To improve conditions of hiring, transferring and promoting employees.
2. To establish an appropriate training program.
3. A means of budgetary control.

Job Description:

Definition: A written record of duties, responsibilities and requirements of a particular job (or a summary of the job analysis).

Job Specification:

Definition: Everything one needs to know concerning the requirements of a job and the qualifications and abilities the worker needs (a complete job description includes a job specification).

JOB ANALYSIS

Job Title:

Department: Section: Department Head:

Number on Job: Location of Job:

Job Summary:

Relation to Other Jobs:

> Promotion from—
>
> Promotion to—
>
> Transfer to and from—

Work Performed:

Equipment, Machines Used:

Skill Involved:

Education and Training:

Responsibility for Material:

Responsibility for Work of Others:

Responsibility for Safety of Others:

Resourcefulness:

Physical Requirements:

Personal Requirements:

Physical Efforts:

Surroundings:

Hazards:

PRELIMINARY INFORMATION NEEDED TO WRITE JOB DESCRIPTIONS

1. Where is position located?
2. What duties are performed regularly?
3. From whom do you receive your work?
4. What do you do with it and where do you send it?
5. What duties are performed at stated periods?
6. What duties are performed at irregular intervals?
7. To whom are you directly responsible?
8. How many employees do you supervise?
9. What instructions do you receive about work to be done?
10. What equipment do you use in your work?
11. What do you feel should be the lowest grade of grammar, high school or college that should be required of a person starting in your position?
12. What special courses would be needed in order to perform your job well?
13. What is the most difficult part of your work?
14. What is the proportion of your time spent in standing, sitting, moving or other physical positions?
15. What are the physical requirements necessary to do your job?
16. What is your responsibility for workers under your supervision?
17. What is your responsibility for money, valuables and so forth?
18. What contact do you have with the general public?
19. What are your regular working hours?

NECESSARY STEPS IN WRITING THE JOB DESCRIPTION OR JOB SPECIFICATIONS

The job description should contain:

    The title of position
    A code for the position, if codes are used
    Department where position is located
    The age range preferred in the position
    Statement as to whether both male and female applicants are acceptable
    Hours of the position and shifts, if any
    Pay rates, pay range and any bonuses

Benefits such as vacations, sick leave, insurance and other privileges

Upgrading possibilities should be included on job description

Job summary should explain the position in detail and work requirements

Experience required for position

Education and training requirements

Performance requirements

Physical activities and working conditions

JOB DESCRIPTION
(A Summary of the Job Analysis)

Job Title: Date:
Job Code: Department: Location:

I.   JOB SUMMARY:

II.   PERFORMANCE REQUIREMENTS:
   a) Responsibilities
   b) Job Knowledge
   c) Mental Application
   d) Dexterity and Accuracy
   e) Equipment Used

III. MINIMUM REQUIREMENTS:
   a) Experience required
   b) Training data (Minimum):
      On-the-job
      Technical or vocational training
      Formal education
      Ability to read and understand English
   c) Age and Sex:
   d) Relation to other jobs:
      Promotions from:
      Promotion to:
   e) Supervision:
      Under general supervision
      Give some supervision to assistant

JOB DESCRIPTION

Job Title: Baker   August 1971
Division: Food Services
Department:

Summary of Duties:

With one assistant, Baker is responsible for the preparation and for the baking of all bakery products, except bread, that are used in the hospital. (e. g. cakes, cookies, pies, pudding, etc.) This includes the mixing of ingredients supplied by the ingredients control girl, and the apportioning and baking of these mixes.

Main Duties:

1. Each morning checks left-over perishables, ingredients in refrigerators and arranges to use these, if possible.
2. Checks production sheets and ingredients on hand and makes up orders for ingredients for hot breads, pastry and desserts. Mixes ingredients, makes dough and bakes.
3. Stocks night refrigerator, desserts for midnight and early morning break.
4. Cleans steam kettles, counters, etc.
5. Makes up storeroom orders for next day.
6. Cleans bake shop refrigerator each week.
7. Makes cookies and birthday cakes for special orders, as required.

Responsible to: Food Service Director

Initiative Required: General

Supervision Required: General

Responsible for: Special equipment used: Oven, mixers, stove

Contacts-inside: Food Service Staff
     -outside: Nil

Education required (academic and/or vocational):   Read and Write

Previous experience required: Not necessary; the Food Service Director will teach a suitable person.

Time required to attain minimum competence: without experience, six months to train.

Usual source of staff: Promoted from among the food service staff.

Normal line of promotion: Promotions not usually available, but employee could go on and do meat and vegetable cookery with possibility of advancing to position as Chef.

Working Hours—hours per day: 6:30-3:30
  —average hours per week
  —weekends: average two days per week off—
  four days every two weeks
  —shifts

JOB SPECIFICATION
Payroll Title:

Department: Occupation Code:

Supervised by:

Job Summary:

Education Status:

Experience Required:

Knowledge and Skills:

Physical Requirements:

Personal Requirements:

References Required:

Wage Code:

Hours:

Tests:

QUALIFICATION REQUIREMENTS
FOR A POSITION

POSITION - FIRST COOK

Function: Food preparation; responsible for cleanliness of cook's area

Tasks:

1. Prepares soups, meats, meat sauces, main luncheon dishes, according to menu and hours of service.

2. Food must meet the standards set for quality and be ready to serve at time scheduled.

3. Standardized recipes which are to be followed are provided.

4. Puts away left-over food and checks with a supervisor for re-use.

5. Responsible for cleanliness of ranges, cook's table and large equipment in preparation area.

6. Directly responsible to supervisor on duty.

7. Responsible for supervision of the work of assistant cooks, not including pastry or salad cooks.

JOB QUALIFICATION REQUIREMENTS - First Cook

Experience in large quantity food preparation

Knowledge of operation of all kitchen equipment

High food standards

Ability to direct work of others

Mental alertness

Good health

Dependability

Honesty

Industry

Neat personal appearance

JOB DESCRIPTIONS FOR SMALL OPERATION

Food Service Director
> Sets standards of the operation
> Plans the menus, food orders, method of preparation and
>   service
> Plans the organization of work
> Selects and trains personnel
> Directs the personnel
> Supervises the food preparation and the service
> Responsible for entire business

Head Cook
> Responsible to Food Service Director
> Prepares and cooks all the food
> May supervise the work in the kitchen and the dining
>   room or counter
> May do the short order cooking
> Responsible for keeping own working areas clean
> Responsible for kitchen operation

Assistant Cook
> Responsible to Cook
> Cooks to order and serves grilled and fried meats, eggs,
>   hot cakes and quickly prepared foods
> May serve food from the steam table or the counter
> May make the sandwiches and salads
> Responsible for keeping own work area clean

Tray Girls or Food Service Helpers
> Responsible to Manager or other person designated in
>   organization chart
> Waits on patients' tables; takes orders, serves food, clears
>   and cleans tables.
> May perform such operations as making coffee, toast,
>   sandwiches, salads, etc. according to need
> Responsible for keeping serving area and tables clean.
>   If mats or linen are used, responsible for keeping up
>   available stock and replacing for patients'
>   service.
> May be responsible for taking dishes to dishwashing area
> May assist with washing and drying dishes
> Polishes the silver, sorts and counts the linen, and does
>   other such jobs related to the dining room work
> Responsible for keeping own work area clean

Head Porter

Responsible to Cook or other persons designated in organization chart

Cleans the kitchen, dining room and the counter

Sweeps and mops the floors

Removes trash and garbage

Washes, dries pots and pans; puts away clean utensils

Cleans ice boxes, windows, does other special cleaning jobs

Keeps storerooms in order

Brings food cases up from main storeroom

Dishwasher and Cleaner

Responsible to Cook or other person designated in organization chart

Washes dishes and puts them away according to an approved method of dishwashing, rinsing and handling

Keeps the dish room clean and orderly

Secretary

Responsible to Food Service Director

Responsible for keeping all required records

Assist in keeping food costs and accounts

Assists with placing of orders

Storeroom Girl

Responsible to Secretary

Checks in and weighs all deliveries

Fills out all requisitions for special area and diets

Typist

Responsible to Secretary

Does all typing required by Food Service Director

Assists in taking inventories and recording prices on perpetual inventory file

Baker

Responsible to Head Cook

Responsible for preparing all baked products for dining room

Prepares special cakes and cookies for special functions

Makes all desserts such as gelatins, pudding, etc.

JOB DESCRIPTION   Job Title: Dietary Consultant

Main Function:
    Plans and directs activities of dietary department to pro-
vide good dietary services for patients and staff.

Duties and Responsibilities:
    Consults, advises and gives necessary instruction
    Establishes departmental regulations and procedures
    Takes active part in menu conferences to assure that the
dietary allowances of the Food and Nutrition Board of the
National Council are met and adjusted for age, sex and activity
    Ensures that the dietary department is meeting the food
and nutritional needs of patients, in accordance with physicians' orders and to the extent medically possible
    Formulates menus for therapeutic diets
    Keeps up with new developments in food items, recipes,
equipment and techniques
    Organizes food inventories, food orders and raw food
costs
    Ascertains that foods are prepared and served with re-
gard to nutritive value, flavor, appearance and temperatures
    Ensures effective sanitary conditions in storage, prepara-
tion and distribution area
    Conducts in-service training programs
    Confers with dietary staff and administration at the end
of each visit

Education Required
    B. S. Degree with major in foods and nutrition
    Membership in the American Dietetic Association
    Registered Dietitian

The Cycle Menu

The Cycle Menu is a very important tool that, used wisely, will help the Food Service Director solve production problems and food cost problems. The menu should be written up on a four-week cycle, tried and then evaluated. Necessary changes should then be made. It is the hub around which all activities in a food service rotate. It will help you operate your food service more efficiently.

The Cycle Menu will help you to operate your food service more efficiently, however, there are still other details that must be kept up to date. A specific time should be set up each day for keeping records. This may be done by the Food Service Director or a specific employee may be assigned this responsibility.

Records

A specific time should be set up for keeping records. Records must be kept up to date continuously. This may be done by the Food Service Director or a specific employee may be assigned this responsibility.

Records are definite points of information written in an organized form. Complete, accurate and legible records are necessary if they are to be used as management tools in the dietary department. Since the records vary with the institution, management must decide which records are to be kept, how they are to be kept, and why they are to be kept. Some records which are essential to the dietary department in health care facilities are:

the meal census   order and receiving records
the diet roster   daily food cost
menus served

The accuracy of certain records is interdependent. For example, an accurate daily food cost depends upon the accuracy of meal census, receiving records and inventory figures.

Other records may include food production record, personnel records, inspection records, records of hours worked daily, equipment inventory and maintenance records.

B - Breakfast
N - Noon
E - Evening

MONTHLY MEAL CENSUS

Month ——————— Year ———————

DAY OF MONTH	RESIDENTS			EMPLOYEES			OTHER			TOTALS			TO-TALS DAY			TOTAL MEALS	
	B	N	E	B	N	E	B	N	E	B	N	E				Today	To Date
1																	
2																	
3																	
4																	
5																	
6																	
7																	
8																	
9																	
10																	
11																	
12																	
13																	
14																	
15																	
16																	
17																	
18																	
19																	
20																	
21																	
22																	
23																	
24																	
25																	
26																	
27																	
28																	
29																	
30																	
31																	

MEAL CENSUS

A record of the number of persons who are served meals in the home is called a meal census. This form is necessary in order to determine the cost of food per person served. It lists the number of residents, employees and others served each meal. The information is recorded every day. This form should be posted on the bulletin boards and filed at the end of the month for future reference. (See form on facing page.)

DIET ROSTER

Rm & Bed No.	Name	Regu-lar	Salt	Dia-betic	No Salt	Low Fat	Other	Modi-fied as:	COMMENTS Needs Help to Eat; Chewing Problem; Food Likes and Dislikes
11-1	Anderson, Mary	x							Extra cream for tea
11-3	Gambini, John	x							No coffee
10-1	Doyle, Tom			x				Diab-1400 (70-60-150)	No teeth, chop food
10-3	Tech, Helen					x			Needs to be fed
12-1	Silvers, Marine					x			
12-2	Jones, Diane	x							Tea for lunch

Note: 1. List all bed numbers consecutively
2. Include empty beds
3. Mark x in proper square for diet order

The Diet Roster is a list of individual residents compiled from the residents' charts. It includes the resident's name and diet as prescribed by the physician. You may list the individual's likes, dislikes, etc.

The Diet Roster should be maintained by the Food Service Director. It must be kept up to date and changes made when necessary. The previous roster should be kept on file and kept as part of the dietary records.

A list should also be kept of all patients served therapeutic or special diets. This list should be available to the employees serving the residents' trays. It should also be filed as part of the dietary records.

Inventory

The inventory is taken by counting all the unopened containers of foods and then writing the count in the count column of the inventory for the appropriate date. All items should be listed by brand, size and unit price. This inventory should be taken once a month, preferably on the last day of the month. Don't include any items that will be used the day the inventory is taken.

All food supplies stored in refrigerator and freezer should be included in the inventory.

It is easier if one person does the counting and a second person makes the entries on the inventory list. It will save time if stock is marked with unit price when it is shelved. A marking crayon is useful. The inventory is easier to work with if foods are classified according to food groups.

Complete the inventory by multiplying count by unit price for each item and enter the result in the Total Cost Column. Add the figures in the Total Cost column to obtain the dollar value of your inventory.

Food cost for the inventory period is determined by adding the dollar value of food of the beginning inventory to the dollars spent for food purchased during the inventory period and then subtracting the dollar value of the ending inventory.

Food Purchase Record

To maintain the Food Purchase Record, the food invoices for the inventory period are entered on the record when they are received. This may be done by food classifications. In this way, it is possible to see exactly what was spent for each food group.

ITEM	BRAND	SIZE	QUAN-TITY	UNIT PRICE	TOTAL
CAFETERIA INVENTORY School ___ Date ___					
CLEANING SUPPLIES					
Ammonia					
Bleach					
Cleanser					
Liquid Soap					
Laundry Soap					
Brillo					
Kurley Kate					
Sponges					

ITEM	BRAND AND SPECIFICATION	UNIT	QUAN-TITY	UNIT PRICE	TOTAL
CAFETERIA INVENTORY					
PAPER GOODS AND SUPPLIES					
Daily balance envelope					
Cash register rolls					
Food dishes No.43					
Cups, hot drinking					
Cups, cold No.58					
Souffle, cups 2 oz.					
Souffle, cups 4 oz.					
Napkins, Jr. compact					
Paper plates 6-in.					
Paper plates 8-in.					
Wax paper rolls					
Freezer paper					
Place mats, lace and french					
Aluminum foil					
Foil dishes					
Rite forks					
Rite spoons					

CAFETERIA INVENTORY					
ITEM	BRAND	SIZE	QUAN-TITY	UNIT PRICE	TOTAL
EXTRACTS & SPICES					
Baking Soda					
Bayleaves					
Thyme					
Nutmeg, whole					
Caraway seeds					
Celery seeds					
Cinnamon					
Cloves					
Cheese, parmesan					
Cocoanut, shredded					
Cream of tartar					
Parsley flakes					
Onion flakes					
Pimento					
Oregano					
Paprika					
Catsup					
Mustard					
Onion salt					

CAFETERIA INVENTORY					
ITEM	BRAND	SIZE	QUAN-TITY	UNIT PRICE	TOTAL
EXTRACTS & SPICES					
Vanilla					
Lemon					
Orange					
Liquid, red color					
Vinegar					
Pepper, White					
Pepper, Black					
Salt, Bulk					
Salt, Boxes					
Brown Sugar					
Granulated Sugar					
Confectioners Sugar					
Wrapped Tablets					
Coffee					
Coffee, instant small					
Tea bags					
Iced tea					

CAFETERIA INVENTORY					
ITEM	BRAND	SIZE	QUAN-TITY	UNIT PRICE	TOTAL
BASES					
Brown gravy					
Chicken gravy					
Turkey gravy					
CEREALS & PASTE					
Cornstarch					
Macaroni					
Noodles-broad					
Noodles-medium					
Noodles-fine					
Noodles-chow mein					
Tapioca					
Spaghetti					

CAFETERIA INVENTORY					
ITEM	BRAND	SIZE	QUAN-TITY	UNIT PRICE	TOTAL
PICKLES					
Pickles					
Relish					
SAUCES					
Spaghetti sauce					
Soy sauce					
Marinara sauce					
MAYONNAISE					
Corn Oil					

CAFETERIA INVENTORY					
ITEM	BRAND	SIZE	QUAN-TITY	UNIT PRICE	TOTAL
SOUPS					
Bean w/bacon					
Beef noodle					
Beef barley					
Vegetarian soup					
Vegetable soup w/beef					
Onion soup					
Chicken noodle					
Chicken rice					
Chicken vegetable					
Cream of chicken					
Turkey noodle					
Turkey, creamed					
Cream of mushroom					
Cream of vegetable					
Cream of tomato					
Minestrone					
Clam chowder					
Tomato					

CAFETERIA INVENTORY					
ITEM	BRAND	SIZE	QUAN-TITY-	UNIT PRICE	TOTAL
JAMS & GELATIN					
Jelly					
Gelatin, assorted red					
CAKES & PUDDING					
Biscuit Mix					
Cake mix, white					
Cake mix, yellow					
Cake mix, devils food					
Brownie mix					
PUDDING					
Chocolate, bakers					
Sprinkles, assorted					
Sprinkles, chocolate					
Nuts					
Raisins					

CAFETERIA INVENTORY					
ITEM	BRAND	SIZE	QUAN-TITY	UNIT PRICE	TOTAL
JUICES					
Apple juice					
Orange juice					
Orange & grapefruit					
Grapefruit juice					
Pineapple juice					
Grape juice					
Tang					
Punch base					
FRUITS					
Apples, sliced					
Applesauce					
Apricots, halves					
Apricots, whole					
Fruit cocktail					
Cherries, maraschino					
Grapefruit, sections					
Peaches, sliced					
Peaches, whole, halved					
Pears, halves					
Pineapple chunks					
Pineapple crushed					
Pineapple tidbits					
Pineapple sliced					

CAFETERIA INVENTORY					
ITEM	BRAND	SIZE	QUAN-TITY	UNIT PRICE	TOTAL
CANNED MEAT & FISH					
Clams					
Chicken, boned					
Chicken,					
Chicken,					
Turkey,					
Meat balls & sauce					
Salmon					
Tuna fish, large					
Tuna fish, small					
Lobster					
Shrimp					

CAFETERIA INVENTORY					
ITEM	BRAND	SIZE	QUAN-TITY	UNIT PRICE	TOTAL
CANNED VEGETABLES					
Beans, baked w/pork					
Beans, vegetarian					
Beets, diced					
Beets, sliced					
Carrots, sliced					
Carrots, diced					
Corn whole kernel					
Mushroom, broken					
Peas					
Tomatoes, whole					
Tomatoes, paste					
Tomatoes, puree					
Potato, sliced					
Potatoes, sweet					
Potato sticks					
Potato, whipped					
Vegetables, chow mein					
Sauerkraut					

CAFETERIA INVENTORY		
ITEM	QUANTITY	TOTAL
ICE CREAM		
Pops		
Sandwiches		
Dixie cups		
Ices		

CAFETERIA INVENTORY		
Government Surplus Foods		
ITEM	QUANTITY	TOTAL

FOOD PURCHASE RECORD

PERIOD			April 1		April 30	
Date of Invoice	Name of Firm	Meats	Fruit Veg.	Groceries & Staples	Milk & Ice Cream	TOTALS
April 2	Smith	$175.20				$175.20
6	Grands				120.00	120.00
7	Jays		125.00			125.00
9	Silver			115.20		115.20
15	Smith	302.00				302.00
TOTALS		$477.20	$477.20	$115.20	$120.00	$837.40

FOOD COST REPORT

The figures from the Food Purchase Record are Transferred directly to the Food Cost Report.

Accounting Period	Date April 1 through Apr. 30	Date May 1 through May 31	Date_____ through
Total Purchases	$1,475.00		
Plus beginning inventory	200.00		
Equals a Total of	1,675.00		
Month ending inventory of	325.00		
Equals cost of food	1,350.00		
Divided by number of meals served	3000		
Equals food cost per capita per meal	31¢		
Multiplied by 3 equals food cost per capita per day	93¢		

REQUISITION FROM MAIN KITCHEN

DATE _____

REQUESTED BY: _____
      (name or area)

	FOOD	AMOUNT	UNIT PRICE	TOTAL PRICE
1.				
2.				
3.				
4.				
5.				
6.				
7.				
8.				
9.				
10.				
11.				
12.				
13.				
14.				
15.				
16.				
17,				
18.				
19.				
20.				

FOOD FLOW DIAGRAM

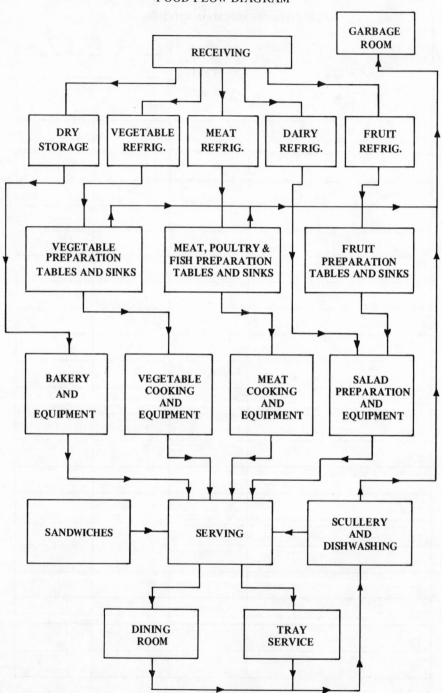

TIME SHEET - DIETARY DEPARTMENT

PERSONNEL	SUNDAY	MONDAY	TUESDAY	WEDNESDAY	THURSDAY	FRIDAY	SATURDAY

Cost Per Serving of Canned Vegetables and Fruits

To obtain the cost per serving, divide the number of servings per can into the cost per can. Example: One No. 10 can sliced peaches = 25 servings; cost per can $1.05. $1.05 divided by 25 = 4+ cents per serving.

The greatest variation in cost per serving occurs with meat and poultry items. It is, therefore, important to pre-cost these items before they are put on the menu.

To pre-cost these items, it is necessary to know:

1. Item—specifications on grade and style—fresh or frozen, bone in or boned, rolled and tied, pre-portioned, etc.

2. Size of portion to be served
Usually 3 ounces at dinner, 2 ounces at lunch or supper.
3. Yield or servings per pound of meat as purchased.
4. Price per pound.
5. Price per serving.

Divide the cost per pound by the yield of servings per pound to obtain the cost per serving. Example: $1.00 (cost per pound) divided by 4 (servings per pound = 25 cents cost per serving).

The projected, budgeted cost of purchased food to serve one person three meals per day is $1.20. Most people find the daily figure easier to work with because it can be related directly to the menu pattern and the cost per serving of each menu item.

BREAKFAST	DINNER	LUNCH OR SUPPER
Fruit or Juice	Meat, Poultry or Fish	Soup or Juice
Cereal	Potato	Main Dish
Egg or Meat	Vegetable or Salad	Vegetable or Salad
Bread and	Dessert	Dessert
Butter	Bread and Butter	Bread and Butter
Beverage	Milk	Milk
	Coffee or Tea	Coffee or Tea

The cost of the menu items selected to fill the basic

menu pattern for a day will establish <u>at the time it is planned</u> the raw food cost of that day's menu.

On the basis of a daily per person food cost of $1.20, an approximate breakdown of this amount to cover the basic menu pattern may be made.

PER SERVING COST

BREAKFAST		DINNER		LUNCH OR SUPPER	
Fruit or Juice	2½-5¢	Meat	28¢	Soup or Juice	2½-5¢
Cereal	2-6¢	Potato	3¢	Meat extended	
W/milk-¼ cup	2¢	Vegetable	2½-5¢	or substitute	20¢
Egg	4¢	Dessert	5-8¢	Vegetable or	
Bread	2½¢	Bread	1¢	Salad	2½-6¢
Butter	2¢	Butter	1¢	Dessert	5-8¢
Beverage	2½¢	Milk	7¢	Bread	2¢
Cream	1¢	Beverage	2½¢	Butter	1¢
	17½-24¢	Cream	1¢	Milk	7¢
			51-56½¢	Cream	1¢
					43½-52½

If the menu items with the lowest per serving cost were consistently used for the above pattern, one day's menu might cost only $1.12 (17½¢ + 51¢ + 43½¢ = $1.12). If all higher cost menu items were selected, the cost could go up to $1.33 (24¢ + 56½¢ + 52½¢ = $1.33). To provide a variety of foods in menus, a wide selection of menu items is offered and these will vary in per serving cost. Therefore, each day's total may go above or below the projected allowance.

The per serving cost of most canned fruits used for desserts will range between four and six cents per serving. Frozen fruits will cost two or three cents more. Ice cream costs approximately five cents per serving.

The choice of fruits, juices and vegetables can be made primarily in terms of color, texture and nutritional values and the cost will usually fall within the range given. For example, ½ cup of reconstituted frozen orange juice will cost approximately 2½ cents, but if a half grapefruit were served instead, the per serving cost would be five cents. Fruits and vegetables do not have a wide variation in per serving cost and the per serving cost of bread, butter, milk, coffee and tea remains almost unchanged over long periods of time.

Purchasing of Food

The purchasing of food for a food service establishment is of great importance.

There are four basics which you should look for.

1. Quality
2. Variety
3. Net Weight
4. Maximum Yield

Serving excellent food while still remaining within your budget will take careful planning and wise buying. Carelessness in buying can mean the success or failure of your operation.

Quality buying pays off; buy the best in fresh produce, meats, fish, poultry, canned and frozen foods and groceries.

Consider your salesmen also. Your relations with the people and firms from whom you buy is important. Know their products. Don't be afraid to ask questions. These gentlemen are a good source of information and are well-informed and willing to help.

How or what you purchase will depend on the numbers you feed, the class of people being served, local tastes and eating habits. The type of menu you serve and how much you can afford to spend per portion must all be considered when setting up a food budget and purchasing food.

Plan menus ahead. A four-or-five-week cycle is suggested. Consider your storage space carefully. Keep in mind the number you are feeding and the amount of money you have to spend.

Keep careful records of all purchases. Food inventory is money in the bank. Check deliveries carefully; make sure they conform to what you ordered.

Keep inventories; they provide operating figures that determine your food cost and reveal errors in buying and controls. Inventories should be taken each month and priced

without delay. Have a systematic method of purchasing, for
example:

Milk	Order daily
Bread	Order daily
Fresh Produce	Order weekly
Meats	Order bi-weekly or weekly
Staples	Order monthly
Ice Cream	Order weekly

SELECTING FOOD PRODUCTS
Fresh Fruits and Vegetables

Since these are perishables, care must be taken in buying
these products. They lose their flavor and saleability. Do not
overstock.

Most fresh fruits and vegetables are graded on the basis
of color, shape, freshness, firmness, freedom from decay. Size
is a grade factor for some fruits and vegetables. The size or
count is stated on the container so that you can purchase the
size most economical for your operation.

When appearance is most important, as in serving whole
fresh fruit, the grades to use are U. S. Extra Fancy, Fancy or
Extra No. 1. When fruit is mixed or used in salads or desserts,
a lesser grade can be used, such as U. S. No. 1. When the
product is to be cooked or cut up, U. S. No. 2 or 3 can be
used.

There are available on the market many pre-prepared
items such as pared and cut apples, potatoes and carrots and
washed spinach, cut cabbage for cole slaw and many other
items. The use of these items eliminates labor and equipment
for these time-consuming preparations.

Canned Goods

Practically all canned vegetables are put in the following
three grades:

U. S. Grade A or Fancy - Carefully selected for color,
tenderness, and freedom from blemishes. They are the most
flavorful, tender and succulent vegetables produced.

U. S. Grade B or Extra Standard - Excellent quality but
not so well selected for color and tenderness as Grade A. Usu-

ally more mature and have a slightly different taste than the Grade A vegetables.

U. S. Grade C or Standard - Not uniform in color and flavor and usually more mature. A thrifty buy when appearance is not too important.

Term "Packed under continuous inspection of the U. S. Department of Agriculture" provides assurance of a wholesome product of at least minimum quality.

When you buy canned vegetables, be sure the cans are not leaking or swelled or bulged at either end. Bulging or swelling indicates spoilage.

When purchasing, consider the type of pack and piece count. There is a wide variety in types of pack. Consider such factors as Whole, Halves, Quarter, Sliced, Cubed, Diced and Crushed. Each has its place on the menu. Buy the type and size you need.

Buy not only the large No. 10 cans but also some of the smaller can sizes for special orders. It is better to open up two or three No. 2½ cans for a special order than to open a large No. 10 and have the leftover contents spoil in the refrigerator.

Frozen Foods and Vegetables - prepared by a quick-freezing process
The original nutritive value, flavor and color of foods are better preserved by freezing than any other method. The cost per serving is usually on a level with that of fresh foods.

Grades - same as those set up for canned vegetables. Grades are based on factors which reflect the quality, characteristics of the finished product, such as color, size, succulence in vegetables, ripeness and shape in fruit, and flavor.

Practically every fruit and vegetable is available the year around. These products are packaged in a large range of weights and sizes to meet individual needs.

Fish
The product is highly perishable and it is necessary to take the utmost care in the purchase, preparation and serving

of this item. It must be constantly kept under refrigeration or it will deteriorate. Characteristics of fresh fish are: (1) Eyes clear and bright, (2) Gills and mouth closed, (3) Flesh firm and elastic, (4) Scales clinging to the skin, and (5) A fresh odor.

For portion control, suppliers can readily supply you with uniform sizes and uniform servings.

"In the round" means fish which are just as they leave the water. You have to clean and trim them yourself. Small fish are usually marketed in this manner.

"Dressed" means eviscerated, head and tail removed.

Fish steaks are cross sections of large size fish. When ordering, specify the weight per steak for portion control.

Fillets are sliced lengthwise of the fish along the backbone.

Avoid overbuying of this product as it does not keep well.

Shellfish
The grades to consider are the size and weight. All shellfish must be strictly fresh. Shrimp are graded prawns which are quite large, jumbo large, medium and small. When purchasing this product, consider the type of dish to be served and the cost by weight of each grade to keep your portion cost controlled.

Frozen Seafood
All items of fish and shellfish are available in frozen form. They must be handled properly, however. They should remain frozen until ready for cooking. It is not wise to thaw and refreeze these products. The bacteria of spoilage have already begun their work and refreezing only arrests their action. Be careful and suspicious.

POULTRY
Chickens and Turkeys
The governing factors are (1) Age, (2) Finish or appearance and (3) Plumpness.

Good quality poultry comes from young birds. When

purchasing poultry, observe the following:
1. Legs: Young chickens—yellow and smooth
            Young turkeys—black and smooth
2. Breastbone—soft and pliable
3. Skin—smooth, soft and glossy
4. Pin Feathers—very few, if any
5. Bones—finger pressure on the bone structure near the
     tail should find soft pliable bone. This is the best sign
     of the young bird.

Market Classes of Poultry - Chicken

BROILER— Chicken under 12 weeks old, either sex,
              not over 2½ lbs. and soft meated to cook
              tender under broiling.

FRYERS— 12 to 20 weeks old, over 2½ lbs. but not
              over 3½ lbs. and sufficiently tender for fry-
              ing or roasting.

BOILING Over-age and otherwise inferior birds are
FOWL—   used for soup and flavoring stocks and as
              flesh for pastry items such as pot pies or
              chicken-a-la-king.

Market Classes of Poultry - Turkey
     It is important that you consider the weight of the bird
which gives you the best return in net usable yield. Twenty
to twenty-five pounds is the most practical size.

     To test for age, press the flesh against the breastbone be-
tween thumb and finger. Your fingertips should almost meet
through to the soft breastbone if the bird is young.

MEAT
     The purchase of meat is of the utmost importance, as it
absorbs the largest percentage of your Food Budget.

     There are three guides to consider in purchasing of meat.
              1. The inspection stamp
              2. The grade stamp
              3. The appearance of the meat itself.

     The inspection stamp deals with the wholesomeness of
the meat, while the grade stamp indicates the quality of the
meat.

INSPECTION MARK   GRADE MARK

The U. S. D. A. has quality grades for beef, calf, veal, lamb, yearling mutton and mutton. It also has grades for pork, but these do not carry through to the retail level as do the grades for other kinds of meat.

U. S. D. A. meat grades, such as U. S. Prime, U. S. Choice, U. S. Good, are based on nationally uniform, federal standards of quality.

The United States' official grades for the different kinds of meat are:

BEEF	VEAL	LAMB	MUTTON
Prime	Prime	Prime	-
Choice	Choice	Choice	Choice
Good	Good	Good	Good
Commercial	Commercial	-	-
Utility	Utility	Utility	Utility
Cutter & canner	Cull	Cull	Cull

Beef

The meat of cattle nearly one year of age or older. The color should be bright cherry red and the flesh firm and fine grained, well marbled with a creamy white fat. The cut surface is smooth and velvety to the sight and touch.

U. S. D. A. PRIME is the ultimate in tenderness, juiciness and flavor. Prime roasts and steaks are excellent for dry heat cooking—roasting and broiling.

U. S. D. A. CHOICE is high quality. Choice roasts and steaks from the loin and rib are tender, juicy and flavorful. They are best suited to dry heat cooking. Many of the less tender cuts, such as those from the rump, round and blade chuck, can also be used when cooked with dry heat.

U. S. D. A. GOOD is fairly tender but because it has less marbling, it lacks some of the juiciness and flavor of the higher grades.

U. S. D. A. STANDARD has a high proportion of lean meat and very little fat. It is fairly tender because it comes from young animals. Because it lacks marbling, it has less flavor and must be cooked in moist heat.

U. S. D. A. COMMERCIAL is produced from mature animals. Not tender, requires long, slow cooking with moist heat to make it tender. But when prepared this way, it will have the full flavor characteristics of mature beef and can be delicious.

Lamb

Lamb is marked under the general classification of Spring, Fall and Yearling. The hardness and color of the bones are the best indication of age. It is important to know the signs of growth in this product. Redness in bones indicates a young animal and whiteness an old one. As the lamb approaches yearling stage, the bones become harder and whiter. The flesh color varies from light to dark pink; as the animal grows older, the color deepens. The flesh of the yearling will be medium pink to light red and as the animal matures into mutton, changes gradually to dark red. Spring lamb is the quality item and usually is hung for aging for about 10 days after killing.

U. S. D. A. grades of Prime or Choice lamb are tender and can be oven roasted or broiled. Lower grades of lamb (U. S. D. A. GOOD, UTILITY AND CULL) are seldom marked with the grade when sold at retail.

Pork

Pork is generally produced from young animals. U. S. Dept. of Agriculture grades for pork are only two levels of quality–ACCEPTABLE and UNACCEPTABLE. Unacceptable pork is graded U. S. UTILITY.

In pork of good quality, the flesh is firm, fine grained, of a grayish pink color and marbled with flecks of fat. There should be a uniform covering of firm white fat on the exterior surfaces.

Eggs–Grades Are U. S. Grade AA, A and B

Grade AA eggs are produced under U. S. D. A.'s quality control program. These eggs reach the market quickly under strictly controlled conditions, guaranteeing a fresh, top-quality product.

The GRADE A eggs are ideal for all purposes but are especially good for frying and poaching where appearance is important.

GRADE B eggs are good for general cooking and baking where appearance is not important.

Size refers to minimum weight per dozen. The size may be shown within the grade shield or elsewhere on the case. Size and quality are not the same. Large eggs may be of high or low quality; high quality eggs may be either large or small. The sizes most often found are:

	Minimum Weight per dozen
Extra Large	27 oz.
Large	24 oz.
Medium	21 oz.

Other sizes sometimes available are:

Jumbo	30 oz.
Small	18 oz.
Peewee	15 oz.

If there is less than 7 cents price spread per dozen eggs between one size and the next smaller size in the same grade, you will get more for your money by buying the larger size.

Butter

U. S. GRADE AA BUTTER - delicate, sweet flavor, fine pleasing aroma. Made from high quality fresh sweet cream. Smooth creamy texture with good spreadability. Salt completely dissolved and blended in just the right amount to enhance savory quality.

U. S. GRADE A BUTTER - pleasing flavor, made from fresh cream, fairly smooth texture, rates close to top grade.

U. S. GRADE B BUTTER - May have slightly acid flavor, generally made from selected sour cream. Readily accepted and preferred by some consumers.

Menu Planning

Planning diets in nursing homes is not an easy task. Meals must provide the right kinds of food for people who may vary greatly in their nutritional needs. These meals must satisfy people who may have very different food likes. And usually the food must be purchased within a definite money allowance. It is essential, therefore, that a food service director know the basic needs within a fairly well defined cost limit.

People of different ages and degrees of physical activity differ in their nutritional needs. Although the kind of nutrients required are the same, the quantities vary. Adults and children, however, can get their nutrients from the same kind of food. Quantities of food energy and the nine nutrients required to meet the needs of persons of different ages and degrees of activity have been recommended by the National Research Council. In general, these nutrients can be obtained from commonly used foods.

Many different combinations of foods will provide an adequate diet. In this country, an adequate diet planned around the food habits of the people usually includes certain groups of foods every day: Leafy, green, and yellow vegetables; citrus fruit and tomatoes; potatoes, sweet potatoes; other vegetables and fruits; dairy products; protein-rich foods such as meat, poultry, fish, eggs, and dry beans, peas, or nuts; enriched, restored, or whole grain cereals and cereal products; and butter or fortified margarine. Such foods as sugar and fats, other than butter and margarine, can then be added as needed for energy and palatability.

For convenience in planning, I have classified the most common everyday foods into eleven groups in the following lists, and the number of servings needed daily to provide an adequate diet is indicated. Although the lists are not complete, they can be used in placing most foods in their proper group. Miscellaneous items such as coffee and tea, seasonings and flavorings, and baking powder and soda are not included in the eleven groups.

LEAFY, GREEN, AND YELLOW VEGETABLES
(Fresh, Canned, Frozen)
Plan to use: 1 or more servings daily

Asparagus, green	Okra
Beans, lima	Peas
Beans, snap, green	Peppers, green
Broccoli	Pumpkin
Brussels sprouts	Spinach
Cabbage, green	Squash, winter yellow
Carrots	Turnip greens
Kale	Wild greens
Mustard greens	Other greens, including salad greens

CITRUS FRUIT, TOMATOES
(Fresh, Canned, Frozen)
Plan to use: 1 or more servings daily

Grapefruit	Oranges
Lemons	Tangerines
Limes	Tomatoes and Tomato products

The following foods are also good sources of vitamin C and may be used to supplement citrus fruit and tomatoes; raw green cabbage, salad greens, raw green peppers, raw turnips, raw strawberries, raw pineapple, cantaloupe (musk-melon).

POTATOES, SWEET POTATOES
(Fresh, Canned)
Plan to use: 1 or more servings daily

Potatoes	Sweet Potatoes

OTHER VEGETABLES AND FRUITS
(Fresh, Canned, Frozen, Dried)
Plan to use: 1 or more servings daily or additional servings of leafy, green or yellow vegetables

Apples	Cherries	Grapes	Plums
Apricots	Corn, Sweet	Melons	Prunes
Bananas	Cranberries	Onions	Radishes
Beets	Cucumbers	Parsnips	Raisins
Berries	Currants	Peaches	Sauerkraut
Cauliflower	Dates	Pears	Summer Squash
Celery	Figs	Pineapple	Turnips
			Watermelons

MILK, CHEESE, ICE CREAM

Plan to use daily the following amounts of milk or its equivalent. The quantities include milk used both for drinking and for cooking. Adults: 2 or more cups. The group includes:

Milk, fluid	Milk, condensed
Milk, skim	Buttermilk
Milk, dry, whole	Cheese
Milk, dry, nonfat	Ice Cream
Milk, evaporated	

MEAT, POULTRY, FISH
(Fresh, Canned, Cured, Frozen, Dried)

Plan to use: One or more servings daily (include liver or other variety meats once a week, if possible). Additional servings of eggs may be used in place of meat on occasion.

Beef	Tongue
Lamb	Sweetbreads
Mutton	Chicken
Pork (except bacon	Duck
and fat back)	Goose
Veal	Turkey
Liver	Fish, all kinds

EGGS

Plan to use: 3 to 5 a week or additional servings of meat, poultry, fish.

DRY BEANS AND PEAS, NUTS

Plan to use: 1 or more servings a week

Dry Beans (all kinds)	Soya flour and grits
Dry Peas	Peanuts
Lentils	Peanut Butter
Soybeans	Nuts, all kinds

FLOUR, CEREALS, BAKED GOODS

Plan to use: Some enriched, whole-grain, or restored cereals or cereal products daily, others as needed for satisfying meals.

Flour, enriched or	Bread, enriched or	Cookies
whole grain, all types	whole grain, all kinds	Crackers
Uncooked cereals	Rolls	Pies
Ready-to-eat cereals	Cakes	

FATS AND OILS

Plan to use: Some butter or fortified margarine daily; other fats as needed in cooking.

Butter	Bacon
Margarine	Salt Pork
Mayonnaise	Shortening
Salad Dressing	Suet
Salad Oil	Drippings

SUGAR, SYRUPS, PRESERVES

Plan to use: As needed for food energy and flavor in meals.

Sugar (cane or beet)	Jams
Sugar, Brown	Jellies
Molasses	Preserves
Syrups	Candies
Honey	

With the basic needs defined in terms of nutrients and the foods that supply them, the next step is to plan to use these foods in attractive and satisfying meals.

The foods that can be served will depend upon such factors as the type of individuals in the institution, the amount of money allowed, availability of foods (especially fresh foods), storage facilities, and staff and equipment for food preparation. Food selection will be influenced somewhat by the type of individuals in an institution. Meals suitable for older people will not satisfy the needs of men doing hard manual labor.

The level of food money allowance will affect the variety of food served, as well as the quantities of the more expensive foods that are used. With a fairly liberal food allowance, more kinds of foods and larger amounts of the more expensive foods such as roasts and chops can be served. As the allowance becomes more limited, larger quantities of the less expensive foods such as breads, cereals, cereal products, potatoes and the cheaper cuts of meat must be used, and greater ingenuity and skill are needed to plan meals that are not monotonous

It is fortunate that diets both nutritionally adequate and satisfying can be obtained at different food cost levels. By careful food selection, costs can be controlled within certain limits without endangering the nutritional adequacy of the diet. For example, milk is an essential part of all normal diets. Although the quantity needed varies with individuals, milk in one of its forms must be included every day. If using all fluid milk makes the bills too high, other less expensive forms such as evaporated milk can be used for many purposes. Nonfat dry milk, although lacking in the fat and the vitamin A value of whole milk, is nevertheless a good source of protein, calcium and riboflavin. It is usually cheaper than fluid whole milk and can be used in baked products, cream sauces, soups and other beverages.

If a nursing home is located in or near a city, obtaining fresh foods may not present a problem. Many nursing homes, however, are a considerable distance from supplies of fresh foods. If deliveries are irregular or infrequent, it may be necessary to use canned foods more often, as well as other types of food that can be kept for some time. Sometimes refrigerated storage is exceedingly limited. This will have an additional effect on the quantity of fresh foods that can be kept on hand for use between infrequent or irregular deliveries.

The form in which food can be served is influenced by the equipment and by the number of persons to be served. If labor-saving equipment is inadequate, foods will have to be planned that take a minimum amount of preparation, especially last minute preparation. For example, it would be very difficult to serve whipped potatoes to a large group, if the potatoes had to be mashed by hand and the number of kitchen employees was small.

Making Menus
The constant longing of many people for a home-cooked meal is often, in part, a desire to escape from the monotony that so often characterizes institutional food. A common criticism is that the food service "gets into a rut"—that the day of the week can be told by the meals that are served. The successful food service director avoids such criticism by considering variety and appetite appeal as well as nutritive value when planning menus. Although one person should be responsible for the planning, it is a good idea to give your people a chance to suggest foods they like. Including one food each day that

someone has asked for will not ruin the menus, nor is it likely to throw costs out of line.

Interest can be added to mealtimes by making festive occasions of holidays and once in a while changing the type of service. Serving Sunday night supper buffet style, for instance, or having a picnic on a spring afternoon, will break the monotony of three meals a day served in the same place and in the same way. Considerations such as these will give people a feeling they count, that they are important. Results will be well worth the little extra effort. If possible, it is well to serve the same menu to all unless special diets have been prescribed.

Menu-Making Suggestions and Guides

Menus that please everyone are difficult to plan. However, certain basic rules and techniques can be used to aid in the planning of attractive meals that are acceptable to the majority of persons to whom they are served. The following suggestions are offered as guides to planning nutritionally well balanced and attractive meals.

PLAN IN ADVANCE. Planning meals for at least a week in advance lessens the chance of repeating a food too often. Rotating weekly menus in entirety is always to be avoided.

HAVE A GENERAL MEAL PATTERN A meal pattern is a design indicating the types of food that are to be included in each meal. Patterns in common use in many nursing homes are similar to the following:

BREAKFAST	LUNCH OR SUPPER	DINNER
Fruit	Main Dish	Main Dish
Cereal	Vegetable or salad	Vegetables (2 or
Main dish	Bread spread	3 or salad in
Bread spread	Fruit or dessert	place of 1
Beverage	Beverage	vegetable)
		Bread spread
		Dessert
		Beverage

The chief difference in meal patterns in different institutions is in the number of food items included. In general, when the food allowance is limited, fewer items are included and the servings of each are somewhat larger than when there is more to spend.

FOLLOW THE FOOD GROUPS. To be reasonably sure that the proper nutrients are being supplied in the diet, follow the food groups in planning menus, including in each day's meals the number of servings indicated from each group. Some dishes, such as ham a la king, salads and butterscotch pudding, combine foods from more than one group.

SERVE SIMPLE FARE. Plain, well-cooked, and attractively served foods usually are more acceptable than fancy or mixed foods. Mixtures often suggest that the same food is being repeated or that left-overs are always being served. This, in turn, suggests poor management. Also, when an unpopular food is used in a mixture, the dish may be refused by many, thereby causing waste.

PROVIDE VARIETY IN TEXTURE, FLAVOR, COLOR. Food served in the same meal should provide variety in texture, flavor and color. A good rule is to include in a menu a crisp, a firm and a soft food. This will guard against meals monotonous in texture, such as one of soup, creamed codfish, mashed potatoes, stewed tomatoes and chocolate pudding. Several highly seasoned foods should not be combined in one meal. Serving flavorful foods with milder ones, a bland food with a relish or sauce that is optional, is usually more acceptable. Seasonings and gravies that give the same flavor to different foods also can become monotonous. Foods that make an attractive color combination tend to stimulate the appetite. A meal that is all-white is most uninteresting, especially on the all-white plate used in many nursing homes.

INCLUDE FOOD WITH "STAYING" QUALITY. Each meal should contain at least one food that has staying quality — one that gives a satisfied feeling so that an individual isn't hungry soon after the meal is over.

LIST SUGGESTIONS FOR VARIETY IN MEALS. Another guide for planning menus is a set of charts listing the different foods suitable for each meal and ways in which they can be prepared. Include in the charts all foods popular in the nursing home that can be purchased within the ration allowance and that can be prepared with available personnel and equipment. As new ways of preparing foods are tried, they can be added to the lists.

USE OF LEFT-OVERS. In spite of careful planning, the problem of left-overs may arise. When foods have been left over, try to fit them into other meals as soon as possible. Even though left-overs lose some food value during storage and re-heating, they usually retain enough to make them worth using.

The suggestions on the list below illustrate some of the kinds of dishes in which left-overs can be used. When making a chart for a particular institution, it is better to list specific dishes than general classifications.

SUGGESTIONS FOR USE OF LEFTOVERS

Cooked Meats	Cooked Potatoes	Cooked Vegetables
Croquettes	Creamed	Soup
Meat Pie	Fried	Meat Pie
Hash	Potato Cakes	Stew
Casserole dishes	Stuffed	Stuffed Peppers
Sandwich	Baked	Salads
fillings	Meat Pie	
Salads	Stew	
	Chowder	
	Hash	

Cooked Cereals	Bread, Cakes	Eggs
Fried	Bread, dry crumbs	Egg yolks
Meat Loaf	Brown Betty	Cakes
Rice, with	Breaded chops	Pie Fillings
tomatoes		Salad Dressing
Croquettes		
Fondue		

Milk	Macaroni	Soft Crumbs
Sour Milk	Noodles	Meat Loaf
Cakes	Tomatoes	Stuffing
Cookies	Cheese	Cake or Cookies
Muffins	Meat Sauce	Brown Betty
Cottage	Tunafish	Ice-box Cake
Cheese		

Egg Whites	Sour Cream	Cooked Eggs
Meringue	Cakes	Deviled
Cake	Cookies	Creamed
Puddings	Salad Dressing	Salads
	Swiss Steak	Sandwich
		fillings

SAMPLE MENUS FOR 2 DAYS SHOWING HOW

FOOD GROUP	BREAKFAST	DINNER	LUNCH OR SUPPER
Leafy, green and yellow vegetable		Broccoli	Green Lettuce
Citrus fruit, tomatoes	Grapefruit Juice		Tomato
Potatoes, sweet-potatoes		Sweet-Potatoes	
Other vegetables and fruit		Celery Sticks Radishes Apples in Pie	Peaches
Milk, cheese, ice cream	Milk		Milk
Meat, poultry fish		Roast Shoulder of Pork	
Eggs	Scrambled Eggs		
Dry beans and peas, nuts			Baked Lima Beans
Flour, cereal, baked goods	Toast Wheat cereal	Rolls Apple Pie	Raisin Bread Oatmeal cookies
Fats, oils,(a)	Butter or Margarine	B or M	B or M Salad Dress.
Sugar, syrups, preserves(b)	Jam		

(a) Other fat used in cooking
(b) Other sugar used in cooking and beverages

FOODS FROM 11 GROUPS CAN BE USED

BREAKFAST	DINNER	LUNCH OR SUPPER
	Green cabbage (salad) Carrots	Green Asparagus
Tomato Juice	Orange	
	Scalloped potatoes	
	Prunes (salad)	Whipped gelatin with bananas
	Meat Loaf	Ham ala King on Toast
		Eggs in Ham ala King
	Nuts (done in salad)	
Toast Scrapple	Bread Butterscotch pudding	Rolls
B or M	B or M Gravy	B or M
Syrup		Jelly

PLANNING FOR NUTRITION

It is a well known fact that most of us do not consume the daily requirements of vitamins for proper body function and growth. In some cases, this deficiency is countered by the intake of vitamin pills; in others, by the eating of specific foods high in vitamin content. However, prolonged absence of the daily requirements of any particular nutrient will result in harmful effects in the body itself and in the function of the senses and capabilities of the person. In an effort to identify these characteristics and the vitamin which may be lacking in particular cases, a list is printed below which associates the signs of poor health that may accompany an insufficient intake of protective food in the diet.

Vitamin A— A dry, scaly or "goose pimple" skin, ingrown hair, low resistance to infection, diarrhea, sensitivity of eyes to bright light, night blindness.

Vitamin B_1 (thiamin chloride)—Lassitude, no energy for work, poor appetite, constipation, nervousness and irritability, poor judgment, sleeplessness, neuralgia.

Vitamin C— (ascorbic acid)—Lassitude, no energy for work, skin hemorrhages, spongy bleeding gums, low resistance to infection, slowly healing wounds, tooth disorders.

Vitamin D— Poor teeth, crooked bones, rickets.

Vitamin B_2 (Riboflavin)—Burning itching eyes sensitive to light, blackheads and "whiteheads," oily skin, sore lips with cracks at corners.

Niacin (formerly known as nicotinic acid)—Sore mouth and tongue, burning of throat, rough, chapped skin particularly in winter, sleeplessness, indigestion, nervousness, constipation, loss in weight.

Calcium— Tooth cavities, poorly developed bones and teeth, muscle soreness.

Iron— Lassitude and fatigue, general weakness, nutritional anemia, mental dullness.

Iodine— Lassitude and fatigue, simple goiter.

Protein Tiredness, general weakness, anemia, loss of weight, edema.

PRINCIPAL SOURCES OF ENERGY FOODS

Starches	Sugars	Fats
Breads	Sugar	Butter
Crackers	Molasses	Cream
Rice	Honey	Lard
Breakfast foods	Preserves	Salt Pork
Other cereal	Jellies	Bacon
products	Dried fruits	Margarine
Tapioca	Candy	Vegetable and
Sago	Cake and Cookies	nut oils
Potatoes	Other sweet	Peanut Butter
Beans and Peas	desserts	Cheese
Macaroni	Syrup	

Protein Rich Foods	Roughage (regulating foods)
Milk	Raw and Cooked
Eggs	vegetables
Cheese	Cooked cereals
Lean Meat	Cooked and raw fruits
Fish	
Poultry	
Dried Peas	
and Beans	
Legumes	
Nuts	

Protective foods which may be used to build up various body building nutrients are listed below beneath the vitamin they furnish.

PROTECTIVE FOODS HIGH IN VITAMIN CONTENT

Vitamin A	Vitamin B$_1$ (Thiamin)	Vitamin C (Ascorbic Acid)
Codliver oil (tsp)	Pork, lean	Rutabaga (cooked)
Liver	Peanuts	Spinach and
Greens, raw, cooked	Squash	mustard greens
Pumpkin	Whole Wheat	Strawberries
Sweet potato	Nuts	Pimientos (1 tbsp.)
Carrots	Wheat germ (1 tbsp.)	Orange juice
Apricots	Apricots and	Grapefruit juice
Squash	Peaches	Cantaloupe
		Cauliflower

Green vege-
tables
Cheese
Pimiento (1tbsp.)
Tomatoes (raw)
Cream
Corn
Tomato Juice
Egg
Peas, creamed,
canned
Butter

Asparagus
Dried Beans
Sweet Corn
Turnip tops
Bread-whole
wheat (enriched)
Liver
Raisins
Oysters
Potatoes (baked)
Milk
Grapefruit
Tomato juice
Oatmeal

Turnips
Peppers, sweet
Asparagus
Other cooked
greens and green
vegetables
Tomatoes
Raw green leaves

Iron
Liver
Molasses
Beef heart
Apricots (dried)
Prunes-fresh or
canned
Nuts
Turkey
Dried fruit
Lean Meat
Eggs
Dried beans
Green leaves
Whole wheat
Oysters
Green vegetables
Dark corn syrup
Peas
Potatoes
Oatmeal

Vitamin B$_2$
(Riboflavin)
Liver
Turnip Tops
Eggplant
Prunes
Sardines
Peanuts
Lean Meats
Dried peaches
Salmon (canned)
Green cooked
peas
Milk
Beans (dried)
Cantaloupe

Vitamin D
Sea fish oils
Steenbock process
irradiated foods
Sea foods
To a less degree in
egg yolk
Butter

Niacin
Liver
Kidney
Heart
Muscle meat
Chicken
Peanuts
Whole wheat
Enriched flour
Beans
Carrots
Oatmeal
Potatoes

A SIMPLE GUIDE FOR MEAL PLANNING

A daily food guide, listing the quantities and kinds of food to use daily to supply body needs, includes:

Milk—1 quart for children, 2 or more cups for adults.

Butter—1 ounce (1 tablespoon); 2 ounces, if skimmed milk is used.

Vegetables—1 serving potatoes, 2 generous servings other vegetables (one raw or leafy).

Fruits—2 servings (one high in vitamin C).

Whole cereals—1 serving: whole grain breakfast cereal, 3-6 slices of bread, muffins, etc., whole grain or enriched.

Meat, poultry, cheese, fish or beans, peas, nuts: 1 or more servings (liver and sea fish once a week).

Eggs— 1 daily (at least 3 to 5 each week).

MENU SUGGESTIONS

ENTREES

Italian Spaghetti
and Meat Balls
Chili Con Carne,
Mexican Style
Braised Beef and
Vegetables
Creamed Ham
and Eggs
Ham Fritters,
Pineapple Sauce
Ham and Macaroni
Au Gratin
Ham and Rice with
Spanish Sauce
Boiled Ham and
Lima Beans
Baked Noodles,
Ham
Escalloped Potatoes
with Ham
Boiled Spareribs,
Red Cabbage
Beef Chop Suey,
Steamed Rice
Potted Sirloin of Beef
Stuffed Green Peppers
Roast Beef Hash
with Potatoes
Corned Beef Hash with

Poached Eggs
Beef Pot Roast
with Noodles
Baked Meat Loaf
Browned Beef Stew
Hungarian Goulash
with Dumplings
Swiss Steak with
Buttered Noodles
Creamed Chipped
Beef with Rice
Creamed Chipped
Beef on Toast
Salisbury Steak with
Browned Onions
Ham and Rice Cakes,
Tomato Sauce
Barbecued Beef on
Bun
Barbecued Pork on
Bun
Broiled Canadian
Bacon
Pork Chop Suey,
Steamed Rice
Creamed Ham and
Green Peppers
Ham Cutlet with
Grilled Tomatoes

Cabbage Rolls
Stuffed with Ham
Veal Fricassee with
Biscuit
Veal Chop Suey,
Steamed Rice
Baked Pork and Bean
Casserole
Chicken Chopped
Salad
Chicken Loaf
Scalloped Chicken
and Macaroni
Lamb Shortcake
with Fresh Peas
Brown Lamb Hash
with Green Peppers
Chopped Beef and
Spaghetti
Turkey Fritters and
Apple Rings
Spaghetti with Mush-
room Sauce
Baked Lima Beans
with Pork
Veal Pot Pie, Flaky
Crust
Irish Lamb Stew,
Dumplings

LAMB

Roast Leg of Lamb,
Mint Jelly
Shepherd Pie
Minced Parsley
Braised Lamb Shank
Boneless Saddle of
Lamb
Baked Lamb Loaf
with Buttered
Noodles
Pan Fried Lamb
Patties
Irish Lamb Stew

Grilled Lamb Chops
Crown Roast of Lamb
Boiled Leg of Lamb,
Horseradish Sauce
Boneless Loin Lamb
Chops
Stuffed Bake Lamb
Chops, Sausage
Stuffing
Breaded Lamb Chops
Pan Fried
Rolled Roast of Lamb,
Rice Stuffing

Lamb and Vegetable
Casserole
Lamb Pot Pie with
Hot Baking Pow-
der Biscuit
Fricassee of Lamb
Stuffed Shoulder of
Lamb, Brown
Sauce
Baked Lamb Loaf,
Tomato Sauce
Lamb Croquettes,
Cream Sauce
Baked Lamb Hash

VEAL

Stuffed Breast of Veal Bread Stuffing
Danish Meat Balls
Chopped Veal Steak
Choice Roast Leg of Veal
Pot Roast of Veal, Vegetables
Crown of Veal Roast

Stuffed Cushion of Veal Brown Sauce
Veal Chops with Buttered Noodles
Pan-Broiled Veal Steak, Mushroom Sauce
Scallopini of Veal
Baked Veal and Ham Loaf, Dill Pickle

Breaded Veal Cutlets, Tomato Sauce
Minced Veal with Green Peppers
Veal Chops with Spanish Sauce
Baked Veal Pie, Hot Biscuits

BEEF

Italian Spaghetti with Meat Balls
Creole Beef with Buttered Noodles
Beef ala Mode with Natural Gravy
Country Fried Steak, Smothered Onions
Baked Salisbury Steak, Spanish Sauce
Boiled Beef with Buttered Noodles
Cold Sliced Beef Plate, Potato Salad
Roast Prime Ribs of Beef, Au Jus
Baked Hamburger Casserole
Baked Hash Vegetable Casserole
Grilled Frankfurters with Spanish Rice
Pan Fried Baby Beef Liver, Bacon
Stuffed Peppers with Tomato Sauce
Creamed Chipped Beef on Toast Points
Yankee Pot Roast with Fresh Vegetables
Boiled Corned Beef and Cabbage
Standing Rib of Beef, Au Jus
Meat Balls and Lima Bean Casserole
Escalloped Hamburger with Potatoes
Braised Flank Steak, Buttered Mushrooms
Home-Made Vegetable Beef Stew

Baked Beef Cutlets, Hungarian Sauce
Choice Top Sirloin Steak, Mushroom Sauce
Braised Round Steak, Swiss Style
Southern Beef Hash with Whipped Yams
American Chop Suey
Beef Pot Pie, Flaky Crust
Hamburger Patties with Boston Baked Beans
Braised Swedish Meat Balls
Baked Corn Beef Hash
Fricassee of Beef, Steamed Rice
Spanish Rice Casserole with Hamburger
Baked Frankfurters with Hot Potato Salad
Simmered Beef Shanks with Parsley Potatoes
Boiled New England Dinner
Baked Swiss Steak, Tomato Sauce
Chili con Carne, Steamed Rice
New England Beef Stew, Boiled Potatoes
Grilled Cubed Steak, Onion Sauce
Baked Shortribs, Barbecue Sauce
Baked Swiss Steak with Dumplings
Beef Kidney Stew, Maryland Style
Baked Beef and Macaroni Loaf, Creole Style
Spanish Meat Loaf
Creamed Chipped Beef on Hot Corn Bread

BEEF (cont.)

Cold Sliced Beef Plate,
  Sliced Tomatoes
Baked Meat Loaf, Brown Gravy
Broiled Sirloin Steak,
  Mushroom Sauce
Boiled Weiners with German
  Sauerkraut

Cold Sliced Beef Tongue
  with Cole Slaw
Porterhouse Steak
Rib Steak
Club Steak
T-Bone Steak

PORK

Roast Loin of Pork
  Baked Apple Rings
Baked Virginia Ham,
  Raisin Sauce
Breaded Pork Tenderloin
Baked Ham Loaf,
  Mustard Sauce
Stuffed Pork Shoulder,
  Applesauce
Broiled Pork Chops,
  Spiced Apple
Grilled Ham Steak,
  Pineapple
Baked Spareribs,
  Barbecue Sauce
Breaded Pork Chops,
  Cream Sauce
Baked Pork Loaf,
  Tomato Sauce
Chipped Ham on Toast
  with Melted Cheese
Ham Croquettes, Cream Sauce
Ham ala King with Hot
  Corn Bread
Baked Ham Souffle with
  Mushrooms
Roast Leg of Pork,
  Applesauce
Boiled Spareribs with
  German Sauerkraut
Boiled Ham and Cabbage
Barbecued Pork Chops
Polish Sausage with
  Sauerkraut
Deviled Pork Chops,
  Glazed Carrots

Jellied Pork Loin,
  Mustard Mayonnaise
Pickled Pig's Feet, Relish
Baked Sugar Cured Ham,
  Cumberland Sauce
Rice and Bacon Casserole,
  Creole Sauce
Breaded Pork Cutlets,
  Glazed Fruit
Cold Pork in Aspic
  Hartford Sauce
Cold Sliced Pork
  Parsley Potatoes
Baked Pork and Bean
  Casserole
Baked Ham with
  Lima Beans
Roast Fresh Pork, Glazed
  Apple Rings
Sliced Cold Boiled Ham
  Sweet Mustard
Smoked Pork Shoulder
Boiled Smoked Pork Jowl,
  Cabbage Wedges
Pork, Cheese and Noodle
  Casserole
Roast Fresh Ham,
  Apple Butter
Baked Pork with Boston
  Baked Beans
Casserole of Pork Steak
  with Riced Potatoes
Scalloped Ham and
  Sweet Potatoes
Cabbage Rolls Stuffed
  with Ham

Diced Ham with Scalloped
  Potatoes
Pork Steak with Country Gravy
Ham Salad on Fruit Plate
Grilled Ham on Toast with
  Cheese Sauce
Fried Pork Liver with
  Grilled Bacon
Ham and Macaroni
Ham Fritters with Pineapple
  Sauce
Creamed Ham and Eggs
Broiled Canadian Bacon
Pork Chop Suey with
  Steamed Rice
Stuffed Pepper with Ham
  and Rice

Cold Baked Ham with
  Potato Salad
Breaded Pork Sausage Patties
Old Fashioned Pork Pie,
  Flaky Crust
Pork Chow Mein, Crispy
  Chinese Noodles
Ham Loaf with Pineapple
  Glaze
Baked Sausages with Whipped
  Potatoes
Ragout of Fresh Pork,
  Hungarian Style
Fluffy Ham Omelette
Noodles with Bacon Strips
Baked Spareribs with
  Buttered Noodles

MEATLESS MAIN DISHES

Macaroni and Eggs with
  Cream Sauce
Baked Macaroni Loaf
Cheese Noodle Loaf
Mexican Spaghetti
Creamed Macaroni with
  Baked Tomatoes
Cabbage Rolls with
  Buttered Noodles
Shrimp Chow Mein
Stuffed Cabbage with Rice
Shrimp and Corn Casserole
Creamed Asparagus on Toast
Home-Baked Beans
Escalloped Cheese and Corn
Corn Fritters
Eggs ala King
Spanish Omelet
Cheese Fondue
Eggs Creamed on Toast
Baked Lima Beans with
  Mushrooms
Chinese Omelet
Baked Macaroni and Cheese
Cheese Souffle
Rice and Tomato Casserole
Vegetable Souffle

Creole Spaghetti
Stuffed Peppers with Rice,
  Tomato Sauce
Escalloped Eggs with Green
  Beans
Rice Croquettes
Eggs, Au Gratin
Welsh Rarebit
Scrambled Eggs
Spanish Rice
Baked Vegetable Pie
Tuna Noodle Casserole
Mushroom Vegetable
  Casserole
Corn Fritters
Potato Pancakes
Mock Chicken Rice with
  Tuna
Vegetable Chop Suey
Baked Lasagna
Creamed Eggs and Shrimp
Macaroni Hash
Egg Cutlets, Cream Sauce
Corn Pudding
Spicy Apple Fritters
Cheese Custard
Cheese Pancakes

MEATLESS MAIN DISHES (cont.)

FISH AND SEAFOOD

New England Codfish Cakes
Baked Fresh Haddock,
  Butter Sauce
Broiled Halibut Steak
Baked Stuffed Mackerel
Poached Salmon Steaks
Pan Fried Perch
Baked Fillets of Fish with
  Spanish Sauce
Creamed Codfish on Toast
Deviled Salmon with Macaroni
Creamed Tuna Fish with Hot
  Buttered Biscuits
Salmon and Potato Casserole
Creamed Salmon with Celery
  and Peas
Tuna Fish ala King
Broiled Maine Lobster
French Fried Oysters
Escalloped Salmon with Eggs
Lobster Newburg
Lobster Thermidor
Baked Salmon Loaf
Tuna Fish and Cheese
  Biscuit Roll

Escalloped Oysters
Baked Scallops in Casserole
Baked Tuna Fish Pie
Seafood Newburg
French Fried Scallops
Shrimp Chop Suey
Tunafish Salad
Salmon Salad
French Fried Shrimp
Baked Salmon Patties
Shrimp Fondue
Tuna Fish Roll
Clam Fricassee
Tuna and Cheese Biscuit Roll
Baked Shrimp and Tuna Newburg
Oyster Pie
Baked Haddock Fillets in
  Spanish Sauce
Broiled Scallops
Fish Sticks with Tartar Sauce
Barbecued Salmon Steaks
Shrimp with Tomato Sauce
Steamed Oysters in the Shell
Tuna Potato Scallop
Fish Stick Burgers

VEGETABLES

Crumbed Cauliflower
Scalloped Green Beans
Boiled Red Cabbage
Stewed Whole Corn
Candied Yams
Glazed Whole Carrots
Fresh Spinach with
  Hard Boiled Egg
Harvard Beets
Buttered Green Asparagus
Baked Succotash
Scalloped Tomatoes with
  Cheese Sauce
Creamed Peas and Carrots
Diced Buttered Turnips
Cold Wax Beans with Vinegar
Mashed Sweet Potatoes on
  Pineapple

Buttered Carrot Strips
Buttered Baby Whole Beets
Boiled Onions with Cheese Sauce
Buttered June Peas
Carrots, Shoestring Style
Corn and Tomato Casserole
Buttered Broccoli with Lemon
  Butter
Spinach
Freshly Cooked Lima Beans
Creamed Cabbage
Creamed Celery
Buttered Corn and Green
  Peppers, Saute
Creamed Small Whole Onions
German Sauerkraut
Stewed Creamed Corn
Baked Corn Pudding

Baked Squash
Stewed Yellow Turnips
Black-Eyed Peas
Baked Stewed Tomatoes
   with Corn
Hot Cole Slaw, Chipped Bacon
Sweet Sour Cabbage
Buttered Brussels Sprouts
Sliced Beets in Orange Sauce
Creamed Broccoli
Baked Stuffed Onions
Corn O'Brien
Baked Shredded Carrots
Corn on the Cob,
   Drawn Butter
Sliced Cucumbers, Vinaigrette
Creamed Mixed Vegetables
Baked Tomatoes Parmesan

Creamed Green Beans
Lima Beans with Tomatoes
Boston Baked Beans
Baked Whole Sweet Potatoes
Braised Carrots
Hot Spiced Beets
Fried Parsnips, Butter Sauce
Au Gratin Carrots
Red Cabbage, German Style
Corn Fritters, Maple Syrup
French Fried Onions
Lyonnaise Carrots
French Fried Eggplant
Baked Beans with Tomatoes
Stewed Navy Beans
Sliced Pickled Beets
Mexican Style Corn with
   Green Peppers

POTATOES

Creamy Whipped Potatoes
Baked Idaho Potato
French Fried Potatoes
Parsley Buttered Potatoes
Hash Brown Potatoes
Hot German Potato Salad
Scalloped Potatoes
Boiled Potatoes
Baked Stuffed Potato
Shoestring Potatoes
Julienne Potatoes
Home Fried Potatoes
Potato Croquettes
German Fried Potatoes
Potato Pancakes
Riced Potatoes

Delmonico Potatoes
Creamed Potatoes
Oven Roasted Potatoes
Potato Dumplings
German Potato Cakes
Chilled Potato Salad,
   Sliced Tomatoes
Potato Chips
Fried Potato Balls
Cottage Fried Potatoes
Potatoes, Au Gratin
Potatoes, O'Brien
Buttered Diced Potatoes
Buttered Steamed Potatoes
Fluffy Mashed Potatoes
Fried Potato Cakes

RICE

Steamed Buttered Rice
Rice Croquettes with
   Mushroom Cream Sauce
Scalloped Rice
Rice Pancakes with
   Maple Syrup

Baked Rice with American
   Cheese
Spanish Rice
Steamed Rice with Tomato
   Sauce
Creamed Rice Casserole

OTHER STARCH FOODS

Boiled Buttered Noodles   Baked Macaroni and Cheese
Macaroni Au Gratin   Macaroni with Tomato Sauce
Chilled Macaroni Salad   Baked Noodles with Spanish Sauce

SUGGESTIONS FOR SALADS

Chilled Fruit Molded Salad
Waldorf Salad
Cole Slaw
Stuffed Celery with Cheese
Cottage Cheese with Sliced
  Tomatoes
Hearts of Lettuce Salad,
  French Dressing
Sliced Cucumber Salad
Grated Carrot and Raisin
  Salad
Pickled Beet and Onion Salad
Chef's Salad
Fruit Salad with Stuffed Prunes
Jellied Vegetable Salad
Egg Salad
Tomato Aspic
Shredded Cabbage and Carrot
  Salad
Perfection Salad
Pineapple Cottage Cheese Salad
Macaroni Salad
Macaroni Coleslaw
Cherry Red Fruit Salad
Jellied Peach Salad
Fruit Salad Ring
Stuffed Beet Salad
Mexican Relish Salad
Wilted Lettuce Salad
Stuffed Pear and Cottage

Cheese Salad
Fresh Fruit Salad,
  Whipped Dressing
Mexican Bean Salad
Carrot Curls with Radish Roses
Shredded Lettuce Salad
Sliced Tomato Salad
Mexican Slaw
Jellied Carrot and Pineapple
  Salad
Deviled Egg Salad
Chilled Macaroni Salad
Head Lettuce with Russian
  Dressing
Chopped Salad Greens,
  Russian Dressing
Stuffed Tomato Salad
Stuffed Prune Salad
Orange and Grapefruit Salad
Asparagus Salad
Sweet-Sour Cucumbers
Mandarin Orange Salad
Jellied Egg Salad
Ginger Ale Fruit Salad
Prune and Cheese Salad
Cabbage, Bacon and Egg
  Salad
String Bean Salad
Frozen Vegetable Salad

SANDWICHES

Lunchmeat Sandwich
Grilled Frankfurter on Bun
Pork Sausage Sandwich
Liverwurst Sandwich
Minced Chicken Sandwich
Sliced Cold Chicken Sandwich
Chicken and Celery Sandwich
Chicken and Ham Sandwich
Chicken Club Sandwich
Egg Salad Sandwich
Hard-Cooked Egg Sandwich
Fried Egg Sandwich
Deviled Egg Sandwich
Scrambled Egg Sandwich
Egg and Celery Sandwich
Egg-Olive-Ham Sandwich
Egg and Bacon Sandwich
Egg and Ham Sandwich
Sardine Sandwich
Tunafish Salad Sandwich
Salmon Salad Sandwich
Shrimp Salad Sandwich
Mock Lobster Salad Sandwich
Fried Oyster Sandwich
Sliced American Cheese
  Sandwich
Toasted Cheese Sandwich
Chopped Cheese and
  Pimiento Sandwich
Grilled Ham Sandwich
Ham and Relish Sandwich
Baked Ham Loaf Sandwich
Minced Ham Sandwich
Ham and Bologna Sandwich .
  with Lettuce
Ham and Cheese Sandwich
Ham-Cheese-Pineapple Sandwich
Deviled Ham Sandwich
Cold Roast Beef Sandwich
Cold Sliced Meat Loaf Sandwich

Hot Roast Beef Sandwich
Meat Loaf and Egg Sandwich
Grilled Hamburger on Bun
Grilled Cheeseburger on Bun
Sliced Corned Beef Sandwich
Sliced Cold Lamb Sandwich
Sliced Baked Veal Loaf
  Sandwich
Beef Tongue Sandwich
Mock Chicken Sandwich
Sliced Cold Pork Sandwich
Pickled Beef Tongue Sandwich
Deviled Meat and Prune Sandwich
Bacon, Lettuce and Tomato
  Sandwich
Bologna Sandwich
Cream Cheese Sandwich on
  Brown Bread
Cream Cheese with Sliced Tomato
Cream Cheese and Raisin Nut
  Sandwich
Spiced Veal Sandwich
Shrimp Salad Sandwich with
  Sliced Tomato
Cream Cheese and Egg Salad
  Sandwich
Toasted Peanut Butter Sandwich
Peanut Butter and Jelly Sandwich
Lettuce and Tomato Sandwich
Hot Roast Pork Sandwich
Chicken Salad Sandwich
Cold Meat Salad Sandwich
Barbecued Hamburger on Bun
Hot Hamburger Sandwich with
  Brown Gravy
Sliced Cold Turkey Sandwich
Turkey Salad Sandwich
Barbecued Beef Sandwich
Barbecued Pork Sandwich
Bacon and Cheese Sandwich

QUICK BREAD AND MUFFINS

Baking Powder Biscuits
Buttered Dropped Biscuits
Apple Biscuits
Bacon Biscuits
Buttermilk Biscuits
Sour Milk Biscuits
Hot Bran Biscuits
Butterscotch Biscuits
Lemon Biscuits
Jam and Jelly Biscuits
Honey Biscuits
Cheese Biscuits
Caraway Seed Biscuits
Chopped Fruit Biscuits
Sour Cream Biscuits
Peanut Butter Biscuits
Pineapple Rolls
Hot Orange Biscuits
Hot Cross Buns
Hot Pecan Rolls
Blueberry Muffins
Sour Cherry Muffins
Oven Scones with Raisins
Cherry Nut Bread
Apple Nut Bread
German Coffee Cake
Fruit Bread
Orange-Filled Coffee Cake
Coffee Fruit Ring
Apple Coffee Cake
Apricot Upside-Down
  Coffee Cake
Jam-Filled Breakfast Cake
Old Fashioned Corn Bread
Sour Milk Corn Bread
Pan-Baked Johnny Cake
Hominy Spoon Bread
Corn Sticks
Plain Sugared Doughnuts
Drop Doughnuts
Fruit Doughnuts
Plain Sugar Crullers
Molasses Doughnuts

Rich Dessert Waffles
Hot Griddle Scones
Date and Nut Muffins
Currant Muffins
Cranberry Muffins
Corn Muffins
Brown Sugar Muffins
Bran Nut Muffins
Apricot Muffins
Cinnamon Apple Muffins
Pecan Muffins
Peanut Butter Muffins
Whole Wheat Fruit Muffins
Spiced Prune Muffins
Banana Muffins
Honey Bran Muffins
Molasses Raisin Muffins
Pecan Nut Bread
Date and Nut Bread
Whole Wheat Nut Bread
Orange Date Nut Loaf
Apricot Luncheon Bread
Apricot Bran Bread
Corn Fritters
Blueberry Fritters
Orange Fritters
Apple Fritters
Banana Fritters
Pineapple Fritters
Buttermilk Pancakes
Sour Milk Pancakes
Applesauce Pancakes
Banana Pancakes
Whole Wheat Pancakes
Buckwheat Cakes
Potato Pancakes
Raw Potato Pancakes
Swedish Pancakes
Apple Waffles
Banana Waffles
Nut Waffles
Buttermilk Waffles
Corn Bread Waffles

YEAST BREAD AND ROLLS

Enriched White Bread
Oatmeal Bread
Orange Bread
Raisin Bread
Rye Bread
Whole Wheat Bread
Cinnamon Twist Bread
Raised Biscuits
Butterhorns
Cinnamon Buns
Refrigerator Rolls
Marmalade Rolls
Parker House Rolls
Pecan Rolls
Whole Wheat Rolls
Danish Pastry
Baking Powder Biscuits

Buttermilk Biscuits
Cheese Biscuits
Quick Caramel Biscuits
Scones
Whole Wheat Biscuits
Cornbread
Sally Lunn
Butter Rolls
Raisin-Orange Rolls
Cloverleaf Rolls
Orange Pinwheels
Honey Date Rolls
Oatmeal Yeast Rolls
Onion Buns
Crescent Rolls
Hot Cross Buns
Poppy Seed Rolls

CAKES

Fluffy White Cake
Home-Made Chocolate Cake
Banana Whipped Cream Cake
Sour Milk Devil's Food Cake
Coffee Devil's Food Cake
Chocolate Layer Cake
Spice Cake with Raisins
Applesauce Spice Cake
Gingerbread Cake,
   Marshmallow Topping
Maple Cream Cake
Chocolate Nut Cake
Marble Swirl Cake
Orange Layer Cake
Gold Pound Cake
Angel Food Cake
Custard Angel Food Cake
Lemon Angel Food Cake
Jiffy Sponge Cake

Jelly Roll
Chocolate Cream Roll
Rum Sponge Cake
Orange Chiffon Cake
Peppermint Chip Cake
Coconut Cake
Southern Pecan Cake
Strawberry Short Cake
Boston Cream Pie
Light and Dark Fruit Cake
Peach Upside-Down Cake
Pear Upside-Down Cake
Pineapple Upside-Down Cake
Cottage Cheese Cake
Chocolate Chip Cake
Coconut Fluff Cake
Strawberry Cake
Maraschino Party Cake
Peppermint Angel Food Cake

COOKIES AND CUPCAKES

Vanilla Cupcakes
Chocolate Cupcakes
Fruit and Nut Cakes
Cocoa Cupcakes
Marshmallow Cakes
Lady Fingers
Brown Sugar Drop Cookies
Fruit Drop Cookies
Nut Drop Cookies
Coconut Drop Cookies
Coffee Spice Cookies
Refrigerator Nut Cookies
Chocolate Refrigerator Cookies
Butter Cookies
Lemon Cookies
Raisin-Filled Cookies
Chocolate Brownies
Crisp Sugar Cookies
Vanilla Drop Cookies
Sour Cream Cookies
Butterscotch Cookies
Brandy Cookies
Butter Balls

Chocolate Chip Cookies
Vanilla Pinwheels
Crispy Oatmeal Cookies
Oatmeal Molasses Cookies
Oatmeal Drop Cookies
Date-Filled Oat Squares
Crisp Ginger Cookies
Thick Molasses Cookies
Spice Raisin Cookies
Hermits
Rolled Date Cookies
Filled Cookies
Fig Cookies
Pineapple Drops
Peanut Butter Cookies
Honey Bars
Pumpkin Cookies
Coconut Icebox Cookies
Almond Cookies
Coconut Macaroons
Meringue Kisses
Cornflake Macaroons
Russian Nut Balls

PUDDINGS AND DESSERTS

Apple Betty
Apple Dumplings
Baked Fruit Pudding
Coconut Bread Pudding
Indian Pudding
Peach Crumble Dessert
Pineapple Betty
Almond Torte
Date Delight
Baked Cherry Pudding
Cottage Cheese Pudding
Devil's Food Pudding
Blueberry Puff
Chocolate Pudding
Lemon Cake Top Pudding
Blueberry Cobbler
Fruit Shortcake

Baked Winesap Apple
Apricot Whip
Biscuit Tortoni
Whipped Fruit Gelatin
Jellied Caramel Pudding
Baked Rice Pudding
Peach Cobbler
Chocolate Ice Box Pudding
Tapioca Cream
Cottage Pudding
Blanc Mange
Lemon Cream Rice Pudding
Floating Island Pudding
Graham-Cracker Date
   and Nut Pudding
Raisin Pudding
Peach Tapioca

Butterscotch Blanc Mange
Pineapple Custard Pudding
Apple Sauce Custard
Cherry Cobbler
Cantaloupe
Apple Crumble
Baked Prune Pudding
Strawberry Short Cake
Upside-Down Cherry Pudding
Brown Sugar Custard
Maple Pudding
Peanut Butter Custard
Chocolate Fudge Pudding
Raisin Nut Pudding
Lemon Bisque

Spanish Pudding
Pineapple Marshmallow Fluff
Grapenut Pudding
Baked Alaska
Strawberry Whip
Apple Raisin Torte
Brownie Pudding
Coffee Cream Puffs
Cookie Shortcake
Pineapple-Marshmallow Whip
Fruit Cocktail Tapioca
Marshmallow Fruit Mold
Pineapple Crisp
Spicy Apple Sauce Torte
Apple Cobbler

DESSERT SAUCES

Brown Sugar Syrup
Butterscotch Sauce
Caramel Sauce
Cherry Sauce
Chocolate Sauce
Custard Sauce
Foamy Fruit Sauce
Hard Sauce
Marshmallow Sauce
Orange Sauce
Peppermint-Marshmallow
 Sauce
Vanilla Sauce
Hot Fudge Sauce
Lemon Sauce

Cocoa Dessert Sauce
Pineapple Sauce
Brandy Sauce
Maple Sauce
Tutti-Frutti Sauce
Peach Sauce
Apricot Sauce
Raisin Sauce
Rum Sauce
Strawberry Sauce
Wine Sauce
Honey Sauce
Chocolate Mint Sauce
Lemon Cream Sauce
Nutmeg Sauce

PIES

Frosty Almond
Peppermint
Coconut Butterscotch
Lemon Chiffon
Chocolate Cream
Fresh Rhubarb
Lemon Cheese

Cherry
Blueberry
Peach
Peach Cream
Pecan
Pineapple

PIES (cont.)

Hot Mincemeat	Raspberry Cream
Strawberry Chiffon	Pineapple Cream
Banana Cream	Boston Cream
Nesselrode	Cheese
Dutch Apple	Cranberry Chiffon
Fresh Apple	Sour Cream Raisin
Apricot Cream	Raisin-Pineapple
Banana Chiffon	Fruit Glazed
Butterscotch	Butterscotch Pecan
Coconut Cream	Mocha Chiffon
Coconut Custard	Sweet Potato
Chocolate Chiffon	Egg Nog Chiffon
Apricot Pineapple	Chocolate Peppermint Cream
Light Shoo Fly	Cherry Whipped Cream
Blueberry Chiffon	Pumpkin
Rum Cream	Strawberry Rhubarb
Pineapple Custard	Apple Cream
Lemon Fluff	Black Bottom
Rhubarb	Cherry Almond Cream

FRUIT CUPS

Canned fruit cocktail is ready to serve chilled as it comes from the can. Other canned fruits may also be combined for the beginning course. Garnishes are many and add to the appetite-appeal of the starter for the meal.

Fruit Cup Suggestions

Fruit cocktail, creme de menthe
Orange-grapefruit sections, grenadine
Pineapple chunks, melon balls
Fruit cocktail, unpeeled red apple wedges
Peach slices, grapefruit sections, blueberries
Pear chunks, pineapple tidbits, seedless grapes

Garnishes for Fruit Cups

Small ball of Sherbet	Sugar-frosted edge of cup
Strawberry with green stem left on	Sprig of mint
	Lemon or lime wedge
Few berries	Cranberry Sauce

SEAFOOD COCKTAILS
Shrimp, lobster, crab meat, tuna salmon or a combination may be served chilled and varied in many ways with interesting dressings.

Seafood Cocktail Suggestions
Crabmeat in half avocado
Shrimp and tuna in hollowed-out tomato
Salmon and capers in lettuce-lined sherbet glass
Shrimp and grapefruit sections in watercress nest
Salmon and tart apple wedges
Tuna and quartered deviled egg

Cocktail Dressing Suggestions
Catsup, prepared horseradish
Seafood-chili sauce dressing
Mayonnaise, pickle relish, curry powder
Mayonnaise, chopped chives, tarragon vinegar
Mayonnaise, prepared mustard, prepared horseradish,
   chopped onion and parsley

JUICE COCKTAILS
Both fruit and vegetable juices make excellent first courses when served chilled, just as they come from the can or jar. Garnishes add zest and attractiveness, and may be as simple as mint leaves or a wedge of lime for fruit drinks, or chopped parsley for vegetable ones. They may be more elaborate, such as tiny squares of a frozen whipped cream-horseradish-chopped chives mixture to float on hot consomme and tomato juice.

Fruit Juice Combinations
Pineapple, grapefruit
Orange juice, apricot nectar,
   ginger-ale
Orange-grapefruit, pepper-
   mint flavor
Cranberry, apple, lemon sherbet
Apple, lime, ginger ale
Grape, lemonade
Unsweetened grapefruit juice,
   syrup from canned fruit

Vegetable Juice Combinations
Vegetable juice cocktail,
   chopped chives
Tomato juice, dash Tabasco
   Worcestershire sauce,
   lemon wedges
Clam, tomato, cold or hot
Sauerkraut, tomato
Consomme, tomato or vege-
   table juice cocktail, hot

Juice with Sherbet Floats—Many combinations of fruit juice and syrup from canned fruits may be featured, spiked with a bit of lemon or lime juice, if needed, and dressed up with a small dipper of sherbet.

Juice Over Fruit—Various fruit cups, such as combinations of grapefruit and orange sections with melon balls, are enhanced when a small quantity of either canned juice or syrup made from canned juice is added.

MEAT AND WHAT TO SERVE WITH IT
Beef

Beef Cut	ROAST
Soup or appetizer	Corn chowder, Split pea, Vegetable
Starchy food	Browned potatoes, Mashed potatoes, Boiled potatoes
Other vegetable	Fresh lima beans, Fried eggplant, Asparagus
Bread, rolls, etc.	Parkerhouse rolls, Bread, Soft bun
Accompaniment	Yorkshire pudding, Sage dressing, Pickles
Salad	Lettuce, Apple and celery, Sliced tomato
Dessert	Lemon pie, Ice cream and cake, Peach shortcake

Beef Cut	POT ROAST
Soup or appetizer	Cream of Celery, Tomato, Potato
Starchy food	Boiled noodles, Baked potatoes
Other vegetable	Buttered carrot strips, Buttered green peas, Buttered succotash
Bread, rolls, etc.	Bread, Cheese biscuits, Hot rolls
Accompaniment	Horseradish, Chili sauce, Pickled onions
Salad	Cabbage and apple, Cucumber and onion, Banana
Dessert	Stewed apricots, Baked custard, Butterscotch Pudding

Beef Cut	STEAK
Soup or appetizer	Cream of asparagus, Bean, Chicken
Starchy food	French fried potatoes, Escalloped potatoes, Hashed brown potatoes
Other vegetable	Fried onions, Cauliflower, Baked corn
Bread, rolls, etc.	Pan rolls, Sour milk biscuits, Hot rolls
Accompaniment	Pickled beets, Carrot sticks, Celery
Salad	Combination sliced cucumber, String bean
Dessert	Coconut cream pie, Chocolate pudding, Baked apple

Beef Cut	STEW
Soup or appetizer	Clam chowder, Tomato consomme, Fruit Juice
Starchy food	Rice, Boiled potatoes, Macaroni

Other vegetable	Onions, Carrots, Rutabagas
Bread, rolls, etc.	Corn bread, Whole wheat bread, White bread
Accompaniment	Piccalilli, Radishes, Spiced crab apples
Salad	Fruit, Pimiento, Raw vegetable
Dessert	Layer cake, Rice pudding, Fruit and cookies

Beef Cut	**CORNED BEEF**
Soup or Appetizer	Rice and tomato, Barley, Cream of Spinach
Starchy food	Boiled potatoes, Parsleyed potatoes, Buttered noodles
Other vegetable	Boiled cabbage, Buttered carrots, Turnips
Bread, rolls, etc.	Rye bread, White bread, Hard rolls
Accompaniment	Mustard sauce, Dill pickles, Marmalade
Salad	Celery, Pineapple, Carrot and raisin
Dessert	Fruit gelatin, Banana pudding, Gingerbread

Beef Cut	**HAMBURGER STEAK**
Soup or appetizer	Lima Bean, Potato and carrot, Cream of Corn
Starchy food	Cream potatoes, Fried potatoes, Au gratin potatoes
Other vegetable	Buttered beets, String beans, Summer squash
Bread, rolls, etc.	Hot biscuits, Raisin bread
Accompaniment	Catsup, Green onions, Jam
Salad	Cole slaw, Lettuce and egg, Beet
Dessert	Bread custard, Chocolate pie, Doughnuts

Lamb

Lamb Cut	**ROAST OR LOAF**
Soup or appetizer	Tomato Juice
Starchy food	Mashed sweet potatoes, Parsleyed potatoes, Browned potatoes
Other vegetable	Buttered broccoli, Mashed turnips, Fritter fried egg plant
Bread, rolls, etc.	Parkerhouse rolls, Bread, Soft bun
Accompaniment	Mint sauce, Mint jelly, Assorted pickles
Salad	Macedoine of vegetables, Carrot and pineapple, Lettuce and radish
Dessert	Ice cream and cake, Peach pie, Cornstarch pudding

Lamb Cut	**CHOPS OR PATTIES**
Soup or appetizer	Rice, Beef bouillon, Onion
Starchy food	Lyonnaise potatoes, French fried potatoes, Spanish rice
Other vegetable	New peas, Butter beans, Glazed carrots
Bread, rolls, etc.	Sandwich buns, Raisin bread, Hot rolls

Accompaniment Tart jelly, Celery-onions, Mint ice
Salad Bacon-combination, Waldorf, Sliced tomato
Dessert Berry shortcake, Custard pie, Cantaloupe

Lamb Cut **STEW**
Soup or appetizer Puree of green pea, Potato chowder, Fruit
  cocktail
Starchy food Steamed rice, Baked noodles, Boiled potatoes
Other vegetable Julienne green beans, Carrot rings, Buttered
  lima beans
Bread, rolls, etc. Hot Biscuits, Corn bread, French bread
Accompaniment Spiced beets, Radishes, Sour pickles
Salad Prune and carrot, Vegetable, Pear and
  grated cheese
Dessert Bread pudding with chocolate sauce, Berry
  pie, Apricot tapioca

Veal
Veal Cut **ROAST**
Soup or appetizer Puree of bean, Green peas, Consomme
Starchy food French baked potatoes, Baked sweet potatoes,
  Mashed potatoes
Other vegetable Mashed squash, Succotash, Steamed spinach
Bread, rolls, etc. Bread, Hot rolls, Baking powder biscuits
Accompaniment Sweet pickles, Raspberry jam, Olives-celery
Salad Tomato and cucumber, Cabbage and pineapple,
  Celery and nut
Dessert Cherry pie, Brown betty, Chocolate ice cream

Veal Cut **CUTLETS OR CHOPS**
Soup or appetizer Noodle, Barley and tomato, Vegetable, Lentil,
  Chicken and rice, Cream of tomato
Starchy food French baked potatoes, Baked sweet potatoes,
  Mashed potatoes, Escalloped potatoes
Other vegetable Harvard beets, Carrots and peas, Wax beans,
  Carrots and onions, Peas, Braised celery
Bread, rolls, etc. Bread, Parkerhouse rolls, Finger rolls, Graham
  Bread
Accompaniment Cranberry sauce, Tomato sauce, Currant jelly
Salad Peach and cottage cheese, Lettuce, Asparagus
Dessert Apple cobbler, White layer cake, Tapioca
  pudding

Pork

Pork Cut	ROAST
Soup or appetizer	Beef broth, Cream of cabbage, French onion
Starchy food	Whipped potatoes, Buttered diced potatoes, Sweet potatoes
Other vegetable	German sauerkraut, Creamed spinach, Broccoli
Bread, rolls, etc.	Bread, Hot rolls, Raisin bread
Accompaniment	Applesauce, Brown gravy, Tart jelly
Salad	Head lettuce, Cole slaw, Banana and nut
Dessert	Lemon ice, Custard pie, Baked pears

Pork Cut	CHOPS
Soup or appetizer	Macaroni, Clam juice, Chicken and rice
Starchy food	Cottage fried potatoes, Baked potatoes, French baked potatoes
Other vegetable	Cabbage au gratin, Glazed carrots, Green peas
Bread, rolls, etc.	French bread, Parkerhouse rolls, Graham bread
Accompaniment	Fried apple rings, Marmalade, Celery
Salad	Pineapple and celery, Combination, Sliced tomato
Dessert	Cherry dumplings, Orange gelatin, Spice cake

Pork Cut	SPARERIBS
Soup or appetizer	Cream of celery, Tomato, Puree of split pea
Starchy food	Boiled potatoes, French fried sweet potatoes, Mashed potatoes
Other vegetable	Buttered corn on the cob, Buttered mixed vegetables, Buttered wax beans
Bread, rolls, etc.	Corn bread, Hot biscuits, Rye bread
Accompaniment	Apple stuffing, Barbecue sauce, Sliced onions
Salad	Fresh fruit, Cabbage and green pepper, Beet and cucumber
Dessert	Lemon cream pie, Fresh fruit and cookies, Caramel custard

Pork Cut	BAKED HAM
Soup or appetizer	Corn chowder
Starchy food	Candied yams, Spanish rice
Other vegetable	Steamed cabbage, Green beans, Asparagus
Bread, rolls, etc.	Vienna bread, Muffins, Bread
Accompaniment	Raisin sauce, Jelly or jam, Radishes, Green onions
Salad	Raw vegetable, Pineapple and cottage cheese
Dessert	Chocolate ice cream, Apricot pie, Fresh fruit and cookies

Pork Cut	**BOILED HAM**
Soup or appetizer	Lentil, Tomato and rice
Starchy food	Mashed sweet potatoes, Parslied potatoes
Other vegetable	Corn pudding, Black-eyed peas, Spinach
Bread, rolls, etc.	Soft bun bread, Pan rolls, Rye bread
Accompaniment	Mustard pickles, Spiced crab apples, Horse-radish
Salad	Apple and date, Onion and cucumber, Cabbage and peanut
Dessert	Banana cream pie, Pineapple ice, Fruit gelatin

Pork Cut	**HAM SLICE**
Soup or appetizer	Pineapple juice, Vegetable, Cream of asparagus
Starchy food	Fried corn meal mush, Baked potatoes, Curried rice
Other vegetable	Baked corn and tomatoes, Fresh lima beans, Creamed carrots
Bread, rolls, etc.	Sour milk biscuits, Bread, Sandwich buns
Accompaniment	Sweet pickles, Cottage cheese, Onion gravy
Salad	Apple, celery and nut, Hearts of lettuce, Tomato
Dessert	Rhubarb pie, Coconut custard, Lemon loaf cake

Pork Cut or Meat Dish	**SAUSAGE**
Soup or appetizer	Puree of potato, Noodle, Macaroni and tomato
Starchy food	Creamed potatoes, Baked sweet potatoes, Fried potatoes
Other vegetable	Hot spiced beets, Boston baked beans, Mexican style corn with green pepper
Bread, rolls, etc.	Corn bread, Bread, Hard rolls
Accompaniment	Browned pineapple, Milk gravy, Watermelon pickles
Salad	Green bean,Carrot and raisin, Spinach and hard-cooked egg
Dessert	Apple pie, Chocolate cake, Chilled melon

MISCELLANEOUS

Meat dish	**CHILI**
Soup or appetizer	Tomato, Cream of potato, Beef broth
Starchy food	Buttered diced potatoes, Steamed rice, Baked potatoes
Other vegetable	Broccoli, Green Beans, Vinegar, Spinach
Bread, Rolls, etc.	French bread, Hard rolls, White bread
Accompaniment	Pickled beets, Dill pickles, Carrot sticks
Salad	Green pepper, Lettuce and tomato, Celery
Dessert	Gelatin and oatmeal cookies, Coconut layer cake

Meat dish	**FRANKFURTERS**
Soup or appetizer	Oyster stew, Split pea, Cream of corn
Starchy food	Hot potato salad, Spanish rice, Baked Macaroni
Other vegetable	Steamed sauerkraut, Baked beans, Whole kernel corn
Bread, rolls, etc.	Rye bread, Sandwich buns, Bread
Accompaniment	Barbecue sauce, Mustard, Catsup
Salad	Cabbage and pineapple, Beet and onion, Sliced tomato
Dessert	Apricot brown betty, Pineapple tapioca, Strawberry shortcake

Meat dish	**MEAT LOAF**
Soup or appetizer	Consomme, Puree of white bean, Tomato juice
Starchy food	Lyonnaise potatoes, Hashed in cream potatoes, Curried rice
Other vegetable	Black-eyed peas, Fried eggplant, Creamed onions
Bread, rolls, etc.	Finger rolls, Graham bread, Corn bread
Accompaniment	Spanish sauce, Chili sauce, Mustard pickles
Salad	Fruit, Combination, Carrot, prune and celery
Dessert	Jelly roll, Coffee ice cream, Peach cobbler

Meat dish	**HEART**
Soup or appetizer	Navy bean, Vegetable chowder, Onion
Starchy food	Buttered noodles, Candied yams, Fried potatoes
Other vegetable	Boiled onions, Fried corn, Escalloped tomatoes
Bread, rolls, etc.	Parkerhouse rolls, Baking powder biscuits, Bread
Accompaniment	Sage stuffing, Spiced gooseberries, Currant jelly
Salad	Cole slaw, Asparagus, Combination Fruit
Dessert	Apricots and brownies, Prune whip, Raisin pie

Meat dish	**LIVER**
Soup or appetizer	Tomato juice, Spring vegetable, Celery
Starchy food	French fried potatoes, Potatoes in jackets, Steamed brown rice
Other vegetable	Hot slaw, Lima beans, French fried onions
Bread, rolls, etc.	White bread, Raisin bread, Hot rolls
Accompaniment	Bacon, Pickled onions, Assorted pickles
Salad	Pineapple and cheese, Endive, Banana
Dessert	Pumpkin pie, Peaches and cream, Cup cakes

Meat dish	**TONGUE**
Soup or appetizer	Noodle, Beef broth with rice
Starchy food	Boiled potatoes, Mashed potatoes, Escalloped potatoes
Other vegetable	Steamed spinach, Wax beans, Braised celery
Bread, rolls, etc.	Rye bread, Hard rolls, Bread
Accompaniment	Raisin sauce, Spanish sauce, Horseradish
Salad	Spiced beet, Pineapple, Lettuce
Dessert	Chocolate pudding, Mince pie, Ice cream with fruit sauce

Meat dish	**ASSORTED COLD MEATS**
Soup or appetizer	Clam chowder, Bean puree, Onion au gratin
Starchy food	Potato salad, Macaroni, Creamed whole potatoes
Other vegetable	Sliced jumbo tomatoes, Sliced cucumbers vinaigrette, Succotash
Bread, rolls, etc.	Cheese biscuits, Bread, Parkerhouse rolls
Accompaniment	Sweet pickles, Sliced cheese, Mustard pickles
Salad	Shredded lettuce, Fruit, String bean and celery
Dessert	Apple turnovers, Rhubarb sauce and cookies, Cottage pudding

Menus for 52 Weeks

In the menus that follow, an item preceded by 🎩 can be prepared from recipe in THE PROFESSIONAL CHEF; an item preceded by 🎩🎩 can be prepared from recipe in THE PROFESSIONAL CHEF'S BAKING RECIPES. Figures in parenthesis after these menu items list page for recipe in designated book. (For more information on menu codes, see p. 8.)

1st Week

SUNDAY	MONDAY

BREAKFAST
 Chilled Melon
 Scrambled Eggs
 Hickory Smoked
  Bacon
 Cinnamon Raisin
  Pecan Rolls
 Beverage(s)

DINNER
 Cranberry Juice
 Fried Chicken
 Mashed Potatoes
 Buttered Asparagus
 Jellied Pineapple and
  Carrot Salad
🍳🍳Clover Leaf
  Rolls (46)
 Butter of Margarine
🍳Sponge Cake (319)
  with Vanilla Sauce
 Beverage(s)

SUPPER
🍳Celery Soup (268)
 Assorted Cold Cuts
 Tomato Slice
🍳Cole Slaw(223)
 Potato Chips
 Bread
 Butter or Margarine
 Catsup-Mustard
🍳🍳Old Fashioned
  Molasses
   Cookies (73)
 Beverage(s)

8:30 P.M.
 Beverage(s)*

BREAKFAST
 Assorted Fruit Juices
 Selected Cold Cereals
  or
 Oatmeal with Cream
 Toast, Buttered
 Jelly
 Beverage(s)

DINNER
 Cherry Juice
 Salisbury Steak
 Browned Potatoes
 Buttered Green Beans
🍳Mixed Vegetable Salad
  (219)
 Bread, white and dark
 Butter or Margarine
 Fruit Gelatin Dessert
 Beverage(s)

SUPPER
 Split Pea Soup
 Grilled Ham Sand-
  wich
 Pickles
🍳Carrot and Raisin
  Salad (229)
 Spice Cake
 Beverage(s)

8:30 P.M.
 Beverage(s)*

TUESDAY

BREAKFAST
  Orange Sections
  Poached Egg on
    Buttered Toast
🍳🍳Hot Rolls (44)
  Butter or Margarine
  Jam
  Beverage(s)

DINNER
  Apple Juice
🍳Pork Roast (87)
🍳Glazed Sweet
    Potatoes (177)
  Tomatoes with
    Celery Sauce
🍳Perfection
    Salad (234)
🍳🍳Cornbread (44)
  Butter or Margarine
    and Jam
  Baked Custard
  Beverage(s)

SUPPER
  Spanish Rice with
    Chopped Meat
🍳Fruit Slaw (223)
  Bread, white and dark
  Butter or Margarine
  Lemon Oatmeal
    Drop Cookies
  Beverage(s)

8:30 P.M.
  Beverage(s)*

WEDNESDAY

BREAKFAST
  Bananas with Cream
  Golden French Toast
  Maple Syrup or Honey
  Canadian Bacon
  Beverage(s)

DINNER
🍳Chicken Pie (104)
  Broccoli, buttered
  Spiced Peaches
  Bread, white and dark
  Butter or Margarine
  Chocolate Pudding
  Beverage(s)

SUPPER
🍳 Beef Rice Soup (256)
🍳Egg Salad Sandwiches
    (white and dark
    bread) (224)
  Apple and Cheese
    Wedges
🍳🍳Prune Whip (77)
  Beverage(s)

8:30 P.M.
  Beverage(s)*

THURSDAY

BREAKFAST
Assorted Juices
Selected Cold Cereal
or
Wheatena with Cream
✺✺Corn Muffins (44)
Butter or Margarine
Jelly
Beverage(s)

DINNER
✺Baked Ham (85)
Carrot Slices
Boiled Potatoes
✺Jellied Perfection
Salad (234)
Bread, white and dark
Butter or Margarine
Butterscotch Ice-
Box Cookies
Beverage(s)

SUPPER
✺Vegetable Soup (261)
Fricassee of Lamb
✺✺on Hot Biscuit (3)
✺Tossed Green Salad
with Italian
Dressing (219)
Chilled Pear Halves
Beverage(s)

8:30 P.M.
Beverage(s)*

FRIDAY

BREAKFAST
Grapefruit Half
Fried Eggs
Plantation Sausage
Toast
Butter or Margarine
Jam
Beverage(s)

DINNER
✺Fried Scallops with
Tartar Sauce (167)
✺Parslied Buttered
Potatoes (192)
Green Beans
Sunshine Salad
Bread, white and dark
Butter or Margarine
Lemon Meringue Pie
Beverage(s)

SUPPER
Cream of Vichoyoisse
Soup
✺Tomato Stuffed with
Tuna Salad (221)
Potato Chips
✺✺Hot Rolls (46)
Butter or Margarine
Pineapple Chunks
Chilled
Beverage(s)

8:30 P.M.
Beverage(s)*

SATURDAY

BREAKFAST
  Assorted Juices
  Buttermilk Pancakes
  Honey Butter
  Warm Maple Syrup
  Grilled Ham
  Beverage(s)

DINNER
  Swiss Steak (49)
  Boiled Potatoes
  Buttered Cauliflower
  Pineapple Slaw (223)
  Bread, white and dark
  Butter or Margarine
  Chilled Peaches
  Beverage(s)

SUPPER
  French Onion Soup (253)
  Toasted Cheese
      Sandwiches with Bacon
  Waldorf Salad (226)
  Peanut Butter
      Cookies (71)
  Beverage(s)

8:30 P.M.
  Beverage(s)*

2nd Week

SUNDAY

BREAKFAST
  Chilled Orange Juice
  Country Fresh Eggs
  Grilled Sausages
  Almond Nut
    Doughnuts
  Butter or Margarine
  Beverage(s)

DINNER
  Apple Juice
  ☕Roast Chicken (106)
  ☕Herb Dressing
    (116-117)
  Mashed Potatoes
  ☕Baked Hubbard
    Squash (188)
  Jellied Cranberry
    Salad
  ☕☕Clover Leaf Rolls (46)
  Butter or Margarine
  Raspberry Sherbet—
    Cookies
  Beverage(s)

SUPPER
  ☕Tomato-Rice
    Bouillon (256)
  Ham and Cheese
    Sandwiches, (dark
    and white bread)
  Relish Tray
  ☕☕Apple Crisp (76)
  Beverage(s)

8:30 P.M.
  Beverage(s)*

MONDAY

BREAKFAST
  Fruit in Season
  Old Fashioned Waffles
  Honey or Maple Syrup
  Soft Butter
  Beverage(s)

DINNER
  Roast Veal
  Browned Potatoes
  Barbecued Lima Beans
  Pineapple and Carrot
    Salad
  ☕☕Rolls (48)
  Butter or Margarine
  ☕☕Chocolate Cake (29)
  Beverage(s)

SUPPER
  Split Pea Soup
  Turkey Salad
  Tomato Slices
  Bread, white and dark
  Butter or Margarine—
    Jelly
  Vanilla Pudding—
    Caramel Sauce
  Beverage(s)

8:30 P.M.
  Beverage(s)*

TUESDAY

BREAKFAST
 Assorted Juices
☕Poached Egg on
  Buttered Toast (19)
 Orange Pineapple
  Danish Roll
 Butter or Margarine
 Jelly
 Beverage(s)

DINNER
 Salisbury Steak
☕Scalloped Potatoes
  (197)
 Asparagus
☕Chopped Cole
  Slaw (223)
 Bread, white and dark
 Butter or Margarine
 Chilled Pears
 Beverage(s)

SUPPER
☕Consomme (255)
 French Toast
 Escalloped Apples
☕Pork Sausage Links
  (20,21)
☕☕ Ice Cream–Cookies (75)
 Beverage(s)

8:30 P.M.
 Beverage(s)*

WEDNESDAY

BREAKFAST
 Grapefruit Half
 Selected Cold Cereal
  or
 Cream of Wheat,
  with Cream
 Golden Toast
 Butter or Margarine
 Jelly
 Beverage(s)

DINNER
 Roast Beef and Gravy
 Mashed Potatoes
 Broccoli, buttered
☕Beet Salad (216)
☕☕Muffins (43)
 Butter or Margarine
☕☕Applesauce Cake (18)
 Beverage(s)

SUPPER
☕Creamed Celery Soup
  (268)
 Broiled Hamburger Sand-
  wich
☕Cole Slaw (223)
 Potato Chips
 Catsup-Mustard-Onions
 Butterscotch Ice Box
  Cookies
 Beverage(s)

8:30 P.M.
 Beverage(s)*

THURSDAY

BREAKFAST
Chilled Fruit Juice
Buttermilk Pancakes
Soft Butter
Warm Maple Syrup
  or Honey
Beverage(s)

DINNER
♨Meat Loaf (65)
♨Potatoes au Gratin
  (196)
Green Beans
♨♨Rolls (46)
Butter or Margarine
Fresh Orange Cake
Beverage(s)

SUPPER
♨Vegetable Soup
  (261)
Cheese Rarebit with
  Bacon on Toast
♨Lettuce Salad/
  dressing (218)
Peach Tapioca
  Pudding
Beverage(s)

8:30 P.M.
Beverage(s)*

FRIDAY

BREAKFAST
Orange Slices
♨Scrambled Eggs (19)
Crisp Bacon
Toast
Butter or Margarine
Jelly
Beverage(s)

DINNER
Tomato Juice
Oven Fried Ocean
  Perch Fillets
♨Scalloped Potatoes
  (197)
Brussel Sprouts,
  buttered
♨Shredded Lettuce
  Salad/dressing
  (238)
♨♨Brownies (36)
Beverage(s)

SUPPER
♨Clam Chowder (252)
♨Savory Shrimp and
  Rice Casserole (150)
Cabbage and Green
  Pepper Salad
♨♨Rolls (47)
Butter or Margarine
Chilled Pineapple
  Chunks
Beverage(s)

8:30 P.M.
Beverage(s)*

SATURDAY

BREAKFAST
  Stewed Prunes,
    Lemon Slices
  Assorted Cold Cereals
    or
  Oatmeal with Cream
  Cinnamon Streusel
    Danish
  Butter or Margarine
  Beverage(s)

DINNER
  ✿Hungarian Goulash
    with Noodles (41)
  Royal Orange and
    Apple Salad
  French Bread
  Butter or Margarine
  ✿✿Coconut Custard Pie
    (58)
  Beverage(s)

SUPPER
  ✿Individual Chicken Pies
    (104)
  ✿Head Lettuce with
    Fruits (227,228)
  ✿✿Cloverleaf Rolls (46)
  Butter or Margarine
  Chocolate Pudding,
    Whipped Cream
  Beverage(s)

8:30 P.M.
  Beverage(s)*

NOTES
(Special Events,
Residents'
Birthdays, etc.)

3rd Week

SUNDAY	MONDAY

BREAKFAST
Grapefruit and
  Orange Sections
🍳Bacon Omelet (20)
Golden Toast
Butter or Margarine
Jam or Marmalade
Beverage(s)

BREAKFAST
Chilled Fruit Juice
Assorted Cold Cereals
  or
Wheatena, with Cream
Cheese Danish Roll
Butter or Margarine
Beverage(s)

DINNER
Veal Roast
Fluffy Mashed
  Potatoes
Cauliflower a la
  Creole
🍳Cucumber and Onion
  Salad (220)
🍳🍳Rolls (45)
Butter or Margarine
🍳🍳Apple Pie a la
  Mode (56)
Beverage(s)

DINNER
🍳Baked Ham (85)
🍳Baked Squash (188,189)
🍳Creamed Spinach (190)
Bread, white and dark
Butter or Margarine
Cabbage and Green
  Pepper Salad
Orange Cake
Beverage(s)

SUPPER
🍳Chicken Noodle
  Soup (256)
Assorted Sandwiches
  (Egg, Cheese,
  Ham, Chicken)
Raw Vegetable Tray
🍳🍳Chocolate Eclair (67)
Beverage(s)

SUPPER
Beef Vegetable Soup
🍳Chicken Chow Mein (100)
🍳Fluffy White Rice (24)
🍳Cottage Cheese and
  Pineapple Salad (229)
🍳Apple Strudel (318)
Beverage(s)

8:30 P.M.
Beverage(s) *

8:30 P.M.
Beverage(s) *

TUESDAY

BREAKFAST
Stewed Apricots
Fried Egg
Hickory Smoked
Bacon
Golden Toast
Butter or Margarine
Jam
Beverage(s)

DINNER
♕ Swiss Steak (60)
Parsley Buttered
Potatoes
Harvard Beets
Corn Relish
Bread, white and
dark
Butter or Margarine
Steamed Prune
Pudding
Beverage(s)

SUPPER
Ham Chowder
♕ Deviled Egg and
Olive Sandwich
Filling (224)
(dark and light
bread)
♕ Scalloped
Tomatoes (187)
Jellied Pineapple
and Carrot Salad
♕♕ Banana Cake (22)
Beverage(s)

8:30 P.M.
Beverage(s)*

WEDNESDAY

BREAKFAST
Chilled Pineapple Juice
Assorted Cold Cereals
or
Oatmeal with Cream
Hot Rolls
Butter or Margarine
Jelly
Beverage(s)

DINNER
Beef Pot Roast and
Gravy
Browned Potatoes
Lima Beans in Butter
Sauce
♕ Green Salad/dressing
(239)
Bread, white and
dark
Butter or Margarine
Snow Pudding
Beverage(s)

SUPPER
Apple Juice
French Toast
Hot Syrup
♕ Sausage Patties (21)
Chilled Pineapple
Chunks—Cookies
Beverage(s)

8:30 P.M.
Beverage(s)*

THURSDAY	FRIDAY
BREAKFAST Grapefruit Sections Grenadine 🍳Poached Egg on Buttered Toast (19) Apple Danish Roll Butter or Margarine Beverage(s)	**BREAKFAST** Chilled Prune Juice Old Fashioned Waffles Honey Butter Warm Maple Syrup Beverage(s)
DINNER Yankee Pot Roast Fresh Vegetables 🍳 Apple Nut Salad (223) Bread, dark and white Butter or Margarine 🍳🍳Iced Yellow Cup Cakes (29,32) Beverage(s)	**DINNER** Fried Ocean Perch Fillets Baked Rice Asparagus Sunshine Salad Bread, white and dark Butter or Margarine Grape-Nut Custard Beverage(s)
SUPPER 🍳Scotch Broth (257) 🍳Macaroni au Gratin (191) 🍳Tomato on Shredded Lettuce with dressing (218) 🍳🍳Warm Rolls (46) Butter or Margarine Vanilla Cream Pudding, Chocolate Sauce Beverage(s)	**SUPPER** 🍳Clam Chowder (252) New England Lasagne with Tomato Sauce Jellied Pineapple and Carrot Salad 🍳🍳Rolls (48) Butter or Margarine Dutch Apple Pie Beverage(s)
8:30 P.M. Beverage(s)*	8:30 P.M. Beverage(s)*

SATURDAY

BREAKFAST
Chilled Fresh Melon
Slice
Assorted Cold Cereals
or
Cream of Wheat,
warm milk
Cinnamon Raisin
Pecan Roll
Butter or Margarine
Beverage(s)

DINNER
Veal Cutlet,
Mushroom Sauce
Delmonico Potatoes
(196)
Buttered Green Beans
Green Salad/dressing
(239)
Pound Cake (21)
Beverage(s)

SUPPER
Potato Chowder (270)
Creamed Chipped Beef
on Toast
Crisp Vegetable Salad/
dressing (221)
Bread, white and dark
Butter or Margarine
Fruited Oatmeal Drops
(75)
Whipped Cherry Gelatin
(231)
Beverage(s)

8:30 P.M.
Beverage(s)*

NOTES
(Special Events,
Residents'
Birthdays, etc.)

4th Week

SUNDAY

BREAKFAST
Chilled Melon
🍳 Scrambled Eggs (19)
Hickory Smoked
  Bacon
Cinnamon Raisin
  Pecan Rolls
Beverage(s)

DINNER
🍳 Roast Pork (87)
🍳 Parsley Buttered
  Potatoes (192)
Chopped Spinach
  with Bacon
  Dressing
Apple Sauce
🍳🍳 Corn Bread (44)
Butter or Margarine
🍳 🍳 Vanilla Ice Cream—
  Cookies (68, 69)
Beverage(s)

SUPPER
Tomato-Barley Soup
Assorted Cold Cuts
  and Cheese
Potato Chips
Relishes
Bread, white and dark
Butter or Margarine
Honey Pecan Tarts
Beverage(s)

8:30 P.M.
Beverage(s)*

MONDAY

BREAKFAST
Assorted Fruit Juices
Selected Cold Cereals
  or
Oatmeal, with Cream
Toast, Buttered
Jelly
Beverage(s)

DINNER
🍳 Meat Loaf (65)
Mashed Potatoes
Buttered Carrot Rings
🍳 Pears and Lime Gelatin
  Salad (233)
Graham Muffins
Butter or Margarine
Peach Tapioca
Beverage(s)

SUPPER
Split Pea Soup
Creamed Chicken
  Almondine
🍳🍳 Hot Biscuits (3)
🍳 Cabbage, Apple, Raisin
  Salad (223)
Lemon Refrigerator
  Dessert
Beverage(s)

8:30 P.M.
Beverage(s)*

TUESDAY

BREAKFAST
  Orange Sections
  ♨ Poached Egg on
    Buttered Toast (19)
♨♨ Hot Rolls (40)
  Butter or Margarine
  Jam
  Beverage(s)

DINNER
  ♨ Baked Ham with
    Raisin Sauce (85)
  ♨ Glazed Sweet
    Potatoes (177)
  ♨ Succotash (185)
♨♨ Clover-Leaf Rolls
    (46)
  Butter or Margarine
  Orange Layer Cake
    with Orange
    Butter Icing
  Beverage(s)

SUPPER
  ♨ Vegetable Soup
    (261)
  Ham Salad Sand-
    wich, (white and
    dark bread)
  ♨ Jellied Tomato Salad
    (234)
  Celery and Carrot
    Sticks
♨♨ Apple Crisp (76)
  Beverage(s)

8:30 P.M.
  Beverage(s)*

WEDNESDAY

BREAKFAST
  Bananas with Cream
  Golden French Toast
  Maple Syrup or Honey
  Canadian Bacon
  Beverage(s)

DINNER
  Braised Chicken Legs
    in Sauce
  ♨ Stuffed Baked Potatoes
    (195)
  Lima Beans
  ♨ Tossed Green Salad/
    dressing (218,221)
  Bread, white and dark
  Butter or Margarine
  Peach Chiffon Pudding
  Beverage(s)

SUPPER
  ♨ Tomato Soup (252)
  Macaroni and Cheese
  Pickled Beet Salad
  Cubed Gelatin
  Honey-Nut Spice Cake
  Beverage(s)

8:30 P.M.
  Beverage(s)*

THURSDAY	FRIDAY
BREAKFAST	**BREAKFAST**

THURSDAY

BREAKFAST
  Assorted Juices
  Selected Cold Cereal
    or
  Wheatena, with cream
♔♔ Corn Muffins (44)·
  Butter or Margarine
  Jelly
  Beverage(s)

DINNER
  Baked Spare Ribs
    and Sauerkraut
  Boiled Potatoes
  Candied Carrot Coins
  Cider Fruit Salad
♔♔ Rolls (48)
  Butter or Margarine
♔♔ Pound Cake-Chilled
    Apple Sauce (21)
  Beverage(s)

SUPPER
  Puree of Lima Bean
    Soup
  Hamburgers on Bun
  Relishes
  Sliced Tomatoes
    on Lettuce
♔♔ Custard Pie (58)
  Beverage(s)

8:30 P.M.
  Beverage(s)*

FRIDAY

BREAKFAST
  Grapefruit Half
  Fried Eggs
  Plantation Sausage
  Toast
  Butter or Margarine
  Jam
  Beverage(s)

DINNER
  Tuna a la King in
    Pastry Shell
  Buttered Peas
  Sliced Tomato and
    Lettuce Salad
♔♔ Rolls (46)
  Butter or Margarine
  Orange Cup Cakes
  Beverage(s)

SUPPER
♔ Manhattan Clam
    Chowder (273)
♔ Welsh Rarebit on
    Buttered Toast
    (259)
♔ Tossed Green Salad
    (239)
  Blue Plums—Cookies
  Beverage(s)

8:30 P.M.
  Beverage(s)*

SATURDAY

BREAKFAST
  Assorted Juices
  Buttermilk Pancakes
  Honey Butter
  Warm Maple Syrup
  Grilled Ham
  Beverage(s)

DINNER
  Pan Fried Lamb Patties
  Mashed Potatoes
  Scalloped Corn
  ♧ Jellied Vegetable
      Salad (234)
  ♧ ♧ Rolls (45)
  Butter or Margarine
  Pineapple Chunks
  Beverage(s)

SUPPER
  ♧ Minestrone Soup (249)
  Beef and Whipped
      Potato au Gratin
  ♧ Waldorf Salad (226)
  Fruit Gelatin with
      Whipped Cream
  Beverage(s)

8:30 P.M.
  Beverage(s)*

NOTES
(Special Events,
Residents'
Birthdays, etc.)

5th Week

SUNDAY

BREAKFAST
    Chilled Orange Juice
    Country Fresh Eggs
    Grilled Sausages
♕♕Almond Nut
        Doughnuts (41)
    Butter or Margarine
    Beverage(s)

DINNER
    Cranberry Juice
    Roast Beef and Gravy
    Browned Potatoes
    Lyonnaise Green
        Beans
♕Lettuce Wedge
        with dressing (240)
♕♕Rolls (48)
    Butter or Margarine
    Fudge Pudding with
        Topping
    Beverage(s)

SUPPER
    Vegetable-Rice Soup
    Chicken Salad
    Sliced Tomatoes
♕Stuffed Celery
        Sticks (222)
♕♕Parker House
        Rolls (46)
    Butter or Margarine
♕♕ Vanilla Ice Cream—
        Cookies (70)
    Beverage(s)

8:30 P.M.
    Beverage(s)*

MONDAY

BREAKFAST
    Fruit in Season
    Old Fashioned Waffles
    Crisp Bacon
    Honey or Maple Syrup
    Soft Butter
    Beverage(s)

DINNER
♕New England Boiled
        Dinner (62) (Corned
        Beef, Cabbage, Boiled
        Parsley Potatoes)
    Bread, white and dark
    Butter or Margarine
    Baked Rice Custard
    Beverage(s)

SUPPER
    Creole Soup
    Assorted Sandwiches
        (Egg, Ham, Cheese,
        Turkey)
    Relishes
♕♕Butterscotch
        Brownies (36)
    Beverage(s)

8:30 P.M.
    Beverage(s)*

TUESDAY

BREAKFAST
  Assorted Juices
  🍳Poached Egg on
    Buttered Toast (19)
  Orange Pineapple
    Danish Roll
  Butter or Margarine
  Jelly
  Beverage(s)

DINNER
  🍳Braised Short Ribs—
    Vegetable
    Gravy (52)
  Boiled Potatoes
  Spinach Souffle
  Royal Orange and
    Apple Salad
  Cinnamon Spice Cake
  Beverage(s)

SUPPER
  Ham and Split Pea
    Soup
  Meat Patties
  🍳Hashed Brown
    Potatoes (194)
  🍳Cucumber and
    Onion Salad (220)
  🍳🍳Rolls (45)
  Butter or Margarine
  Chilled Pears—
  🍳 Cookies (317)

8:30 P.M.
  Beverage(s)*

WEDNESDAY

BREAKFAST
  Half Grapefruit
  Selected Cold Cereal
    or
  Cream of Wheat,
    with cream
  Golden Toast
  Butter or Margarine
  Jelly
  Beverage(s)

DINNER
  Breaded Veal Cutlets
    in Tomatoes
  🍳Scalloped Potatoes
    (197)
  Harvard Beets
  🍳Pineapple Slaw
    Salad (223)
  Bread, white and dark
  Butter or Margarine
  Apple Cobbler
  Beverage(s)

SUPPER
  🍳Cream of Celery
    Soup (268)
  Beef Pot Pie
  Buttered Carrots
  🍳🍳Rolls, home-made (46)
  Butter or Margarine
  🍳🍳Chocolate Cake (29)
  Beverage(s)

8:30 P.M.
  Beverage(s)*

THURSDAY	FRIDAY

BREAKFAST
  Chilled Fruit Juice
  Buttermilk Pancakes
  Soft Butter
  Warm Maple Syrup
    or Honey
  Beverage(s)

BREAKFAST
  Orange Slices
  ♕ Scrambled Eggs (19)
  Crisp Bacon
  Toast
  Butter or Margarine
  Jelly
  Beverage(s)

DINNER
  ♕ Baked Liver covered
    with Bacon
    Strips (36)
  Buttered Mashed
    Turnips
  Spinach with Chopped
    Bacon Dressing
  Oatmeal Rolls
  Butter or Margarine
  ♕ Tomato Aspic with
    Cottage Cheese (234)
  Crumb Spice Cake
  Beverage(s)

DINNER
  ♕ Fried Scallops (167)
  ♕ Potato Puff (Duchess)
    (193)
  Carrot and Raisin Slaw
  ♕ ♕ Crispy Corn Bread (44)
  Butter or Margarine
  Cherry Gelatin Squares
  Beverage(s)

SUPPER
  Corned Beef Hash
  Buttered Green Beans
  Bread, white and dark
  Butter or Margarine
  Vanilla Pudding with
    Caramel Sauce
  Beverage(s)

SUPPER
  ♕ French Onion
    Soup (253)
  Stuffed Peppers in
    Tomato Sauce
  Fruit Salad
  Buttered Asparagus
  Bread
  Butter or Margarine
  Peaches and Cookies
  Beverage(s)

8:30 P.M.
  Beverage(s)*

8:30 P.M.
  Beverage(s)*

SATURDAY

BREAKFAST
Stewed Prunes,
Lemon Slices
Assorted Cold Cereals
or
Oatmeal, with Cream
Cinnamon Streusel
Danish
Butter or Margarine
Beverage(s)

DINNER
Lamb Roast with
Mint Jelly (358)
Stuffed Baked
Potatoes (195)
Buttered Cauliflower
Perfection Salad (234)
Bread
Butter or Margarine
Butterscotch Bars (36)
Beverage(s)

SUPPER
Chicken Rice Soup (256)
Tuna a la King
Buttered Corn
Sunshine Salad
Cherry Pie (62)
Beverage(s)

8:30 P.M.
Beverage(s)*

6th Week

SUNDAY	MONDAY

BREAKFAST
  Grapefruit and
    Orange Sections
  🍳Bacon Omelet (20)
  Golden Toast
  Butter or Margarine
  Jam or Marmalade
  Beverage(s)

BREAKFAST
  Chilled Fruit Juice
  Assorted Cold Cereals
    or
  Wheatena, with Cream
  Cheese Danish Roll
  Butter or Margarine
  Beverage(s)

DINNER
  Oven Baked
    Chicken Legs
  🍳Potatoes au
    Gratin (196)
  Buttered Broccoli
  🍳Endive Salad/dressing (219)
  Rolls, whole wheat or
    graham
  Butter or Margarine
  Mocha Nut Cake
    with Topping
  Beverage(s)

DINNER
  🍳Swiss Steak
    Smothered in
    Tomatoes and
    Onions (60)
  🍳Browned Potatoes (359)
  Buttered Cauliflower
  🍳Shredded Lettuce
    Salad/dressing (218)
  🍳🍳Roll (48)
  Butter or Margarine
  Baked Apples
  Beverage(s)

SUPPER
  🍳English Beef Broth
    (256)
  Cold Meat Cuts
    and Cheese
  Relishes, Green and
    Black Olives
  Bread, white and dark
  Butter or Margarine
  Strawberry Ice Cream
  Beverage(s)

SUPPER
  Ground Beef
    and Spaghetti
  Lyonnaise Green Beans
  French Bread
  Butter or Margarine
  Chilled Pears
  Beverage(s)

8:30 P.M.
  Beverage(s)*

8:30 P.M.
  Beverage(s)*

TUESDAY	WEDNESDAY

BREAKFAST
Stewed Apricots
Fried Egg
Hickory Smoked
  Bacon
Golden Toast
Butter or Margarine
Jam
Beverage(s)

DINNER
Liver Creole
Mashed Potatoes
Harvard Beets
Bread, white and dark
Butter or Margarine
Strawberry-Banana
  Mold
Beverage(s)

SUPPER
Vegetable Soup (261)
Toasted Cheese Sandwich
Head Lettuce Salad/
  dressing (218)
Bread, white and dark
Butter or Margarine
Peaches–Cookies (71)
Beverage(s)

8:30 P.M.
Beverage(s)*

BREAKFAST
Chilled Pineapple Juice
Assorted Cold Cereals
  or
Oatmeal, with Cream
Hot Rolls (40)
Butter or Margarine
Jelly
Beverage(s)

DINNER
Ham Patties on a
  Pineapple Slice
Buttered Peas
Hashed Brown Potatoes
  (194)
Cabbage-Raisin-Nut
  Salad
Bread, white and dark
Butter or Margarine
Cherry Brown Betty
  (76)
Beverage(s)

SUPPER
Fiesta Hamburgers
Potato Chips
Green Beans
Grapefruit Salad,
  Cherry Topped
Fudge Pudding
Beverage(s)

8:30 P.M.
Beverage(s)*

THURSDAY	FRIDAY

BREAKFAST
    Grapefruit Sections,
       Grenadine
🍳Poached Egg on
       Buttered Toast (19)
    Apple Danish Roll
    Butter or Margarine
    Beverage(s)
	BREAKFAST
	    Chilled Prune Juice
	    Old Fashioned Waffles
	    Honey Butter
	    Warm Maple Syrup
	    Beverage(s)

DINNER
    Apple Juice
🍳Roast Chicken and
       Gravy (106)
    Buttered Rice
    Scalloped Corn
🍳Peppy Beet Salad (216)
🍳🍳Rolls (45)
    Butter or Margarine
    Mincemeat Squares
    Beverage(s)
	DINNER
	    V-8 Juice
	🍳Fried Scallops (167)
	    Buttered Spinach
	    Salad Greens/dressing
	    Plain Muffins
	    Fruit Pudding, served
	       with Hot Custard
	       Sauce
	    Beverage(s)

SUPPER
🍳Rice-Tomato
       Bouillon (256)
    Ham and Egg
       Salad Plate
🍳🍳Corn Muffins (44)
    Butter or Margarine
    Butterscotch Pudding
    Beverage(s)
	SUPPER
	🍳Cream of Asparagus
	       Soup (268)
	    Cheese Souffle
	    Lima Beans
	    Bread, white and dark
	    Butter or Margarine
	    Baked Apples
	    Beverage(s)

8:30 P.M.
    Beverage(s)*
	8:30 P.M.
	    Beverage(s)*

SATURDAY

BREAKFAST
Chilled Fresh
  Melon Slice
Assorted Cold Cereals
  or
Cream of Wheat,
  warm milk
Cinnamon Raisin
  Pecan Roll
Butter or Margarine
Beverage(s)

DINNER
Shepherd's Pie
Buttered Carrots
Cabbage Relish
Bread, white and dark
Butter or Margarine
🍳Fruit Cup (15)
Beverage(s)

SUPPER
🍳Chicken Rice Soup (256)
Beef Barbecue on Bun
🍳Potato Salad (225)
Green Beans
Chilled Peaches
Bran Applesauce
  Cookies
Beverage(s)

8:30 P.M.
Beverage(s)*

NOTES
**Special Events,
Residents'
Birthdays, etc.)**

7th Week

SUNDAY	MONDAY

BREAKFAST
Chilled Melon
Scrambled Eggs
Hickory Smoked
   Bacon
Cinnamon Raisin
   Pecan Rolls
Beverage(s)

DINNER
☕Roast Pork Loin (87)
Mashed Potatoes
Buttered Green Beans
☕Gingerale Fruit Salad
   (217)
☕☕Homemade Rolls (46)
Butter or Margarine
☕☕Golden Chiffon Cake/
   Topping (10)
Beverage(s)

SUPPER
☕Tomato Rice
   Bouillon (256)
☕Tuna Salad (221)
Shoestring Potatoes
Bread, white and dark
Butter or Margarine
☕☕Easy Mix Cookies (73)
Beverage(s)

8:30 P.M.
   Beverage(s)*

BREAKFAST
Assorted Fruit Juices
Selected Cold Cereals
   or
Oatmeal, with Cream
Toast, Buttered
Jelly
Beverage(s)

DINNER
Oven Fried Chicken
Mashed Potatoes
Baby Lima Beans
Cabbage and Green
   Pepper Salad
☕☕Rolls (45)
Butter or Margarine
☕☕Bread Pudding, Fruit
   Sauce (76)
Beverage(s)

SUPPER
☕Vegetable Soup (261)
Cheese Sandwiches and
   Ham Sandwiches
Orange, Apple and
   Banana Salad
Honey-Nut Spice
   Cake
Beverage(s)

8:30 P.M.
   Beverage(s)*

TUESDAY	WEDNESDAY

BREAKFAST
 Orange Sections
 🍳Poached Egg on
  Buttered Toast (19)
 👨‍🍳🍳Hot Rolls (48)
 Butter or Margarine
 Jam
 Beverage(s)

BREAKFAST
 Bananas with Cream
 Golden French Toast
 Maple Syrup or Honey
 Canadian Bacon
 Beverage(s)

DINNER
 Baked Lamb Loaf
 Buttered Peas
 Jellied Pineapple
  and Carrot Salad
 👨‍🍳🍳Rolls (46)
 Butter or Margarine
 Orange and Raisin
  Cup Cakes
 Beverage(s)

DINNER
 🍳Pot Roast of Beef (53)
 Browned Potatoes
 Buttered Green Peas
 🍳Pear and Cheese
  Salad/dressing (229)
 Butter or Margarine
 👨‍🍳🍳Rolls (48)
 Fruited Tapioca
 Beverage(s)

SUPPER
 🍳Chicken Soup (258)
 Bacon, Lettuce and
  Tomato Sandwich
 Potato Chips
 🍳Tossed Salad/dressing
  (218)
 Butterscotch Pudding—
  Topping
 Beverage(s)

SUPPER
 🍳Cream of Asparagus
  Soup (268)
 Denver Egg Sandwich
 Grated Carrot and
  Peanut Salad ·
 Chocolate Pudding
 Beverage(s)

8:30 P.M.
 Beverage(s)*

8:30 P.M.
 Beverage(s)*

THURSDAY

BREAKFAST
Assorted Juices
Selected Cold Cereal
or
Wheatena, with Cream
🧑‍🍳🧑‍🍳Corn Muffins (44)
Butter or Margarine
Jelly
Beverage(s)

DINNER
🧑‍🍳Meat Loaf (65)
🧑‍🍳Scalloped Potatoes
(197)
🧑‍🍳Shredded Cabbage
Salad (223)
Harvard Beets
Cherry Cobbler
Beverage(s)

SUPPER
🧑‍🍳Cream of Celery
Soup (268)
Sliced Cold Cuts
Jellied Cranberry
Salad
White and Dark Bread
Butter or Margarine
Baked Rice Custard
Beverage(s)

8:30 P.M.
Beverage(s)*

FRIDAY

BREAKFAST
Grapefruit Half
Fried Eggs
Plantation Sausage
Toast
Butter or Margarine
Jam
Beverage(s)

DINNER
Baked Fish Buena
Vista
Mashed Potatoes
Broccoli, Buttered
Graham Rolls
Butter or Margarine
Banana Cream Pie
Beverage(s)

SUPPER
🧑‍🍳New England Clam
Chowder (252)
🧑‍🍳Macaroni and Cheese
(191)
Jellied Pineapple and
Carrot Salad
🧑‍🍳🧑‍🍳Rolls (46)
Butter or Margarine
🧑‍🍳🧑‍🍳Oatmeal Drop
Cookies (75)
Beverage(s)

8:30 P.M.
Beverage(s)*

SATURDAY

BREAKFAST
  Assorted Juices
  Buttermilk Pancakes
  Honey Butter
  Warm Maple Syrup
  Grilled Ham
  Beverage(s)

DINNER
🍲Goulash and Buttered
    Noodles (41)
  Vegetable and Egg
    Salad
  Bread, white and dark
  Butter or Margarine
  Chilled Peaches
  Beverage(s)

SUPPER
🍲Cream of Vegetable
    Soup (269)
  Cheeseburger
  Potato Chips
  Whole Kernel Corn
  Lemon Refrigerator
    Dessert
  Beverage(s)

8:30 P.M.
  Beverage(s)*

**NOTES
Special Events,
Residents'
Birthdays, etc.)**

8th Week

SUNDAY	**MONDAY**

BREAKFAST
   Chilled Orange Juice
   Country Fresh Eggs
   Grilled Sausages
☕🍽Almond Nut
      Doughnuts (41)
   Butter or Margarine
   Beverage(s)

BREAKFAST
   Fruit in Season
   Old Fashioned Waffles
   Crisp Bacon
   Honey or Maple Syrup
   Soft Butter
   Beverage(s)

DINNER
🍽 Chicken Chow Mein
      with Chinese
      Noodles (100)
   Buttered Rice
🍽Mixed Salad Greens/
      Dressing (239)
   Sesame Rolls
   Butter or Margarine
   Ice Cream—Fortune
      Cookies

DINNER
   Salisbury Steak
   Parsley on Buttered
      Potatoes
   Carrot Coins
🍽 Molded Lime and
      Pear Salad (233)
☕🍽Rolls (48)
   Butter or Margarine
☕🍽Prune Cake (26)
   Beverage(s)

SUPPER
🍽Split Pea Soup (264)
   Sliced Ham Sand-
      wiches on ½ black
      and ½ white bread
🍽Hot Potato Salad
      (225)
   Relishes
   Chilled Pineapple
      Chunks
   Beverage(s)

SUPPER
🍽Cream of Corn Soup (271)
   Pimiento Cheese Sand-
      wiches
   Buttered Green Beans
   Apple, Celery, Tokay
      Grape Salad
   Pineapple Cream
      Pudding
   Beverage(s)

8:30 P.M.
   Beverage(s)*

8:30 P.M.
   Beverage(s)*

TUESDAY

BREAKFAST
  Assorted Juice
  ☕Poached Egg on
    Buttered Toast (19)
  Orange Pineapple
    Danish Roll
  Butter or Margarine
  Jelly
  Beverage(s)

DINNER
  ☕Ham Loaf (89)
  Mashed Sweet Potatoes
  Buttered Asparagus
  ☕Tossed Green Salad/
    Dressing (218)
  Bread, white and dark
  Butter or Margarine
  ☕☕Old Fashioned Bread
    Pudding with Cust-
    ard Sauce (76)
  Beverage(s)

SUPPER
  ☕French Onion Soup
    (253)
  Hot Beef Sandwich
  French Fried Potatoes
  Boiled Lima Beans
  ☕Carrot and Raisin
    Salad (229)
  Orange Cake
  Beverage(s)

8:30 P.M.
  Beverage(s)*

WEDNESDAY

BREAKFAST
  Half Grapefruit
  Selected Cold Cereal
    or
  Wheatena, with Cream
  Golden Toast
  Butter or Margarine
  Jelly
  Beverage(s)

DINNER
  ☕Beef Vegetable Soup (256)
  ☕Meat Loaf (65)
  Browned Potatoes
  Buttered Carrots
  Red Cabbage and
    Apple Salad
  ☕☕Chocolate Brownies
    (36)
  Beverage(s)

SUPPER
  ☕Chicken Rice Soup (258)
  Bacon and Peanut
    Butter Sand-
    wich and
  Roast Beef
    Sandwiches
  ☕Fruit Salad (227)
  Oatmeal Crispies
    Cookies
  Beverage(s)

8:30 P.M.
  Beverage(s)*

THURSDAY	FRIDAY
BREAKFAST Chilled Fruit Juice Buttermilk Pancakes Soft Butter Warm Maple Syrup or Honey Beverage(s)	**BREAKFAST** Orange Slices Scrambled Eggs (19) Crisp Bacon Toast Butter or Margarine Jelly Beverage(s)
DINNER Liver and Bacon (36) Buttered Potatoes Baked Onions with Tomatoes Jellied Vegetable Salad (234) Apricot Upside- Down Cake Beverage(s)	**DINNER** Tuna Fish a la King served on Corn Bread (44) Buttered Peas Jellied Tomato Salad (234) Chilled Pears Beverage(s)
SUPPER Cream of Mushroom Soup (268) Ham Salad and Egg Salad Sandwiches Bowl Salad Cinnamon Drop Cookies Beverage(s)	**SUPPER** Mulligatawny Soup (263) French Toast Warm Maple Syrup Pineapple Cottage Cheese Salad (229) Stewed Dried Peaches Beverage(s)
8:30 P.M. Beverage(s)*	**8:30 P.M.** Beverage(s)*

SATURDAY

BREAKFAST
Stewed Prunes,
    Lemon Slices
Assorted Cold Cereals
    or
Oatmeal, with Cream
Apple Streusel Danish
Butter or Margarine
Beverage(s)

DINNER
♨ Baked Spareribs
    and Sauerkraut (86)
Boiled Potatoes
Bread, white and dark
Butter or Margarine
♨♨ Ice Cream, Cookies (75)
Beverage(s)

SUPPER
Apple Cider
Turkey Salad
♨♨ Rolls (46)
Butter or Margarine
Baked Rice Custard
Beverage(s)

8:30 P.M.
Beverage(s)*

NOTES
Special Events,
Residents'
Birthdays, etc.)

9th Week

SUNDAY	MONDAY

BREAKFAST
Grapefruit and
   Orange Sections
♨ Bacon Omelet (20)
Golden Toast
Butter or Margarine
Jam or Marmalade
Beverage(s)

BREAKFAST
Chilled Fruit Juice
Assorted Cold Cereals
   or
Wheatena, with Cream
Apricot Danish Roll
Butter or Margarine
Beverage(s)

DINNER
Oven Fried Golden
   Brown Chicken
Mashed Potatoes
Buttered Green Peas
Royal Orange and
   Apple Salad
♨ ♨ Rolls (45)
Butter or Margarine
Apricot Whip
Beverage(s)

DINNER
♨ Veal Scallopine (40)
Buttered Noodles
Buttered Broccoli
♨ ♨ Rolls (48)
Butter or Margarine
♨ ♨ Vanilla Ice Cream—
   Cookies (73)
Beverage(s)

SUPPER
Puree of Lima
   Bean Soup
Denver Egg Sandwich
Tomatoes with Celery
♨ Tossed Vegetable
   Salad (221)
Blueberry Cobbler
Beverage(s)

SUPPER
♨ Chicken Rice Soup (256)
♨ Potato Pancakes (197)
Applesauce, warm
Butterscotch Pudding
Beverage(s)

8:30 P.M.
   Beverage(s)*

8:30 P.M.
   Beverage(s)*

TUESDAY	WEDNESDAY

BREAKFAST
Stewed Apricots
Fried Egg
Hickory Smoked
  Bacon
Golden Toast
Butter or Margarine
Jam
Beverage(s)

DINNER
🎩 New England Boiled
  Dinner (62)
  (including potatoes,
  carrots, onions,
  cabbage)
Sliced Tomato on
  Lettuce
🎩 🎩 Rolls (45)
Butter or Margarine
🎩 Angel Food Cake (316)
Beverage(s)

SUPPER
🎩 Cream of Mushroom
  Soup (269)
🎩 Welsh Rarebit on
  Toast (Cheese)
  (259)
🎩 Tossed Green Salad
  (221)
Sliced Pineapple—
  Cookies
Beverage(s)

8:30 P.M.
Beverage(s)*

BREAKFAST
Chilled Pineapple Juice
Assorted Cold Cereals
  or
Oatmeal, with cream
🎩 🎩 Hot Rolls (40)
Butter or Margarine
Jelly
Beverage(s)

DINNER
🎩 Broiled Lamb Patties
  on Grilled Pine-
  apple (84)
🎩 Delmonico Potatoes
  (196)
🎩 🎩 Rolls (46)
Butter or Margarine
Jellied Cranberry
  Salad
Lemon Refrigerator
  Dessert
Beverage(s)

SUPPER
🎩 Corn Chowder (271)
Ham and Pickle Sand-
  wich Filling on
  dark bread
Buttered Green Beans
Cherry Gelatin Cubes
Beverage(s)

8:30 P.M.
Beverage(s)*

THURSDAY

BREAKFAST
 Grapefruit Sections,
  Grenadine
 Poached Egg on
  Buttered Toast (19)
 Apple Danish Roll
 Butter or Margarine
 Beverage(s)

DINNER
 Beef Stroganoff (53)
  served with rice
 Cucumber and Onion
  Salad (220)
 Roll (48)
 Butter or Margarine
 Rainbow Sherbet
 Beverage(s)

SUPPER
 Pineapple Juice
 Stuffed Peppers,
  Tomato Sauce
 Orange-Apple Salad
  with Banana
 Bread, white and dark
 Butter or Margarine
 Butterscotch Bars (36)
 Beverage(s)

8:30 P.M.
 Beverage(s)*

FRIDAY

BREAKFAST
 Chilled Prune Juice
 Old Fashioned Waffles
 Honey Butter
 Warm Maple Syrup
 Beverage(s)

DINNER
 Macaroni and Cheese
  (191)
 Julienne Green Beans
 Chopped Green
  Salad (218)
 Rolls (48)
 Butter or Margarine
 Fruited Oatmeal Drop
  Cookies (75)
 Beverage(s)

SUPPER
 Cream of Celery
  Soup (268)
 Fish Sticks
 French Fried Potatoes
 Sliced Tomatoes and
  Lettuce Salad
 Bread
 Sausage(s)
 Apricot Whip
 Beverage(s)

8:30 P.M.
 Beverage(s)*

SATURDAY

BREAKFAST
Chilled Fresh Melon
Slice
Assorted Cold Cereals
or
Cream of Wheat,
warm milk
Cinnamon Coffeecake,
butter or margarine
Beverage(s)

DINNER
🍳Hungarian Goulash on
Poppy Seed Noodles
(41)
Bread, white and dark,
also Crackers
Butter or Margarine
Jellied Pineapple and
Carrot salad
🍳 🍳Lemon Pie (57)
Beverage(s)

SUPPER
🍳Scotch Broth (257)
Baked Frankfurters
and Rice
🍳Marinated Bean Salad
(214)
🍳 🍳Southern Corn Muffins
(44)
Cherry Gelatin/whipped
topping
Beverage(s)

8:30 P.M.
Beverage(s)*

NOTES
(Special Events,
Residents'
Birthdays, etc.)

10th Week

SUNDAY	MONDAY

BREAKFAST
Chilled Melon
🍳 Scrambled Eggs (19)
Hickory Smoked
 Bacon
🍳🍳 Corn Muffin (44)
Beverage(s)

BREAKFAST
Assorted Fruit Juices
Selected Cold Cereals
 or
Oatmeal, with Cream
Toast, Buttered
Beverage(s)

DINNER
Cranberry Juice
🍳 Roast Pork (87)
🍳 Glazed Sweet
 Potatoes (177)
Pickled Crab Apples
Three-Bean Vegetable
 Salad
Pineapple Upside
 Down Cake/
 Topping
Beverage(s)

DINNER
🍳 Baked Beef Hash (61)
Buttered Spinach
🍳 Tossed Green Salad/
 Dressing (239)
🍳🍳 Rolls (45)
Butter or Margarine
Mocha Nut Cake
Beverage(s)

SUPPER
🍳 Corn Chowder (273)
Ham Salad Sandwich
Sliced Tomato and
 Lettuce
🍳🍳 Ice Cream and Raisin
 Cookies (70)
Beverage(s)

SUPPER
🍳 Creamy Potato Soup
 (265)
🍳 Beef Macaroni Salad
 (215)
🍳 Deviled Eggs (224)
Hermit Cookies
Beverage(s)

8:30 P.M.
Beverage(s)*

8:30 P.M.
Beverage(s)*

TUESDAY	WEDNESDAY

BREAKFAST
Orange Sections
🍳 Poached Egg on
    Buttered Toast
    (19)
🍳🍳 Hot Rolls (45)
    Butter or Margarine
    Jam
    Beverage(s)

DINNER
🍳 Barbecued Spare Ribs,
    with Sauce (79)
    Baked Potatoes, with
    butter
    Green Beans, Julienne
🍳 Tossed Green Salad
    (218)
    Roll, wholewheat
    Butter or Margarine
    Chocolate Drop
    Cookies
    Beverage(s)

SUPPER
    Pork Chop Suey
    with Rice
    Sunshine Salad
🍳🍳 Rolls (46)
    Butter or Margarine
    Baked Apple
    Beverage(s)

8:30 P.M.
    Beverage(s)*

BREAKFAST
    Bananas with Cream
    Golden French Toast
    Maple Syrup or Honey
    Canadian Bacon
    Beverage(s)

DINNER
    Scalloped Ham with
    Potatoes
    Buttered Peas and
    Carrots
🍳 Pineapple Slaw (223)
🍳🍳 Rolls (47)
    Butter or Margarine
🍳🍳 Prune Cake (26)
    Beverage(s)

SUPPER
🍳 Spaghetti with Tomato
    Meat Sauce (291)
    Buttered Broccoli
    Bread, white and dark
    Butter or Margarine
    Chilled Pears
    Beverage(s)

8:30 P.M.
    Beverage(s)*

THURSDAY

BREAKFAST
  Assorted Juices
  Selected Cold Cereal
       or
  Wheatena, with Cream
  Apple Muffins
  Butter or Margarine
  Jelly
  Beverage(s)

DINNER
  Salisbury Steak
  Hashed Brown
       Potatoes (194)
  Buttered Cauliflower
  Jellied Pineapple and
       Carrot Salad/
       dressing (233)
  Rolls (46)
  Butter or Margarine
  Apple Brown Betty (76)
  Beverage(s)

SUPPER
  Cream of Vegetable
       Soup (269)
  Chicken and Noodle
       Casserole
  Buttered Asparagus
  Whipped Grape Gelatin
  Beverage(s)

8:30 P.M.
  Beverage(s)*

FRIDAY

BREAKFAST
  Grapefruit Half
  Fried Eggs
  Plantation Sausage
  Toast
  Butter or Margarine
  Jam
  Beverage(s)

DINNER
  Salmon Loaf
  Au Gratin Potatoes
       (196)
  Buttered Peas
  Tomato Aspic (234)
  Rolls (45)
  Butter or Margarine
  Apricot Tapioca
  Beverage(s)

SUPPER
  Cream of Mushroom
       Soup (268)
  Welsh or Cheese Rarebit
       (259)
  Pickles—Celery
  Buttered Carrots
  Purple Plums—Cookies
  Beverage(s)

8:30 P.M.
  Beverage(s)*

SATURDAY

BREAKFAST
  Assorted Juices
  Buttermilk Pancakes
  Honey Butter
  Warm Maple Syrup
  Grilled Ham
  Beverage(s)

DINNER
  Apple Juice
  ☙ Burgundy Beef Stew
    (69)
  Buttered Spinach
  Bread, white and dark
  Butter or Margarine
  Lemon Coconut Cake
  Beverage(s)

SUPPER
  ☙ French Onion Soup (253)
  Hamburger on Bun
    (barbecued)
  French Fried Potatoes
  Pineapple and Grated
    Cheese Salad
  Grapenut Custard
    Pudding
  Beverage(s)

8:30 P.M.
  Beverage(s)*

NOTES
(Special Events,
Residents'
Birthdays, etc.)

11th Week

SUNDAY	MONDAY

BREAKFAST
    Chilled Orange Juice
    Country Fresh Eggs
    Grilled Sausages
🍳🍳 Sugar Doughnuts (41)
    Beverage(s)

BREAKFAST
    Fruit in Season
    Old Fashioned Waffles
    Crisp Bacon
    Honey or Maple Syrup
    Soft Butter
    Beverage(s)

DINNER
    Fried Chicken
    Whipped Potatoes
    Corn, cream style
🍳 Carrot and Raisin
    Salad (229)
🍳🍳 Rolls (45)
    Butter or Margarine
    Chocolate Cream Pie
    Beverage(s)

DINNER
🍳 Swiss Steak (49)
🍳 Hashed Brown
    Potatoes (194)
    Buttered Green Peas
    Sunshine Salad
    Bread
    Butter or Margarine
    Chilled Pears
    Beverage(s)

SUPPER
    Cream of Pea Soup
🍳 Large Fruit Salad
    (main dish) (227)
🍳🍳 Corn Muffins, warm
    (44)
    Butter or Margarine
    Almond Nut Cookies
    Beverage(s)

SUPPER
🍳 Celery Soup (268)
    Turkey or Chicken
    Spread Sandwiches
    Escalloped Tomatoes
    Butterscotch Ice Box
    Cookies
    Beverage(s)

8:30 P.M.
    Beverage(s)*

8:30 P.M.
    Beverage(s)*

TUESDAY	WEDNESDAY

BREAKFAST
Assorted Juices
🍳 Poached Egg on
   Buttered Toast (19)
Orange Pineapple
Danish Roll
Butter or Margarine
Jelly
Beverage(s)

DINNER
🍳 Beef Vegetable Stew
   (59)
Asparagus
🍳 Pineapple and Cottage
   Cheese Salad (229)
Bread
Butter or Margarine
Crumb Spice Cake
Beverage(s)

SUPPER
Onion Tomato Soup
🍳 Chicken Pot Pie (104)
🍳 Lettuce Salad–
   Dressing (218)
🍳🍳 Date Bars (71)
Beverage(s)

8:30 P.M.
Beverage(s)*

BREAKFAST
Half Grapefruit
Selected Cold Cereal
   or
Cream of Wheat, with
   cream
Golden Toast
Butter or Margarine
Jelly
Beverage(s)

DINNER
Oven Baked Veal Chops
   and Gravy
Boiled Potatoes
Buttered Spinach
🍳 Raw Carrot and Raisin
   Salad (229)
Butterscotch Pudding
Beverage(s)

SUPPER
🍳 Tomato-Rice Bouillon
   (256)
🍳 Baked Macaroni and
   Cheese (191)
Buttered Broccoli
Prune Crunch
Beverage(s)

8:30 P.M.
Beverage(s)*

THURSDAY	FRIDAY
THURSDAY	**FRIDAY**
BREAKFAST	BREAKFAST
Chilled Fruit Juice	Orange Slices
Buttermilk Pancakes	Scrambled Eggs (19)
Soft Butter	Crisp Bacon
Warm Maple Syrup	Toast
or Honey	Butter or Margarine
Beverage(s)	Jelly
	Beverage(s)

THURSDAY

BREAKFAST
  Chilled Fruit Juice
  Buttermilk Pancakes
  Soft Butter
  Warm Maple Syrup
    or Honey
  Beverage(s)

DINNER
  Grilled Liver and
    Bacon (36)
  Creamed Potatoes
    and Parsley
  Buttered Whole Beets
  Rolls (46)
  Butter or Margarine
  Baked Custard (58)
  Beverage(s)

SUPPER
  Swedish Rice Soup
  Ham Salad and Egg
    Salad Sandwiches
  Relishes
  Apricot-Prune Pie
  Beverage(s)

8:30 P.M.
  Beverage(s)*

FRIDAY

BREAKFAST
  Orange Slices
  Scrambled Eggs (19)
  Crisp Bacon
  Toast
  Butter or Margarine
  Jelly
  Beverage(s)

DINNER
  Oven Fried Ocean
    Perch Fillets
  Baked Potatoes
  Stewed Tomatoes
    and Celery (187)
  Cabbage with Tart
    Sauce
  Rolls (45)
  Butter or Margarine
  Baked Apple
  Beverage(s)

SUPPER
  Beef Barley Soup
  Creamed Codfish and
    Hard Cooked Eggs
    on Toast (132)
  Whipped Cherry Gelatin,
    Topping
  Beverage(s)

8:30 P.M.
  Beverage(s)*

SATURDAY

BREAKFAST
    Stewed Prunes, Lemon
        Slices
    Assorted Cold Cereals
        or
    Oatmeal, with Cream
🍪 🍪 Blueberry Muffin (43)
    Butter or Margarine
    Beverage(s)

DINNER
🍪 Baked Ham (85),
        Raisin Sauce (289)
🍪 Hot German Potato
        Salad (225)
    Asparagus, Buttered
🍪 Lettuce or Mixed Green
        Salad/Dressing (239)
    Bread, white and dark
    Butter or Margarine
    Chilled Queen Anne
        Cherries
    Beverage(s)

SUPPER
🍪 Bean Soup (262)
    Spanish Rice with Meat
🍪 🍪 Rolls (46)
    Butter or Margarine
    Caramel Pudding
    Beverage(s)

8:30 P.M.
    Beverage(s)*

NOTES
(Special Events,
Residents'
Birthdays, etc.)

12th Week

SUNDAY	**MONDAY**

BREAKFAST
  Grapefruit and
    Orange Sections
  ♨Bacon Omelet (20)
  Golden Toast
  Butter or Margarine
  Jam or Marmalade
  Beverage(s)

BREAKFAST
  Chilled Fruit Juice
  Assorted Cold Cereals
    or
  Wheatena, with Cream
  Cheese Danish Roll
  Butter or Margarine
  Beverage(s)

DINNER
  ♨Roast Beef and
    Gravy (53)
  Browned Potatoes
  Harvard Beets
  ♨Chopped Cabbage and
    Raisin Slaw (223)
  ♨♨Rolls (48)
  Butter or Margarine
  Honey Apple Pie
  Beverage(s)

DINNER
  Breaded Veal Drumsticks
  ♨Potatoes au Gratin(196)
  Buttered Lima Beans
  ♨Chopped Raw Salad(221)
  ♨♨Rolls (45)
  Butter or Margarine
  Whipped Fruit Gelatin
  Beverage(s)

SUPPER
  Chilled V-8 Juice
  Cold Plate, (Cheese,
    Ham, Roast Beef)
  Cottage Cheese
  Bread, white and dark
  Butter or Margarine
  ♨♨Golden Chiffon
    Cake (10)
  Beverage(s)

SUPPER
  ♨Chicken Rice Soup
    (256)
  Baked Green Peppers
    stuffed with Ground
    Meat and Tomato
    Sauce
  Cider Fruit Salad
  Bread, white and dark
  Butter or Margarine
  ♨♨Brownies (36)
  Beverage(s)

8:30 P.M.
  Beverage(s)*

8:30 P.M.
  Beverage(s)*

TUESDAY	WEDNESDAY

BREAKFAST

TUESDAY:
Stewed Apricots
Fried Egg
Hickory Smoked
Bacon
Golden Toast
Butter or Margarine
Jam
Beverage(s)

WEDNESDAY:
BREAKFAST
Chilled Pineapple Juice
Assorted Cold Cereals
or
Oatmeal, with Cream
Hot Rolls (40)
Butter or Margarine
Jelly
Beverage(s)

DINNER

TUESDAY:
Meat Balls (64) in
Mushroom Sauce
(288)
Parsley Buttered
Potatoes
Tomatoes and Celery
Tossed Vegetable
Salad/dressing (221)
Rolls (45)
Butter or Margarine
Banana Cake (22)
Beverage(s)

WEDNESDAY:
DINNER
Veal Loaf
French Fried Potatoes
Cauliflower, creamed
Chef's Salad, Thousand
Island Dressing (237)
Rolls (46)
Butter or Margarine
Cherry Nut Cookies
Beverage(s)

SUPPER

TUESDAY:
Vegetable Soup (261)
Fricassee of Chicken
(108)
Buttered Rice
Carrot and Raisin Salad
(229)
Whipped Red Rasp-
berry gelatin,
topping
Beverage(s)

WEDNESDAY:
SUPPER
Rice and Tomato Soup
(256)
Corned Beef Sandwich
or Egg Salad
Sandwich
Succotash (185)
Pineapple and Celery
in Apple Gelatin
Banana Pudding
Beverage(s)

8:30 P.M.
Beverage(s)*

8:30 P.M.
Beverage(s)*

THURSDAY	FRIDAY

BREAKFAST
  Grapefruit Sections
    Grenadine
  🍳 Poached Egg on
    Buttered Toast (19)
  Apple Danish Roll
  Butter or Margarine
  Beverage(s)

BREAKFAST
  Chilled Prune Juice
  Old Fashioned Waffles
  Honey Butter
  Warm Maple Syrup
  Beverage(s)

DINNER
  🍳 Hungarian Goulash
    Poppyseed Noodles
    (41)
  Buttered Asparagus
  Apricot-Raisin-Marsh-
    mallow Salad
  Wholewheat Rolls
  Butter or Margarine
  Caramel Custard
  Beverage(s)

DINNER
  Fish Baked in White
    Wine
  Buttered Potatoes
    with Parsley
  Broccoli Spears
  🍳 Tomato Aspic (234)
  Bread, white and dark
  Butter or Margarine
  Pineapple Chunks,
    chilled
  Beverage(s)

SUPPER
  Beef Vegetable Soup
  🍳🍳 American Pizza (50)
  Spring Salad Bowl/
    dressing
  Coconut Cake
  Beverage(s)

SUPPER
  V-8 Juice
  Salmon Salad
  Potato Chips
  Cottage Cheese with
    Chopped Spinach
  Graham Rolls
  Butter or Margarine
  Grape-Nut Custard
    Pudding
  Beverage(s)

8:30 P.M.
  Beverage(s)*

8:30 P.M.
  Beverage(s)*

SATURDAY

BREAKFAST
Chilled Fresh Melon
Slice
Assorted Cold Cereals
or
Cream of Wheat,
warm milk
Cherry Coffeecake
Butter or Margarine
Beverage(s)

DINNER
Apple Juice
Turkey Macaroni Casserole
Buttered Carrots and Peas
👨‍🍳 Waldorf Salad (226)
Bread, white and dark
Butter or Margarine, jelly
Coconut Pineapple Squares
(cookies)
Beverage(s)

SUPPER
👨‍🍳 Chicken Gumbo Soup
(259)
Frankfurters and Sauer-
kraut
Black Bread
Butter or Margarine
👨‍🍳 German Potato Salad(225)
Mustard, Horseradish, Catsup
Whipped Fruit Gelatin
Beverage(s)

8:30 P.M.
Beverage(s)*

13th Week

SUNDAY	MONDAY

BREAKFAST
Chilled Melon
🍳 Scrambled Eggs (19)
Hickory Smoked
   Bacon
Cinnamon Raisin
   Pecan Rolls
Beverage(s)

DINNER
🍳 Pork Roast (87)
Whipped Sweet
   Potatoes
Red Cinnamon
   Apples
Buttered Peas
🍳 Pineapple and Carrot
   in Gelatin Salad (233)
🍳🍳 Blueberry Muffins (43)
Butter or Margarine
Lemon Refrigerator
   Dessert
Beverage(s)

SUPPER
🍳 Cream of Celery Soup
   (268)
Cold Plate (Pork, Cheese,
   Ham, Potato Salad)
Bread, white and dark
Catsup
🍳 Cherry Tapioca—
   Cookies (317)
Beverage(s)

8:30 P.M.
Beverage(s)*

BREAKFAST
Assorted Fruit Juices
Selected Cold Cereals
   or
Oatmeal, with Cream
Toast, Buttered
Jelly
Beverage(s)

DINNER
🍳 New England Boiled
   Dinner (includes)
   potatoes) (62)
🍳 Jellied Tomato Salad (234)
🍳🍳 Corn Bread (44)
Butter, Margarine, Syrup
Stewed Apricots
Beverage(s)

SUPPER
V-8 Juice
🍳 Liver and Bacon (36)
French Fried Potatoes
Buttered Broccoli
🍳🍳 Rolls (45)
Butter or Margarine
Peach Chiffon Dessert
Beverage(s)

8:30 P.M.
Beverage(s)*

TUESDAY

BREAKFAST
Orange Sections
⚜Poached Egg on
Buttered Toast (19)
⚜⚜ Hot Rolls (40)
Butter or Margarine
Jam
Beverage(s)

DINNER
⚜Turkey (118) and
Dressing (117) and
Giblet Gravy (122)
Mashed Potatoes
Brussel Sprouts,
buttered
Carrots, buttered
Jellied Orange and
Cranberry Sauce
⚜⚜ Rolls (45)
Butter or Margarine
⚜Baked Meringue Kisses
(311)
Beverage(s)

SUPPER
⚜Turkey Soup (259)
Open-faced Cheese
and Tomato
Sandwich, grilled
⚜Chopped Cabbage Slaw
(233)
Whipped Raspberry
Gelatin—cookies
Beverage(s)

8:30 P.M.
Beverage(s)*

WEDNESDAY

BREAKFAST
Bananas with Cream
Golden French Toast
Maple Syrup or Honey
Canadian Bacon
Beverage(s)

DINNER
⚜Baked Beef Hash with
Potatoes (61)
Jullienne Green Beans
Jellied Royal Orange
and Apple Salad
⚜⚜Rolls (45)
Butter or Margarine
⚜⚜ Baked Custard (58)
Beverage(s)

SUPPER
⚜Cream of Vegetable
Soup (269)
⚜Corn Fritters (166)
Crisp Bacon
Warm Maple Syrup
Stuffed Celery Sticks
with American
Cheddar Cheese
Fresh Fruits—selection
of Bananas, Apples,
Tangerines, Grapes
Beverage(s)

8:30 P.M.
Beverage(s)*

THURSDAY

BREAKFAST
  Assorted Juices
  Selected Cold Cereal
    or
  Wheatena, with Cream
🍳🍳Corn Muffins (44)
  Butter or Margarine
  Jelly
  Beverage(s)

DINNER
  Veal Roast
  🍳Baked, Buttered Squash
    with brown sugar (188)
  Browned Potatoes
  Lettuce or Mixed Green
    Salad/Parisian dress-
    ing
🍳🍳Hard Rolls (48)
  Butter or Margarine
  Honey Apple Pie
  Beverage(s)

SUPPER
  Apple Juice
  Chicken a la King
  Fresh Frozen Peas
  Royal Orange and
    Apple Salad
  Bread, white and dark
  Butter or Margarine
🍳🍳Peanut Crunch Cookies
    (71)
  Beverage(s)

  8:30 P.M.
    Beverage(s)*

FRIDAY

BREAKFAST
  Grapefruit Half
  Fried Egg
  Plantation Sausage
  Toast
  Butter or Margarine
  Jam
  Beverage(s)

DINNER
  Baked Fish Buena Vista
  Buttered Parsley Potatoes
  Carrots, buttered
  🍳Molded Perfection Salad
    (234)
🍳🍳Rolls (46)
  Butter or Margarine
  Orange and Raisin
    Cupcakes
  Beverage(s)

SUPPER
  🍳Tomato Rice Bouillon
    (256)
  Cheese Fondue
  Buttered Cauliflower
  Jellied Beet Salad
🍳🍳Rolls (45)
  Butter or Margarine
🍳🍳Pineapple Chiffon
    Pie (64)
  Beverage(s)

  8:30 P.M.
    Beverage(s)*

SATURDAY

BREAKFAST
Assorted Juices
Buttermilk Pancakes
Honey Butter
Warm Maple Syrup
Grilled Ham
Beverage(s)

DINNER
Salisbury Steak
🍳 Scalloped Potatoes (197)
Buttered Lima Beans
Head Lettuce, Vinegar
    and Oil Dressing
Bread, white and dark
Butter or Margarine
Baked Rice Custard
Beverage(s)

SUPPER
Baked Lasagna
🍳 Tossed Green Salad/
    Dressing (239)
French Bread
Butter or Margarine
Blackberry Cobbler
Beverage(s)

8:30 P.M.
Beverage(s)*

NOTES
(Special Events,
Residents'
Birthdays, etc.)

14th Week

SUNDAY	MONDAY

BREAKFAST
Chilled Orange Juice
Country Fresh Egg
Grilled Sausages
♕♕ Almond Nut Dough-
   nuts (41)
Butter or Margarine
Beverage(s)

BREAKFAST
Fruit in Season
Old Fashioned Waffles
Crisp Bacon
Honey or Maple Syrup
Soft Butter
Beverage(s)

DINNER
♕ Roast Turkey (118)
Mashed Potatoes
Zucchini and Tomatoes
Asparagus
♕♕ Rolls (46)
Butter or Margarine
Jellied Cranberry Salad
♕♕ Brownies (36)
Beverage(s)

DINNER
Apple Cider
Braised Pork Chops
♕ Glazed Sweet
   Potatoes (177)
Sliced Buttered Carrots
Orange-Apple-Banana
   Salad
♕♕ Rolls (47)
Butter or Margarine
Chilled Peaches
Beverage(s)

SUPPER
Beef Noodle Soup
Cold Plate (Beef, Ham,
   Cheese Cuts)
Buttered Carrots
Bread, white and dark
Butter or Margarine
♕♕ Vanilla Ice Cream,
   Cookies (69)
Beverage(s)

SUPPER
♕ Vegetable Soup (261)
Frankfurter and Roll
   (buttered)
Catsup
Boston Baked Beans
♕ Perfection Salad
   Squares (234)
Butterscotch Ice Box
   Cookies
Beverage(s)

8:30 P.M.
Beverage(s)*

8:30 P.M.
Beverage(s)*

TUESDAY

BREAKFAST
Assorted Juices
🎩 Poached Egg on
  Buttered Toast (19)
Apricot Danish Roll
Butter or Margarine
Jelly
Beverage(s)

DINNER
🎩 Oven Fried Chicken
  (97)
Whipped Potatoes
  and Gravy
Creamed Spinach
  with Onion and
  Crunchy Bacon
Buttered Peas
Sliced Tomato and
  Lettuce Salad
Rolls, wholewheat
Butter or Margarine
Cubed Chilled Pine-
  apple
Beverage(s)

SUPPER
🎩 Bean Soup (262)
Minced Ham Sandwich
🎩 Tossed Green Salad
  (239)
Fig-Nut Tapioca (nuts
  should be ground)
Beverage(s)

8:30 P.M.
  Beverage(s)*

WEDNESDAY

BREAKFAST
Half Grapefruit
Selected Cold Cereal
  or
Cream of Wheat,
  with cream
Golden Toast
Butter or Margarine
Jelly
Beverage(s)

DINNER
🎩 Barbecued Spare
  Ribs (79)
Boiled Potatoes
Buttered Brussel
  Sprouts
Bread, white and dark
Butter or Margarine
🎩 Watercress/French
  Dressing (238)
🎩🎩 Angel Food Cake (31)
Beverage(s)

SUPPER
🎩 Split Pea Soup (264)
Swedish Meat Balls,
  Buttered Rice
🎩 Cooked Vegetable Salad,
  (222)
Chocolate Pudding,
  Whipped Cream
Beverage(s)

8: 30 P.M.
  Beverage(s)*

THURSDAY	FRIDAY

BREAKFAST
- Chilled Fruit Juice
- Buttermilk Pancakes
- Soft Butter
- Warm Maple Syrup
  - or Honey
- Beverage(s)

BREAKFAST
- Orange Slices
- Scrambled Eggs (19)
- Crisp Bacon
- Toast
- Butter or Margarine
- Jelly
- Beverage(s)

DINNER
- Liver Creole
- Baked Potatoes
- Buttered Asparagus
- Jellied Pineapple and
  - Carrot Salad
- Baking Powder
  - Biscuits (3)
- Butter or Margarine,
  - Jam
- Chilled Pear Halves
- Beverage(s)

DINNER
- Shrimp and Crabmeat
  - Newburg (153)
- French Fried Potatoes
- Harvard Beets
- Tossed Salad (239)
- Bread, white and dark
- Butter or Margarine
- Jelly Roll (17)
- Beverage(s)

SUPPER
- Lima Bean Soup
- Swiss Steak (60)
- Carrots and Peas
- Warm Apple Sauce
- Bread, white and dark
- Butter or Margarine
- Peanut Butter Cake
- Beverage(s)

SUPPER
- Cream of Tomato Soup
  - (252)
- Pancakes
- Warm Butter or
  - Margarine
- Warm Maple Syrup
- Fresh Fruits (selection
  - of Apples, Oranges,
  - Bananas, Grapes)
- Beverage(s)

8:30 P.M.
- Beverage(s)*

8:30 P.M.
- Beverage(s)*

SATURDAY

BREAKFAST
  Stewed Prunes,
    Lemon Slices
  Assorted Cold Cereals
    or
  Oatmeal, with Cream
  Assorted Danish (40)
  Butter or Margarine
  Beverage(s)

DINNER
  Swiss Steak
    (includes onions and
    tomatoes) (60)
  Hashed Brown
    Potatoes (194)
  Chopped Spinach with
    Bacon Dressing
  German Cucumber Salad
  Butterscotch Bars (36)
  Beverage(s)

SUPPER
  Onion Soup (253)
  Shepherd's Pie
  Royal Lime and
    Apple Salad
  Apricot Whip
  Beverage(s)

8:30 P.M.
  Beverage(s)*

15th Week

SUNDAY

BREAKFAST
Grapefruit and
  Orange Sections
🍳 Bacon Omelet (20)
Golden Toast
Butter or Margarine
Jam or Marmalade
Beverage(s)

DINNER
🍳 Chicken Roasted (106)
  with Stuffing (117)
  and Giblet Gravy
  (122)
🍳 Baked Hubbard Squash
  (188)
Green Beans, French
  Style
Jellied Cranberry and
  Orange Salad
🍳🍳 Rolls (46)
Butter or Margarine
🍳🍳 Blueberry Pie (62)
Beverage(s)

SUPPER
Beef Rice Soup
Cold Plate (Ham,
  Cheese, Sausage Loaf,
  Pickles and Olives)
Potato Chips
Bread, white and dark
Butter or Margarine
Lemon Coconut Cake
Beverage(s)

8:30 P.M.
Beverage(s)*

MONDAY

BREAKFAST
Chilled Fruit Juice
Assorted Cold Cereals
  or
Wheatena, with Cream
Cheese Danish Roll
Butter or Margarine
Beverage(s)

DINNER
🍳 Baked Ham (85)
🍳 Potatoes au Gratin (196)
Buttered Lima Beans
Bread, white and dark
Butter or Margarine
🍳 Head Lettuce, Roquefort
  Dressing (239)
Cherry Tapioca
Beverage(s)

SUPPER
Baked Green Peppers,
  Stuffed with Ground
  Meat and Tomato
  Sauce
Cider-Fruit Salad
Rolls, Graham
Butter or Margarine
🍳🍳 Brownies (36)
Beverage(s)

8:30 P. M.
Beverage(s)*

TUESDAY

BREAKFAST
  Stewed Apricots
  Fried Egg
  Hickory Smoked
    Bacon
  Golden Toast
  Butter or Margarine
  Jam
  Beverage(s)

DINNER
  🍳Liver and Bacon
    (36)
  Buttered Parsley
    Potatoes
  Mixed Vegetables
  Carrot-Apple-Raisin
    Salad
  🍳🍳Rolls (48)
  Butter or Margarine
  Baked Peach Halves
  Beverage(s)

SUPPER
  🍳Corn Chowder (271)
  🍳Stuffed Beef and
    Cabbage Rolls (65)
  🍳Tomato Aspic (234)
  Pineapple Upside
    Down Cake
  Beverage(s)

8:30 P. M.
  Beverage(s)*

WEDNESDAY

BREAKFAST
  Chilled Pineapple Juice
  Assorted Cold Cereals
    or
  Oatmeal, with Cream
  🍳🍳Hot Rolls (46)
  Butter or Margarine
  Jelly
  Beverage(s)

DINNER
  Fried Veal Chops
    and Gravy
  Boiled Potatoes
  Buttered Chopped
    Spinach
  🍳Cole Slaw (223)
  🍳🍳Rolls (45)
  Butter or Margarine
  🍳Charlotte Russe
    (gelatin) (314)
  Beverage(s)

SUPPER
  Beef Vegetable Soup
  Meat and Cheese
    Salad Plate
  🍳Succotash (185)
  Pineapple and
    Lettuce Salad
  Bread, white and dark
  Butter or Margarine
  Apple Turnovers
  Beverage(s)

8:30 P.M.
  Beverage(s)*

THURSDAY

BREAKFAST
Grapefruit Sections,
   Grenadine
☙ Poached Egg on
   Buttered Toast (19)
Apple Danish Roll
Butter or Margarine
Beverage(s)

DINNER
Breaded Pork Chops,
   Cream Gravy
Boiled Potatoes
☙ Carrots and Peas (186)
Jellied Cranberries on
   Lettuce
☙☙ Rolls (46)
Butter or Margarine
☙☙ Apple Pie (56)
Beverage(s)

SUPPER
☙ Boston Clam
   Chowder (252)
☙ Broiled Beef Patties
   (57)
Lettuce—Tomato
   Salad/dressing
Baked Potato
☙ Fruited Gelatin (232)
Beverage(s)

8:30 P.M.
Beverage(s)*

FRIDAY

BREAKFAST
Chilled Prune Juice
Old Fashioned Waffles
Honey Butter
Warm Maple Syrup
Beverage(s)

DINNER
☙ Filet of Sole, (139)
   Tartar Sauce (287)
French Fried Potatoes
Buttered, Sliced Carrots
Red Cabbage and
   Apple Salad
☙☙ Rolls (45)
Butter or Margarine
Cream Pie
Beverage(s)

SUPPER
☙ Minestrone Soup and
   Crackers (249)
☙ Chicken Chow Mein,
   Rice (100)
Beet and Egg Salad
Fruit Whip
Beverage(s)

8:30 P.M.
Beverage(s)*

SATURDAY

BREAKFAST
 Chilled Melon
   Slice
 Assorted Cold Cereals
   or
 Cream of Wheat,
   warm milk
 Cinnamon Raisin
   Pecan Roll
 Butter or Margarine
 Beverage(s)

DINNER
🎩Meat Balls (64),
   Spaghetti Milani
 Green Beans, buttered
🎩Tossed Green Salad/
   dressing (221)
🎩🎩Rolls (48)
 Butter or Margarine
🎩🎩Applesauce Cake (18)
 Beverage(s)

SUPPER
🎩French Onion Soup (253)
 Tomato Stuffed with
   Chicken Salad
 Buttered Asparagus
🎩🎩Corn Bread (44)
 Butter or
   Margarine—Syrup
 Spice Cake with Frosting
 Beverage(s)

8:30 P.M.
 Beverage(s)*

16th Week

SUNDAY	MONDAY

BREAKFAST
Chilled Melon
🍳 Scrambled Eggs (19)
Hickory Smoked
   Bacon
🍳🍳 Sugar Doughnuts (41)
Beverage(s)

BREAKFAST
Assorted Fruit Juices
Selected Cold Cereals
   or
Oatmeal, with Cream
Toast, buttered
Jelly
Beverage(s)

DINNER
Apple Juice
🍳 Roast Turkey and
   Gravy (118)
🍳 Bread Stuffing (117)
Mashed Potatoes
Buttered Mixed
   Vegetables
Cranberry Sauce
🍳🍳 Nut Bread (8)
Butter or Margarine
🍳🍳 Ice Cream—Cookies (73)
Beverage(s)

DINNER
🍳 Baked Meat Loaf (65)
Browned Potatoes
Lima Beans
🍳 Cole Slaw (223)
Bread, white and dark
Butter or Margarine
Cherry Tapioca
Beverage(s)

SUPPER
🍳 Tomato-Rice
   Bouillon (256)
Corned Beef Sand-
   wiches,
   Rye Bread
Potato Chips
🍳 Stuffed Celery Sticks (222)
   and Carrot Sticks
Apricot Whip
Beverage(s)

SUPPER
Beef Noodle Soup
Scalloped Egg Plant
   with Mushrooms
   on Toast
Fresh Fruits (Apples,
   Bananas, Oranges,
   Grapes)
Beverage(s)

8:30 P.M.
Beverage(s)*

8:30 P.M.
Beverage(s)*

| TUESDAY | WEDNESDAY |

TUESDAY   **WEDNESDAY**

BREAKFAST
  Orange Sections
  🍳 Poached Egg on
    Buttered Toast (19)
  🍳🍳 Hot Rolls (40)
  Butter or Margarine
  Jam
  Beverage(s)

BREAKFAST
  Bananas with Cream
  Golden French Toast
  Maple Syrup or Honey
  Canadian Bacon
  Beverage(s)

DINNER
  🍳 Pot Roast of Beef,
    Natural Gravy (53)
  Mashed Potatoes
  🍳 Beets with Orange
    Sauce (182)
  🍳 Mixed Green Salad/
    dressing (239)
  Bread, white and dark
  Butter or Margarine
  🍳🍳 Bread Pudding with
    Vanilla Sauce (76)
  Beverage(s)

DINNER
  🍳 Baked Virginia Ham (85)
    Raisin Sauce (289)
  Mashed Sweet Potatoes
  🍳 Stewed Tomatoes
    with Celery (187)
  Spiced Peach Salad
  Bread, white and dark
  Butter or Margarine
  🍳🍳 Lemon Cream Pie (57)
  Beverage(s)

SUPPER
  🍳 Chicken Noodle
    Soup (256)
  🍳 Sirloin Patties (57)
  Buttered Wax Beans
  Cabbage and Green
    Pepper Salad
  🍳🍳 Rolls (47)
  Butter or Margarine
  Chilled Queen Anne
    Cherries
  Beverage(s)

SUPPER
  Onion Tomato Soup
  Grilled Frankfurter
  Hot Potato Salad
  Brown Bread
  Butter or Margarine
  Chilled Pears
  Beverage(s)

8:30 P.M.
  Beverage(s)*

8:30 P.M.
  Beverage(s)*

THURSDAY

BREAKFAST
Assorted Juices
Selected Cold Cereal
or
Wheatena, with Cream
♟♟Corn Muffins (44)
Butter or Margarine
Jelly
Beverage(s)

DINNER
City Chicken Legs
and Cream Gravy
Boiled Potatoes
Green Beans
♟Perfection Salad/
dressing (234)
Bread
Butter or Margarine
♟♟Devils Food Cake (29)
Beverage(s)

SUPPER
♟Split Pea Soup (264)
♟Macaroni and Cheese
Casserole (191)
♟Orange and Grapefruit
Salad (230)
Bread, white or dark
Butter or Margarine
♟♟Raisin Cookies (70)
Beverage(s)

8:30 P.M.
Beverage(s)*

FRIDAY

BREAKFAST
Grapefruit Half
Fried Egg
Plantation Sausage
Toast
Butter or Margarine
Jam
Beverage(s)

DINNER
Golden Tuna Casserole
Buttered Asparagus
Royal Orange and
Apple Salad
♟♟Rolls (46)
Butter or Margarine
Stewed Dried Peaches
Beverage(s)

SUPPER
♟Cream of Potato
Soup (265)
♟Fruit Salad (15)
Cottage Cheese
♟♟Corn Muffins (44)
Butter or Margarine,
Jelly
♟♟Angel Food Cake /
Topping (31)
Beverage(s)

8:30 P.M.
Beverage(s)*

SATURDAY

BREAKFAST
  Stewed Prunes
  Buttered Pancakes
  Honey Butter
  Warm Maple Syrup
  Grilled Ham
  Beverage(s)

DINNER
  ☕ Swiss Steak, gravy (60)
  Mashed Potatoes
  Cut Green Beans,
    Buttered
  ☕ Tossed Green Salad (218)
  ☕☕ Corn Bread (44)
  Butter or Margarine,
    Syrup
  Orange Sherbet
  Beverage(s)

SUPPER
  ☕ Cream of Chicken Soup
    (269)
  Hot Sliced Pork Roast
    and Gravy Sandwich
  ☕ Beet and Onion Salad (216)
  Whipped Fruit Gelatin
  Beverage(s)

8:30 P.M.
  Beverage(s)*

17th Week

SUNDAY

BREAKFAST
Chilled Orange Juice
Country Fresh Eggs
Grilled Sausages
🎩 🎩 Coconut Doughnuts
   (41)
Beverage(s)

DINNER
🎩 Roast Beef au Jus
   (55)
Mashed Potatoes
Buttered Cauliflower
🎩 🎩 Cloverleaf Rolls (46)
Butter or Margarine
Cherry Cobbler
Beverage(s)

SUPPER
Apple Juice
🎩 Chicken Fricassee (108),
   Hot Biscuits (3)
🎩 Pear and Cottage
   Cheese on Romaine
   with dressing (229)
Butter or Margarine
Ginger Cookies
Beverage(s)

8:30 P.M.
Beverage(s)*

MONDAY

BREAKFAST
Fruit in Season
Old Fashioned Waffles
Crisp Bacon
Honey or Maple Syrup
Soft Butter
Beverage(s)

DINNER
🎩 Braised Beef with
   Vegetables (53)
Boiled Potatoes
Buttered Green Beans
🎩 Cabbage-Apple-Pine-
   apple Salad (223)
🎩 🎩 Rolls (47)
Butter or Margarine
Vanilla Cream Pudding
Beverage(s)

SUPPER
🎩 Vegetable Soup (261)
Egg Salad Sandwich
   or Ham Sandwich
🎩 Jellied Fruit Salad (231)
Prune Cookies
Beverage(s)

8:30 P.M.
Beverage(s)*

TUESDAY	**WEDNESDAY**

BREAKFAST
Assorted Juices
🍳Poached Egg on
Buttered Toast (19)
Orange-Pineapple
Danish Roll
Butter or Margarine
Jelly
Beverage(s)

BREAKFAST
Half Grapefruit
Selected Cold Cereal
or
Cream of Wheat,
with Cream
Golden Toast
Butter or Margarine
Jelly
Beverage(s)

DINNER
🍳Breaded Veal
Cutlet (37)
Whipped Potatoes
Creamed Spinach
🍳🍳Rolls (48)
Butter or Margarine
🍳🍳Gingerbread with
Lemon Sauce (19)
Beverage(s)

DINNER
🍳Roast Loin of Pork.
(87)
Mashed Yams
🍳Tossed Green Salad
(221)
🍳Beets with Orange
Sauce (182)
🍳🍳Rolls (45)
Butter or Margarine
🍳🍳Devil's Food Cake
(29)
Beverage(s)

SUPPER
Chilled V-8 Juice
🍳Potato Pancakes (197)
Apple Sauce
🍳Mixed Green Salad/
dressing (218)
Chilled Pear Half
Beverage(s)

SUPPER
🍳Veal Scallopini (40)
Buttered Cut Corn
🍳🍳Corn Muffins (44)
Butter or Margarine
Prune and Cottage
Cheese Salad
Pineapple Cream
Pudding
Beverage(s)

8:30 P.M.
Beverage(s)*

8:30 P.M.
Beverage(s)*

THURSDAY	FRIDAY
BREAKFAST Chilled Fruit Juice Buttermilk Pancakes Soft Butter Warm Maple Syrup or Honey Beverage(s)	**BREAKFAST** Orange Slices Scrambled Eggs (19) Crisp Bacon Toast Butter or Margarine Jelly Beverage(s)

DINNER
Beef Pot Roast (53)
Potatoes au Gratin (196)
Diced Buttered
  Turnips and Peas
Orange and Grapefruit
  Sections Salad/
  dressing (230)
Rolls (45)
Butter or Margarine
Butterscotch Custard
  Pie
Beverage(s)
	DINNER
	Oven Fried Ocean
	  Perch Fillets
	Potato Puff
	  (Duchess) (193)
	Buttered Broccoli
	  Spears
	Chopped Salad Greens/
	  Russian Dressing
	Rolls (45)
	Butter or Margarine
	Apple Pie (56)
	Beverage(s)

SUPPER
Minestrone Soup (249)
Weiner and Baked Beans
Spinach
Bread, white and dark
Golden Chiffon Cake
  with Icing (10)
Beverage(s)
	SUPPER
	Cream of Asparagus
	  Soup (268)
	Rice and Cheese Omelet
	Lima Beans
	Bread, white and dark
	Butter or Margarine
	Chilled Peaches
	Beverage(s)

8:30 P.M. Beverage(s)*	8:30 P.M. Beverage(s)*

SATURDAY

BREAKFAST
    Stewed Prunes,
        Lemon Slices
    Assorted Cold Cereals
        or
    Oatmeal, with Cream
    Cinnamon Streusel
        Danish (45)
    Butter or Margarine
    Beverage(s)

DINNER
    Salisbury Steak, gravy
    Mashed Sweet Potatoes
    Buttered Peas
    Pan Rolls (46)
    Butter or Margarine
    Cabbage and Ground
        Peanut Salad
    Pineapple Chunks,
        chilled
    Beverage(s)

SUPPER
    Potato and Onion
        Soup (266)
    Barbecued Ground
        Beef on Bun
    Jellied Vegetable
        Salad (234)
    Blueberry Cobbler (16)
    Beverage(s)

8:30 P.M.
    Beverage(s)*

**NOTES
(Special Events,
Residents'
Birthdays, etc.)**

18th Week

SUNDAY

BREAKFAST
    Grapefruit and
        Orange Sections
  Bacon Omelet (20)
    Golden Toast
    Butter or Margarine
    Jam or Marmalade
    Beverage(s)

DINNER
  Roast Leg of Lamb,
    Mint Jelly (80)
    Baked Potato
    Buttered Broccoli
        Cuts
    Assorted Pickles
    Carrot and Pineapple
        Salad
  Rolls (48)
    Butter or Margarine
  Peach Pie (65)
    Beverage(s)

SUPPER
  Tomato Bouillon
    (256)
    Spanish Rice with
        chopped meat
    Bread—Butter or
        Margarine
    Pear and Grated Cheese
        Salad/dressing
    Grapenut Pudding
    Beverage(s)

8:30 P.M.
    Beverage(s)*

MONDAY

BREAKFAST
    Chilled Fruit Juice
    Assorted Cold Cereals
        or
    Wheatena, with Cream
    Cheese Danish Roll
    Butter or Margarine
    Beverage(s)

DINNER
    Baked Veal Shoulder
        with Stuffing,
        Natural Gravy
    Boiled Potatoes
    Buttered Cauliflower
  Lettuce Salad/
        dressing (239)
  Rolls (46)
    Butter or Margarine
  Bread Pudding with
        Chocolate Sauce (76)
    Beverage(s)

SUPPER
    Chicken-Pimiento Soup
    Sliced Cold Meats
  Hot Potato Salad (225)
    Assorted Pickles
    Wholewheat Bread
    Butter or Margarine
  Fruit Cup (15)
    Beverage(s)

8:30 P.M.
    Beverage(s)*

TUESDAY	WEDNESDAY

BREAKFAST
Stewed Apricots
Fried Egg
Hickory Smoked
   Bacon
Golden Toast
Butter or Margarine
Jam
Beverage(s)

BREAKFAST
Chilled Pineapple Juice
Assorted Cold Cereals
   or
Oatmeal, with Cream
Hot Rolls (46)
Butter or Margarine
Jelly
Beverage(s)

DINNER
Braised Chopped
   Beef Steaks
Creamed Potatoes (196)
Buttered Corn and
   Green Peppers Saute
Shredded Cabbage and
   Carrot Salad
Rolls (45)
Butter or Margarine
Brown Sugar Custard
Beverage(s)

DINNER
German Pot Roast
   (Sauerbraten)
   (66,67)
Oven Browned Potatoes
Buttered Cut Green
   Beans
Vegetable Salad,
   Jellied (234)
Rolls (47)
Butter or Margarine
Gingerbread (19)/
   Topping
Beverage(s)

SUPPER
Clam Chowder (252)
Cheese Rarebit with
   Bacon (259)
Baked Stuffed
   Tomatoes
Shredded Lettuce
   Salad (218)
Whipped Fruit Gelatin
Beverage(s)

SUPPER
Cream of Spinach
   Soup (268)
Barbecued Ham-
   burgers on Bun
Potato Chips
Carrot Sticks
Tapioca Pudding
Beverage(s)

8:30 P.M.
   Beverage(s)*

8:30 P.M.
   Beverage(s)*

| **THURSDAY** | **FRIDAY** |

THURSDAY

BREAKFAST
  Grapefruit Sections,
    Grenadine
  ☕Poached Egg on
    Buttered Toast (19)
  Apricot Danish Roll
  Butter or Margarine
  Beverage(s)

DINNER
  Ham with Potatoes
    au Gratin
  Buttered Asparagus
  ☕Ginger Ale Fruit Salad/
    dressing (217)
  Bread, wholewheat
  Butter or Margarine
  ☕ ☕Thick Molasses
    Cookies (73)
  Beverage(s)

SUPPER
  ☕Mushroom Soup (269)
  Chicken Salad
    Sandwiches
  ☕Tomato Aspic (234)
  ☕☕Gold Pound Cake/
    Topping (21)
  Beverage(s)

8:30 P.M.
  Beverage(s)*

FRIDAY

BREAKFAST
  Chilled Prune Juice
  Old Fashioned Waffles
  Honey Butter
  Warm Maple Syrup
  Beverage(s)

DINNER
  V-8 Juice
  ☕Scallops, deep fried
    with lemon (167)
  ☕Lyonnaise Potatoes (194)
  Buttered Broccoli
  Bread, white and dark
  Butter or Margarine
  ☕☕Fruit Shortcake (37)
  Beverage(s)

SUPPER
  ☕Baked Macaroni and
    Cheese (191)
  ☕Red Cabbage, German
    Style (365)
  ☕Fruit Salad with Stuffed
    Prunes (227)
  ☕☕Rolls (45)
  Butter or Margarine
  ☕☕Apple Pie (56)
  Beverage(s)

8:30 P.M.
  Beverage(s)*

SATURDAY

NOTES
(Special Events,
Residents'
Birthdays, etc.)

BREAKFAST
 Chilled Fresh Melon Slice
 Assorted Cold Cereals
  or
 Cream of Wheat,
  warm milk
🍳🍳 Blueberry Muffin (43)
 Butter or Margarine
 Beverage(s)

DINNER
 Beef and Pepper Steak
🍳 Tossed Vegetable Salad
  (221)
 Bread, wholewheat
 Butter or Margarine
 Cantaloupe, chilled
 Beverage(s)

SUPPER
🍳 Vegetable Soup (261)
🍳 Chicken Chow Mein (100)
  over Chinese Noodles
 Rice, mound
 Celery and String Bean
  Salad
🍳🍳 Yellow Cup Cakes/
  Frosting (29,32)
 Beverage(s)

8:30 P.M.
 Beverage(s)*

19th Week

SUNDAY	MONDAY

BREAKFAST
Chilled Melon
♔Scrambled Eggs (19)
Hickory Smoked
  Bacon
Cinnamon Raisin
  Pecan Rolls
Beverage(s)

BREAKFAST
Assorted Fruit Juices
Selected Cold Cereals
    or
Oatmeal, with Cream
Toast, with butter
Jelly
Beverage(s)

DINNER
♔Baked Meat Loaf
  with Gravy (65)
♔Home Fried Potatoes
  (194)
♔Glazed Carrot Slices
  (184)
Peas, buttered
Three-Bean Salad
♔♔Rolls (45)
Butter or Margarine
Vanilla Ice Cream—
  Butterscotch Sauce
Beverage(s)

DINNER
♔Sirloin Tips, gravy (64)
Shelled Macaroni
  Florentine
Broccoli, buttered
Pineapple and Rasp-
  berry Gelatin Salad
♔♔Rolls (48)
Butter or Margarine
Cottage Pudding with
  Lemon Sauce
Beverage(s)

SUPPER
♔Tomato Rice Soup
  (256)
♔Chicken Pie (104)
Yankee Slaw
Bread, white and dark
Butter or Margarine
Chilled Peaches—
♔♔ Cookies (74)
Beverage(s)

SUPPER
♔Chicken Mushroom
  Soup (260)
Ham and Potatoes au
  Gratin
Creamed Corn
Bread, white and dark
Butter or Margarine
♔♔Devils Food Cake
  Squares (29)
Beverage(s)

8:30 P.M.
Beverage(s)*

8:30 P.M.
Beverage(s)*

TUESDAY	WEDNESDAY

BREAKFAST
Orange Sections
🍳 Poached Egg on
    Buttered Toast (19)
👨‍🍳🍳 Hot Rolls (45)
    Butter or Margarine
    Jam
    Beverage(s)

BREAKFAST
Bananas with Cream
Golden French Toast
Maple Syrup or Honey
Canadian Bacon
Beverage(s)

DINNER
Barbecued Short Ribs
Oven Browned Potatoes
Buttered Spinach
🍳 Tossed Lettuce and
    Orange Section
    Salad (230)
👨‍🍳🍳 Rolls (46)
    Butter or Margarine
    Lemon Fluff
    Beverage(s)

DINNER
🍳 Braised Minute Steaks
    and Gravy (57)
    Mashed Potatoes
    Green Buttered Beans
🍳 Stuffed Prune
    Salad (227)
    Roll, wholewheat
    Butter or Margarine
    Pineapple Upside
    Down Cake
    Beverage(s)

SUPPER
🍳 Beef Soup with
    Barley (256)
    Barbecued Meat Balls
    on Fluffy Rice
🍳 Grated Carrot and
    Raisin Salad (229)
👨‍🍳🍳 Baked Cherry
    Pudding (76)
    Beverage(s)

SUPPER
🍳 Corn Chowder (273)
🍳 Chicken Salad (221)
    Potato Chips
    Relishes
    Bread, white and dark
    Butter or Margarine
    Rice Pudding
    Beverage(s)

8:30 P.M.
Beverage(s)*

8:30 P.M.
Beverage(s)*

THURSDAY

BREAKFAST
Assorted Juices
Selected Cold Cereal
    or
Wheatena, with Cream
Corn Muffins (44)
Butter or Margarine
Jelly
Beverage(s)

DINNER
Roast Lamb and
    Mint Jelly (80)
Buttered Parsley
    Potatoes
Fritter Fried Egg
    Plant (185)
Parker House Rolls
    (46)
Butter or Margarine
Sliced Tomato Salad
Apricot Tapioca
Beverage(s)

SUPPER
Beef Bouillon (256)
Creamed Egg Golden-
    rod on Toast
Baby Lima Beans
Cream Puffs, Choco-
    late Icing (302)
Beverage(s)

8:30 P.M.
Beverage(s)*

FRIDAY

BREAKFAST
Grapefruit Half
Fried Egg
Plantation Sausage
Toast
Butter or Margarine
Jam
Beverage(s)

DINNER
Broiled Haddock
Delmonico Potatoes
    (196)
Swiss Chard
Strawberry Aspic with
    Cottage Cheese Layer
Rolls (45)
Butter or Margarine
Banana Shortcake—
    Topping
Beverage(s)

SUPPER
Cream of Asparagus
    Soup (268)
Tunafish Salad on
    Lettuce Leaf (221)
Potato Chips
Celery and Olives
Bread, wholewheat
Butter or Margarine
Honey Drop
    Cookies (70)
Beverage(s)

8:30 P.M.
Beverage(s)*

SATURDAY

BREAKFAST
    Assorted Juices
    Buttermilk Pancakes
    Honey Butter
    Warm Maple Syrup
    Grilled Ham
    Beverage(s)

DINNER
👨‍🍳 Spare Ribs and
        Sauerkraut (86)
    Boiled Potatoes
👨‍🍳 Tomato Aspic (234)
👨‍🍳 👨‍🍳 Rolls (47)
    Butter or Margarine
    Spice Cake/topping
    Beverage(s)

SUPPER
    Fried Vienna Sausages
👨‍🍳 Spaghetti with Butter
        sauce (24)
    Green Beans, buttered
👨‍🍳 Tomato and Lettuce
        Salad (218)
    Bread, white and dark
    Butter or Margarine
    Whipped Fruit Gelatin
    Beverage(s)

8:30 P.M.
    Beverage(s)*

20th Week

SUNDAY

BREAKFAST
  Chilled Orange Juice
  Country Fresh Egg
  Grilled Sausages
  🍳🍳Chocolate Dough-
    nuts (41)
  Butter or Margarine
  Beverage(s)

DINNER
  🍳Creamed Chicken in
    Individual Shells
    (99)
  Baked Potato, Sour
    Cream and Chives
  Asparagus and Pimiento
  🍳Tossed Salad (green)/
    dressing (221)
  🍳🍳Rolls (45)
  Butter or Margarine
  Orange-Cranberry Pie
  Beverage(s)

SUPPER
  🍳Tomato Rice
    Bouillon (256)
  Choice of Bologna,
    Egg Salad and
    Cheese Sandwiches
  Relishes–Pickles
  Catsup, Horseradish Mustard
  Raw Vegetable Salad/
    dressing
  🍳🍳Apple Crisp (76)
  Beverage(s)

  8:30 P.M.
    Beverage(s)*

MONDAY

BREAKFAST
  Fruit in Season
  Old Fashioned Waffles
  Crisp Bacon
  Honey or Maple Syrup
  Soft Butter
  Beverage(s)

DINNER
  Spanish Rice with Meat
  Cauliflower with Buttered
    Bread Crumbs
  🍳Pear Salad with Cream
    Cheese (229)
  Rolls, wholewheat
  Butter or Margarine
  Fruit Pudding–Custard
    Sauce
  Beverage(s)

SUPPER
  🍳Cream of Celery Soup
    (268)
  🍳Welsh Rarebit on Toast
    (259)
  Green Peas, buttered
  🍳Jellied Fruit Salad/
    Cream Dressing (231)
  🍳🍳Oatmeal Date Bars (71)
  Beverage(s)

  8:30 P.M.
    Beverage(s)*

TUESDAY

BREAKFAST
Assorted Juices
🍳 Poached Egg on
   Buttered Toast (19)
Apricot Danish Roll
Butter or Margarine
Jelly
Beverage(s)

DINNER
Veal Breasts with
   Stuffing
Buttered Parsley
   Potatoes
Fried Egg Plant
🍳 Lettuce and Tomato
   Salad (218)
Bread, white and dark
Butter or Margarine
🍳🍳 Strawberry Chiffon
   Pie (65)
Beverage(s)

SUPPER
Pork and Veal
   Chop Suey
Chinese Noodles
Buttered Rice
🍳 Lime Pear Aspic
   (233)
Bread, white and dark
Butter or Margarine
🍳🍳 Fluffy White Cake with
   Orange Frosting (29)
Beverage(s)
8:30 P.M.
   Beverage(s)*

WEDNESDAY

BREAKFAST
Half Grapefruit
Selected Cold Cereal
   or
Cream of Wheat,
   with Cream
Golden Toast
Butter or Margarine
Jelly
Beverage(s)

DINNER
🍳 Grilled Liver and
   Bacon (36)
Buttered Parsley
   Potatoes
🍳 Scalloped Tomatoes
   (187)
🍳 Watercress with
   French Dressing (238)
Bread, white and dark
Butter or Margarine
Chocolate Cottage
   Pudding with
   Custard Sauce
Beverage(s)

SUPPER
Cranberry Juice
Ham and Sweet Potato
   Casserole
Green Beans
Bread, white and dark
Butter or Margarine
Whipped Gelatin with
   Topping
Beverage(s)

8:30 P.M.
   Beverage(s)*

THURSDAY

BREAKFAST
  Chilled Fruit Juice
  Buttermilk Pancakes
  Soft Butter
  Warm Maple Syrup
    or Honey
  Beverage(s)

DINNER
  🍳Braised Beef with
    Potatoes, Carrots,
    and Peas (63)
  Bread, white and dark
  Butter or Margarine
  🍳Jellied Crushed Pine-
    apple in Lemon
    Gelatin Salad (233)
  Peach Cobbler
  Beverage(s)

SUPPER
  Beef Noodle Soup
  Baked Green Pepper
    stuffed, Tomato
    sauce
  Roll, wholewheat
  Butter or Margarine
  Chilled Queen Anne
    Cherries
  Beverage(s)

8:30 P.M.
  Beverage(s)*

FRIDAY

BREAKFAST
  Orange Slices
  🍳Scrambled Eggs (19)
  Crisp Bacon
  Toast
  Butter or Margarine
  Jelly
  Beverage(s)

DINNER
  🍳Scallops and Shrimp
    Newburg with
    Green Peas (153)
  Potato Chips
  Buttered Broccoli
    Spears
  🍳🍳Rolls (48)
  Butter or Margarine
  Grape Nut Custard
  Beverage(s)

SUPPER
  🍳Cream of Asparagus
    Soup (268)
  Salmon Loaf
  Apple, Celery and
    Date Salad
  Bread, white and dark
  Butter or Margarine
  🍳🍳Crispy Oatmeal
    Cookies (75)
  Beverage(s)

8:30 P.M.
  Beverage(s)*

SATURDAY

BREAKFAST
  Stewed Prunes,
    Lemon Slices
  Assorted Cold Cereals
    or
  Oatmeal, with Cream
  Prune Danish
  Butter or Margarine
  Beverage(s)

DINNER
  ☙Hamburger Steak
    with Fried Onions
    (57)
  Buttered Noodles
  ☙Cole Slaw (223)
  Harvard Beets
  ☙☙Rolls (46)
  Butter or Margarine
  Brown Sugar Custard
  Beverage(s)

SUPPER
  ☙Scotch Broth with
    Barley (257)
  Shepherd's Pie,
    Whipped Potato
    Crust
  Bread, white and dark
  Butter or Margarine
  Pineapple Sherbet
  Beverage(s)

8:30 P.M.
  Beverage(s)*

NOTES
(Special Events,
Residents'
Birthdays, etc.)

21st Week

SUNDAY

BREAKFAST
  Grapefruit and Orange
    Sections
  ✡ Bacon Omelet (20)
  Golden Toast
  Butter or Margarine
  Jam or Marmalade
  Beverage(s)

DINNER
  ✡ Roast Loin of
    Pork (87)
  Brown Gravy
  Mashed Potatoes
  Buttered Baby
    Lima Beans
  ✡ Carrot and Raisin
    Salad (229)
  ✡✡ Hot Biscuits (3)
  Butter or Margarine
  ✡✡ Lemon Pie (57)
  Beverage(s)

SUPPER
  ✡ Tomato Barley
    Soup (256)
  ½ Liverwurst Sand-
    wich (dark bread)
  ½ Deviled Egg Sand-
    wich (white bread)
  Relishes
  Potato Chips
  Spice Cake with
    Whipped Cream
  Beverage(s)

8:30 P.M.
  Beverage(s)*

MONDAY

BREAKFAST
  Chilled Fruit Juice
  Assorted Cold Cereals
    or
  Wheatena, with Cream
  Lemon Doughnut
  Beverage(s)

DINNER
  Boiled Weiners with
  ✡   German Sauerkraut (187)
  Boiled Potatoes
  Harvard Beets
  Bread, white and dark
  Butter or Margarine
  Baked Rice Custard
  Beverage(s)

SUPPER
  ✡ Vegetable Soup,
    saltines (261)
  Broiled Cheeseburger
    on large Bun
  Green Beans, buttered
  Whipped Apple Gelatin
    with Bananas
  Beverage(s)

8:30 P.M.
  Beverage(s)*

TUESDAY

BREAKFAST
  Stewed Apricots
  Fried Egg
  Hickory Smoked
    Bacon
  Golden Toast
  Butter or Margarine
  Jam
  Beverage(s)

DINNER
  ᗰ Breaded Veal
    Chops (37)
  Baked Sweet Potatoes
  ᗰ Succotash (185)
  ᗰᗰ Baking Powder
    Biscuits, hot (3)
  Butter or Margarine—
    Raspberry Jam
  ᗰ Cabbage and Pineapple
    Salad (223)
  ᗰᗰ Apple Brown Betty
    (76)
  Beverage(s)

SUPPER
  ᗰ Spaghetti with
    Tomato and Meat
    Sauce (291)
  ᗰ Carrots, glazed (184)
  ᗰ Mixed Fruit Salad (227)
  Roll, wholewheat
  Butter or Margarine
  ᗰᗰ Orange Pie (64)
  Beverage(s)

8:30 P.M.
  Beverage(s)*

WEDNESDAY

BREAKFAST
  Chilled Pineapple Juice
  Assorted Cold Cereals
    or
  Oatmeal with Cream
  ᗰᗰ Hot Rolls (40)
  Butter or Margarine
  Jelly
  Beverage(s)

DINNER
  ᗰ Baked Spanish Steak
    (60)
  Boiled Potatoes
  Frenched Green Beans
  ᗰ Tossed Vegetable
    Salad (221)
  ᗰᗰ Rolls (48)
  Butter or Margarine
  Refrigerator Pudding
  Beverage(s)

SUPPER
  ᗰ Chicken Soup (258)
  ᗰ Beef Stroganoff,
    Buttered Noodles
    (53)
  ᗰ Stuffed Celery Sticks (222)
  Buttered Peas
  Bread, white or dark
  Butter or Margarine
  Raisin Nut Pudding
  Beverage(s)

8:30 P.M.
  Beverage(s)*

THURSDAY	FRIDAY
BREAKFAST	**BREAKFAST**
Grapefruit Sections, Grenadine	Chilled Prune Juice
⚕ Poached Egg on Buttered Toast (19)	Old Fashioned Waffles
Apple Danish Roll	Honey Butter
Butter or Margarine	Warm Maple Syrup
Beverage(s)	Beverage(s)

THURSDAY

BREAKFAST
Grapefruit Sections,
    Grenadine
⚕ Poached Egg on
    Buttered Toast (19)
Apple Danish Roll
Butter or Margarine
Beverage(s)

DINNER
⚕ Broiled Liver (36)
⚕ Potatoes au Gratin
    (196)
Broccoli
⚕ Tomato Aspic
    Salad (234)
⚕⚕ Rolls (45)
Butter or Margarine
⚕⚕ Gingerbread/Whipped
    Cream (19)
Beverage(s)

SUPPER
⚕ Cream of Corn
    Soup (273)
Crackers
Assorted Sandwiches
⚕ Molded Green Salad
    (233)
⚕⚕ Oatmeal Rocks
    (cookies) (75)
Beverage(s)

8:30 P.M.
Beverage(s)*

FRIDAY

BREAKFAST
Chilled Prune Juice
Old Fashioned Waffles
Honey Butter
Warm Maple Syrup
Beverage(s)

DINNER
Shrimp Rarebit in
    Cheddar Cheese Sauce
Buttered Carrots and
    Peas
⚕⚕ Rolls (46)
Butter or Margarine–
    Jelly
Fresh Strawberry-
    Rhubarb Sauce
Beverage(s)

SUPPER
⚕ Cream of Mushroom
    Soup (268)
⚕ Codfish Cakes (138)
French Fries
Stuffed Tomato with
    Apples and Celery
Chilled Apricots
Beverage(s)

8:30 P.M.
Beverage(s)*

SATURDAY

BREAKFAST
  Chilled Fresh Melon
    Slice
  Assorted Cold Cereals
    or
  Cream of Wheat,
    warm milk
  Pecan Roll
  Butter or Margarine
  Beverage(s)

DINNER
  ♧ Lamb or Irish Stew
    (79,83,84)
  Savory Beets
  ♧ ♧ Rolls (48)
  Butter or Margarine
  Prune and Carrot Salad
  ♧ ♧ Bread Pudding with
    Lemon Sauce (76)
  Beverage(s)

SUPPER
  ♧ Potato Onion Soup (265)
  Turkey Cheese Puff
  Malaga Grape and
    Orange Salad
  Bread, white and dark
  Butter or Margarine
  ♧ ♧ Date Torte (78)
  Beverage(s)

8:30 P.M.
  Beverage(s)*

NOTES
(Special Events,
Residents'
Birthdays, etc.)

22nd Week

SUNDAY

BREAKFAST
Chilled Melon
🍳 Scrambled Eggs (19)
Hickory Smoked Bacon
Cinnamon Raisin Rolls
Beverage(s)

DINNER
🍳 Roast Chicken,
    Dressing (106)
🍳 Giblet Gravy (122)
Mashed Potatoes
Cauliflower with
    Cheese Sauce
🍳 Carrot and Raisin
    Salad (229)
🍳🍳 Rolls (45)
Butter or Margarine
🍳🍳 Strawberry Shortcake/
    Whipped Cream (37)
Beverage(s)

SUPPER
Cream of Pea Soup
Assorted Sandwiches
Grapefruit and
    Romaine/Salad
    dressing
Chocolate Pudding
Beverage(s)

8:30 P.M.
Beverage(s)*

MONDAY

BREAKFAST
Assorted Fruit Juices
Selected Cold Cereals
    or
Oatmeal, with Cream
Toast, buttered
Jelly
Beverage(s)

DINNER
🍳 Roast Fresh Ham (85)
Buttered Parsley Potatoes
Buttered Baby Whole
    Beets
Apple Sauce, Warm
🍳🍳 Roll (46)
Butter or Margarine
🍳🍳 Fruit Pudding
    Custard Sauce (77)
Beverage(s)

SUPPER
🍳 Cream of Tomato
    Soup, with
    croutons (252)
Broiled Veal Pattie
Marinated Green
    Bean Salad
Buttered Broccoli
Spice Cake, with
    Frosting
Beverage(s)

8:30 P.M.
Beverage(s)*

TUESDAY

BREAKFAST
Orange Sections
☕Poached Egg on
Buttered Toast (19)
👨‍🍳☕Hot Rolls (40)
Butter or Margarine
Jam
Beverage(s)

DINNER
☕Barbecued Spareribs
(79)
French Fried
Potatoes
Creamed Celery
👨‍🍳☕Corn Bread—butter
or margarine (44)
Cabbage and Green
Pepper Salad
👨‍🍳☕Lemon Cream Pie (57)
Beverage(s)

SUPPER
Chili Con Carne
☕Tossed Crisp Vegetable
Salad/dressing (221)
👨‍🍳☕Hard Roll (48)
Butter or Margarine
Pineapple Tapioca
Beverage(s)

8:30 P.M.
Beverage(s)*

WEDNESDAY

BREAKFAST
Bananas with Cream
Golden French Toast
Maple Syrup or Honey
Canadian Bacon
Beverage(s)

DINNER
Salisbury Steak, gravy
Buttered Parsley Potatoes
☕Glazed Carrots (184)
☕Wilted Lettuce (bacon
drippings and vinegar,
etc.) (241)
👨‍🍳☕Rolls (45)
Butter or Margarine
☕Chilled Peaches—Cookies (317)
Beverage(s)

SUPPER
Cream of Lima
Bean Soup
Stuffed Green Pepper
with Ham and Rice
☕Jellied Fruit
Salad/dressing (231)
Bread, white and dark
Butter or Margarine
Spicy Applesauce Torte
with Topping
Beverage(s)

8:30 P.M.
Beverage(s)*

THURSDAY

BREAKFAST
  Assorted Juices
  Selected Cold Cereal
      or
  Wheatena, with cream
  Corn Muffins
  Butter or Margarine
  Jelly
  Beverage(s)

DINNER
  Liver Patties
  Baked Potato with
      Butter
  Fried Parsnips
  Buttered Peas
  ௸ Jellied Vegetable
      Salad Square/
      dressing (234)
  Rhubarb Pie
  Beverage(s)

SUPPER
  Split Pea Soup
  ௸ Flaky Crusted Beef
      Pot Pie (59)
  Peach and Cheese Salad
  ௸௸ Parker House Roll (46)
  Butter or Margarine
  Whipped Orange
      Gelatin/Cream
  Beverage(s)

8:30 P.M.
  Beverage(s)*

FRIDAY

BREAKFAST
  Grapefruit Half
  Fried Egg
  Plantation Sausage
  Toast
  Butter or Margarine—
      Jam
  Beverage(s)

DINNER
  ௸ Macaroni and
      Cheese (191)
  Buttered Peas
  ௸ Stewed Tomatoes,
      with buttered crumb
      topping (187)
  ௸௸ Rolls (46)
  Butter or Margarine
  Pineapple Upside
      Down Cake/
      Topping
  Beverage(s)

SUPPER
  ௸ Cream of Tomato Soup
      (252)
  ௸ Tuna Fish Sandwich
      (221) and
  Swiss Cheese Sandwich
  ௸ Fruit Salad/dressing (240)
  ௸ Fruited Gelatin (232)—
  ௸௸ Peanut Butter
      Cookies (71)
  Beverage(s)

8:30 P.M.
  Beverage(s)*

SATURDAY

BREAKFAST
Assorted Juices
Buttermilk Pancakes
Honey Butter
Warm Maple Syrup
Canadian Bacon
Beverage(s)

DINNER
℘ Ham Loaf with Horse-
radish Sauce (287)
Steamed Rice with
Butter
Sliced Warm Beets
℘ Fresh Garden Salad
(221)
Bread, white and dark
Butter or Margarine
℘℘ Baked Apple with
topping (37)
Beverage(s)

SUPPER
℘ French Onion Soup
(253)
Sliced Cold Meat Platter
℘ Potato Salad (225)
Buttered Peas and Carrots
Bread, white and dark
Butter or Margarine
℘℘ Peach Crisp with
topping (76)
Beverage(s)

8:30 P.M.
Beverage(s)*

23rd Week

SUNDAY

BREAKFAST
    Chilled Orange Juice
    Country Fresh Egg
    Grilled Sausages
👨‍🍳👨‍🍳Apple Cinnamon
      Doughnuts (41)
    Butter or Margarine
    Beverage(s)

DINNER
    Fried Chicken
👨‍🍳Giblet Gravy (122)
    Mashed Potatoes
    Baby Lima Beans
👨‍🍳Pear/Cream Cheese on
      Lettuce Salad (229)
    Corn Meal Rolls
    Butter or Margarine
    Vanilla Ice Cream/Fresh
      Strawberry Sauce
    Beverage(s)

SUPPER
👨‍🍳Vegetable Soup (261)
    Assorted Cold Meats
      and Cheese
👨‍🍳Perfection Salad
      Squares (234)
    Potato Chips
👨‍🍳Macaroni Salad (215)
    Bread, white and dark
    Butter or Margarine
    Grapenut Custard
    Beverage(s)

8:30 P.M.
    Beverage(s)*

MONDAY

BREAKFAST
    Fruit in Season
    Old Fashioned Waffles
    Crisp Bacon
    Honey or Maple Syrup
    Soft Butter
    Beverage(s)

DINNER
👨‍🍳Braised Beef with
      Potatoes and Carrots
      (63)
👨‍🍳Apple Gelatin Waldorf
      Salad (226) with
      Lettuce and Dressing
👨‍🍳👨‍🍳Bran Muffins (43)
    Butter or Margarine
    Tapioca Pudding with
      Chocolate Sauce
    Beverage(s)

SUPPER
    Beef Noodle Soup
    Turkey Salad with
      Celery and Hard
      Cooked Eggs
    Bread, white and dark
    Butter or Margarine
    Green Beans
👨‍🍳👨‍🍳Angel Food Cake with
      Butterscotch Sauce
      (31)
    Beverage(s)

8:30 P.M.
    Beverage(s)*

TUESDAY

BREAKFAST
  Assorted Juices
  ☙Poached Egg on
    Buttered Toast (19)
  Raspberry Danish Roll
  Butter or Margarine
  Jelly
  Beverage(s)

DINNER
  ☙Meat Stew with
    Dumplings
    (59, 275)
  Buttered Broccoli
  ☙Tomato Aspic (234)
  ☙ ☙Boysenberry Pie (62)
  Beverage(s)

SUPPER
  ☙Minestrone Soup
    (249)
  Saltines
  ☙Italian Spaghetti
    with Meat
    Sauce (291)
  ☙Tossed Green Salad/
    French Dressing
    (238)
  French Bread—butter
    or margarine
  Cinnamon Apple Cup-
    cakes/Lemon Sauce
  Beverage(s)

8:30 P.M.
  Beverage(s)*

WEDNESDAY

BREAKFAST
  Half Grapefruit
  Selected Cold Cereal
    or
  Cream of Wheat,
    with cream
  Golden Toast
  Butter or Margarine
  Jelly
  Beverage(s)

DINNER
  ☙Fried Liver and
    Bacon (36)
  Buttered Parsley
    Potatoes
  Honey Glazed Carrots
  Chef's Salad
  ☙ ☙Muffins (43)
  Butter or Margarine
  Coconut Cream Pie
  Beverage(s)

SUPPER
  ☙Cream of Fresh Carrot
    Soup (268)
  ½ Ham Salad Sandwich
    on Rye Bread
  ½ Egg Salad Sandwich
    on Whole Wheat
    Bread
  Buttered Celery
    with Peas
  Grapefruit Salad
  Graham Cracker
    Chocolate Cookies
  Beverage(s)

8:30 P.M.
  Beverage(s)*

THURSDAY

BREAKFAST
  Chilled Fruit Juice
  Buttermilk Pancakes
  Soft Butter
  Warm Maple Syrup
    or Honey
  Beverage(s)

DINNER
  Meat Loaf, gravy (65)
  Baked Potatoes and
    Butter
  Corn, creamed style
  Pineapple Cottage
    Cheese Salad
    (229)
  Lemon Oatmeal Drop
    Cookies
  Beverage(s)

SUPPER
  V-8 Juice
  Crabmeat Casserole
  Tossed Green Salad
    (218)
  Bread, white and dark
  Butter or Margarine
  Refrigerator Pudding
  Beverage(s)

8:30 P.M.
  Beverage(s)*

FRIDAY

BREAKFAST
  Orange Slices
  Scrambled Eggs (19)
  Crisp Bacon
  Toast
  Butter or Margarine—
    Jelly
  Beverage(s)

DINNER
  Salmon and Potato
    Casserole, uce
    Parsley Sauce
  Brussels Sprouts
  Perfection Salad
    (234) with
    mayonnaise
  Rolls (46)
  Butter or Margarine
  Bread Pudding with
    Dates and Vanilla
    Sauce (76)
  Beverage(s)

SUPPER
  Cream of Mushroom
    Soup (268)
  Tomato Stuffed with
    Egg Salad (224)
  Potato Chips
  Celery and Carrot
    Curls
  Bread, white and dark
  Butter or Margarine
  Apple Pie (56)
  Beverage(s)

8:30 P.M.
  Beverage(s)*

SATURDAY

BREAKFAST
Stewed Prunes, Lemon
  Slices
Assorted Cold Cereals
  or
Oatmeal, with Cream
Cinnamon Streusel
  Danish
Butter or Margarine
Beverage(s)

DINNER
♕Italian Spaghetti and
  Meat Sauce (291)
♕Tossed Green Salad/
  dressing (239)
♕♕Poppy Seed Hard Rolls
  (48)
Garlic Butter
Lemon Meringue Pie
Beverage(s)

SUPPER
Beef Broth
Skinned Bologna, Holland
♕German Potato Salad,
  hot (225)
Horseradish-Mustard and
  Catsup
Green Beans
Chilled Pears
Beverage(s)

8:30 P.M.
Beverage(s)*

NOTES
(Special Events,
Residents'
Birthdays, etc.)

24th Week

SUNDAY	MONDAY

BREAKFAST
Grapefruit and
  Orange Sections
🍴Bacon Omelet (20)
Golden Toast
Butter or Margarine
Jam or Marmalade
Beverage(s)

BREAKFAST
Chilled Fruit Juice
Assorted Cold Cereals
  or
Wheatena, with Cream
Cheese Danish Roll
Butter or Margarine
Beverage(s)

DINNER
🍴Roast Loin of
  Pork (87)
Baked Apple Rings
Mashed Sweet Potatoes
Steamed Spinach
🍴Jellied Fruit Salad
  (231)
🍴🍴Roll (45)
Butter or Margarine
Lemon Sherbet—
Cookies
Beverage(s)

DINNER
🍴Baked Beef Hash
  (includes potatoes)
  (61)
Buttered Green Beans
Creamed Onions
🍴Grapefruit Salad/
  dressing (238)
🍴🍴Rolls (45)
Butter or Margarine
Vanilla Pudding with
  Chocolate Sauce
Beverage(s)

SUPPER
🍴Chicken Rice Soup
  with Crackers
  (256)
🍴Cottage Cheese and
  Peach Salad (229)
Raisin Toast
Butter or Margarine
🍴🍴Devils Food Cake,
  Frosted (29)
Beverage(s)

SUPPER
🍴Cream of Celery
  Soup (268)
Tomato, Beef and
  Cheese Sandwiches
🍴Tossed Vegetable
  Salad (221)
Chilled Pear Halves
Beverage(s)

8:30 P.M.
Beverage(s)*

8:30 P.M.
Beverage(s)*

TUESDAY	WEDNESDAY

BREAKFAST
Stewed Apricots
Fried Egg
Hickory Smoked
    Bacon
Golden Toast
Butter or Margarine
Jam
Beverage(s)

BREAKFAST
Chilled Pineapple Juice
Assorted Cold Cereals
    or
Oatmeal, with Cream
⚜️⚜️ Hot Rolls (46)
Butter or Margarine
Jelly
Beverage(s)

DINNER
⚜️ Barbecued Spare Ribs
    (79)
Browned Potatoes
Brussel Sprouts
⚜️ French Endive Salad/
    dressing(219)
Orange Sherbet—
⚜️⚜️   Cookies(71)
Beverage(s)

DINNER
⚜️ Pan Fried Lamb
    Patties (84)
⚜️ Lyonnaise
    Potatoes (194)
Buttered Peas
⚜️⚜️ Rolls—Mint Jelly (48)
Butter or Margarine
Lettuce and Tomato
    Salad
⚜️⚜️ Custard Pie (58)
Beverage(s)

SUPPER
Creamed Chipped
    Beef on Toast
Buttered Asparagus
⚜️ Jellied Fruit Salad (231)
⚜️⚜️ Raisin Cookies (70)
Beverage(s)

SUPPER
⚜️ Corn Chowder (271)
Cold Meat Salad
    Sandwich
Baked Lima Beans
    in Tomato Sauce
⚜️ Perfection Salad
    Squares (234)
Baked Rice Pudding
    with Apricot Sauce
Beverage(s)

8:30 P.M.
    Beverage(s)*

8:30 P.M.
    Beverage(s)*

THURSDAY	FRIDAY
BREAKFAST	**BREAKFAST**

BREAKFAST
Grapefruit Sections,
  Grenadine
♕ Poached Egg on
  Buttered Toast (19)
Apple Danish Roll
Butter or Margarine
Beverage(s)

BREAKFAST
Chilled Prune Juice
Old Fashioned Waffles
Honey Butter
Warm Maple Syrup
Beverage(s)

DINNER
♕ Chicken Fricassee (108)
♕ Dumplings and Gravy
  (275)
French Green Beans,
  Buttered
♕ Jellied Fruit Salad
  (231)
Red Raspberry Sherbet—
♕   Cookies (317)
Beverage(s)

DINNER
Salmon Loaf Florentine
Whipped Potatoes
Buttered Mixed
  Vegetables
♕ Stuffed Celery Sticks
  (222)
Bread, white and dark
Butter or Margarine
♕♕ Nut and Raisin
  Cookies (70)
Beverage(s)

SUPPER
♕ Bouillon (256)
Fried Sausage Links
Baked Potato
Mixed Vegetables
Bread—Butter or
  Margarine
♕♕ Yellow Cupcakes
  with Icing (29)
Beverage(s)

SUPPER
♕ Cream of Asparagus
  Soup (268)
Assorted Sandwiches
Buttered, Whole Kernel
  Corn
♕ Grated Carrot and
  Raisin Salad (229)
Chocolate Pudding
Beverage(s)

8:30 P.M.
Beverage(s)*

8:30 P.M.
Beverage(s)*

SATURDAY

BREAKFAST
Chilled Fresh Melon
Slice
Assorted Cold Cereals
or
Cream of Wheat,
warm milk
Cinnamon Raisin
Pecan Roll
Butter or Margarine
Beverage(s)

DINNER
🍳 Corned Beef and
Cabbage (62,63)
Boiled Potatoes
🍳 Molded Vegetable
Salad (234)
Rye Bread
Butter or Margarine
🍳🍳 Baked Custard (58)
Beverage(s)

SUPPER
🍳 Vegetable Soup (261)
Bologna Sandwich on
Black Bread–White
Bread
Butter or Margarine
🍳 Hot German Potato
Salad (225)
Mustard–Catsup
Brown Sugar Cake
Beverage(s)

8:30 P.M.
Beverage(s)*

NOTES
(Special Events,
Residents'
Birthdays, etc.)

25th Week

SUNDAY	**MONDAY**

BREAKFAST
Chilled Melon
🍳 Scrambled Eggs (19)
Hickory Smoked
   Bacon
🍳 🍳 Honey Dip Dough-
   nuts (41)
Beverage(s)

BREAKFAST
Assorted Fruit Juices
Selected Cold Cereals
   or
Oatmeal, with Cream
Toast, buttered
Jelly
Beverage(s)

DINNER
Tomato Juice
🍳 Roast Beef (53)
Oven Browned
   Potatoes
🍳 Beets with Orange
   Sauce (182)
🍳 Cabbage, Apple and
   Pineapple Salad
   (223)
🍳 🍳 Cloverleaf Rolls (46)
Butter or Margarine
Gelatin with Mixed
   Fruit, Whipped
   Topping
Beverage(s)

DINNER
🍳 Meat Balls (64) in
   Mushroom Sauce
   (288)
🍳 Hashed Brown Potatoes
   (194)
Parslied Cole Slaw
Carrots, shoestring
   style
Bread, white and dark
Butter or Margarine
🍳 🍳 Fluffy White Cake,
   Orange Cream
   Frosting (29)
Beverage(s)

SUPPER
🍳 Cream of Mushrrom
   Soup (261)
Hamburger on Bun
Celery Sticks
Pickles—Relish
🍳 🍳 Strawberry Short-
   cake (37)
Beverage(s)

SUPPER
🍳 Chicken Rice
   Soup (256)
🍳 Beef Stew (59)
🍳 🍳   on Hot Biscuit (3)
Apple and Celery Salad
Bran Applesauce
   Cookies
Beverage(s)

8:30 P.M.
Beverage(s)*

8:30 P.M.
Beverage(s)*

TUESDAY

BREAKFAST
  Orange Sections
  ☕Poached Egg on
    Buttered Toast (19)
  ☕☕Hot Rolls (40)
  Butter or Margarine
  Jam
  Beverage(s)

DINNER
  ☕ Baked Stuffed
    Pork Chop (87)
  Whipped Potatoes
  Buttered Spinach
  ☕☕Corn Muffins,(44)
    Apple Jelly
  Butter or Margarine
  Whipped Fruit
    Gelatin
  Beverage(s)

SUPPER
  Beef Noodle Soup
  Chicken Salad
  Bread, white and dark
  Potato Chips
  ☕Tossed Vegetable Salad/
    Russian Dressing (218)
  Butter or Margarine
  ☕☕Dutch Apple Cake (18)
  Beverage(s)

8:30 P.M.
  Beverage(s)*

WEDNESDAY

BREAKFAST
  Bananas with Cream
  Golden French Toast
  Maple Syrup or Honey
  Canadian Bacon
  Beverage(s)

DINNER
  ☕Pot Roast of Beef
    (53)
  Cottage Fried Potatoes
  Diced Summer Squash
    in Sour Cream
  Fresh Green Beans
  ☕Cucumber Slices/
    Vinegar and Oil (220)
  ☕☕Apple Betty (76)
  Beverage(s)

SUPPER
  ☕French Onion
    Soup (253)
  ☕Braised Liver and
    Bacon (36)
  Asparagus, creamed
  Bread, white and dark
  Butter or Margarine
  Old Fashioned Rice
    Pudding
  Beverage(s)

8:30 P.M.
  Beverage(s)*

THURSDAY

BREAKFAST
Assorted Juices
Selected Cold Cereal
    or
Wheatena, with Cream
Blueberry Muffin
Butter or Margarine
    Jelly
Beverage(s)

DINNER
Salisbury Steak
Buttered Noodles
Harvard Beets
🍲Carrot and Raisin
    Salad (229)
🍲🍲Rolls (46)
Butter or Margarine
Peach Cobbler
Beverage(s)

SUPPER
🍲Minestrone Soup
    (249)
🍲Spaghetti with
    Tomato-Meat
    Sauce (291)
🍲Tossed Green Salad/
    Italian Dressing (221)
French Bread
Butter or Margarine
Chilled Pears
Beverage(s)

8:30 P.M.
Beverage(s)*

FRIDAY

BREAKFAST
Grapefruit Half
Fried Egg
Plantation Sausage
Toast
Butter or Margarine
Jam
Beverage(s)

DINNER
Fried Filet of Perch
🍲Au Gratin
    Potatoes (196)
Buttered Green Peas
🍲Tomato Aspic (234)
🍲🍲Rolls (45)
Butter or Margarine
Lemon Meringue Pie
Beverage(s)

SUPPER
🍲Vegetable Soup (261)
🍲Tunafish Salad
    Sandwiches (221)
Potato Chips
🍲Mixed Green Salad/
    French Dressing (238)
🍲🍲Pineapple Cheese Cake
    (35)
Beverage(s)

8:30 P.M.
Beverage(s)*

SATURDAY

BREAKFAST
   Assorted Juices
   Buttermilk Pancakes
   Honey Butter
   Warm Maple Syrup
   Grilled Ham
   Beverage(s)

DINNER
𝒲Braised Short Ribs of
   Beef with natural
   gravy (52)
   Mashed Potatoes
   Buttered String Beans
𝒲 Lettuce Salad/Thousand
   Isalnd Dressing (218)
   Bread, white and dark
   Butter or Margarine
   Creamed Coconut Cake
   Beverage(s)

SUPPER
𝒲 Tomato Soup (256)
   Escalloped Ham and
      Potatoes
   Lima Beans
𝒲 Jellied Fruit Salad (231)
𝒲𝒲 Rolls (48)
   Butter or Margarine
   Refrigerator Pudding
   Beverage(s)

8:30 P.M.
   Beverage(s)*

26th Week

SUNDAY

BREAKFAST
    Chilled Orange Juice
    Country Fresh Egg
    Grilled Sausages
    Almond Nut
      Doughnuts (41)
    Butter or Margarine
    Beverage(s)

DINNER
    Baked Virginia
      Ham (85)
    Baked Yams with
      Butter
    Peas, Buttered
    Tossed Salad/
      dressing (221)
    Rolls (45)
    Butter or Margarine
    Peach Shortcake/
      Topping (37)
    Beverage(s)

SUPPER
    Vegetable Soup (261)
    Pizza (50)
    Buttered Green
      Beans, french style
    Pineapple Sherbet
    Beverage(s)

8:30 P.M.
    Beverage(s)*

MONDAY

BREAKFAST
    Fruit in Season
    Old Fashioned Waffles
    Crisp Bacon
    Honey or Maple Syrup
    Soft Butter
    Beverage(s)

DINNER
    Beef Pot Roast (53)
    Buttered Noodles
    Glazed Carrot
      Rings (184)
    Cheese Biscuits—Butter
      or Margarine
    Cabbage and Apple
      Salad (223)
    Butterscotch Pudding
    Beverage(s)

SUPPER
    Spanish Rice and Bacon
    Peach-Cottage Cheese
      Salad (229)
    Bread, white and dark
    Butter or Margarine
    Nut and Raisin
      Cookies (70)
    Beverage(s)

8:30 P.M.
    Beverage(s)*

TUESDAY

BREAKFAST
Assorted Juices
🍴Poached Egg on
    Buttered Toast (19)
Orange Danish Roll
Butter or Margarine
Jelly
Beverage(s)

DINNER
🍴Breaded Veal Cutlet
    (37) with Tomato
    Sauce (282)
Mashed Potatoes
🍴Vegetable Medley
    Salad (218)
Carrots and Peas
🍴🍴Rolls (48)
    Butter or Margarine
Butterscotch Pie
Beverage(s)

SUPPER
Sweet and Sour Pork
Buttered Rice
🍴Green Tossed Salad/
    dressing (218)
Roll, wholewheat
Butter or Margarine
Whipped Gelatin
    with Bananas
Beverage(s)

8:30 P.M.
Beverage(s)*

WEDNESDAY

BREAKFAST
Half Grapefruit
Selected Cold Cereal
    or
Cream of Wheat,
    with cream
Golden Toast
Butter or Margarine—
    Jelly
Beverage(s)

DINNER
🍴Swiss Steak (58)
Buttered Noodles
Spinach
🍴Lettuce and
    Tomato Salad (218)
🍴🍴Rolls (47)
Butter or Margarine
🍴🍴Chocolate
    Brownies (36)
Beverage(s)

SUPPER
🍴Cream of Celery
    Soup (268)
Meat Salad Plate
🍴Chef's Salad, French
    Dressing (241)
Potato Chips
Bread, white and dark
Butter or Margarine
Apricot Whip
Beverage(s)

8:30 P.M.
Beverage(s)*

THURSDAY

BREAKFAST
Chilled Fruit Juice
Buttermilk Pancakes
Soft Butter
Warm Maple Syrup
or Honey
Beverage(s)

DINNER
Braised Beef and
Vegetables (63)
Baked Potato
Perfection Salad (234)
Bread, white and dark
Butter or Margarine
Baked Custard (58)
Beverage(s)

SUPPER
Grilled Frankfurter
on Bun
German Potato
Salad (225)
Relishes and Pickles
Three Bean Salad
Ice Cream—Cookies (75)
Beverage(s)

8:30 P.M.
Beverage(s)*

FRIDAY

BREAKFAST
Orange Slices
Scrambled Eggs (19)
Crisp Bacon
Toast
Butter or Margarine—
Jelly
Beverage(s)

DINNER
Baked Fillet of
Fish (135) with
Spanish Sauce (291)
French Fried Potatoes
Green Beans, french
style
Molded Beet Salad
Bread, white and dark
Butter or Margarine
Chocolate Chip
Cookies
Beverage(s)

SUPPER
Cream of Mushroom
Soup (268)
Assorted Sandwiches
Summer Fruit Salad/
dressing (227)
Coconut Pudding
Beverage(s)

8:30 P.M.
Beverage(s)*

SATURDAY

BREAKFAST
  Stewed Prunes,
    Lemon Slices
  Assorted Cold Cereals
    or
  Oatmeal, with Cream
  Cherry Streusel Danish
  Butter or Margarine
  Beverage(s)

DINNER
  👨‍🍳 Corned Beef and
    Cabbage (62)
  Boiled Potatoes
  Cottage Cheese Salad
  👨‍🍳👨‍🍳 Rolls (46)
  Butter or Margarine
  👨‍🍳👨‍🍳 Applesauce Cake/
    Topping (18)
  Beverage(s)

SUPPER
  👨‍🍳 Beef Broth (256)
  👨‍🍳 Chef's Salad Bowl (214)
    Pickles—Olives—Radishes
  👨‍🍳 Jellied Fruit Salad (232)
  Toffee Squares (cookies)
  Beverage(s)

8:30 P.M.
  Beverage(s)

NOTES
(Special Events,
  Residents'
Birthdays, etc.)

27th Week

SUNDAY	MONDAY

BREAKFAST
Grapefruit and
  Orange Sections
♨Bacon Omelet (20)
Golden Toast
Butter or Margarine
Jam or Marmalade
Beverage(s)

BREAKFAST
Chilled Fruit Juice
Assorted Cold Cereals
  or
Wheatena, with Cream
Cheese Danish Roll
Butter or Margarine
Beverage(s)

DINNER
♨Roast Loin of
  Pork (87)
Mashed Potatoes
Broccoli Spears,
  buttered
Warm Applesauce
♨♨Rolls (45)
Butter or Margarine
♨♨Ice Cream–Cookies (72)
Beverage(s)

DINNER
V-8 Juice
Veal Pot Pie, flaky crust
Mashed Potatoes
Creamed Spinach
Bread, white and dark
Butter or Margarine
♨♨Pineapple Cake (19)
Beverage(s)

SUPPER
Corned Beef Hash
  with Poached Egg
♨Gingerale Fruit Salad/
  dressing (217)
Roll, wholewheat
Butter or Margarine
♨♨Yellow Pound Cake (21)
Beverage(s)

SUPPER
♨Cream of Mushroom
  Soup (268)
Baked Omelet with
  Currant Jelly
♨Jellied Fruit Salad (232)
Bread, white and dark
Butter or Margarine
♨♨Chocolate Fudge
  Cookies (74)
Beverage(s)

8:30 P.M.
  Beverage(s)*

8:30 P.M.
  Beverage(s)*

TUESDAY

BREAKFAST
Stewed Apricots
Fried Egg
Hickory Smoked
Bacon
Golden Toast
Butter or Margarine–
Jam
Beverage(s)

DINNER
Liver and Bacon (36)
French Fried Onion
Rings (169)
Parsley Buttered
Potatoes
Spiced Peach Salad
Bread
Butter or Margarine
Sponge Cake/
Topping (22)
Beverage(s)

SUPPER
Tomato Bouillon (256)
Main Dish–Fruit
Salad with Cottage
Cheese (227)
Raisin Toast
Butter or Margarine
Pineapple Sherbet,
Spice Cookies (70)
Beverage(s)

8:30 P.M.
Beverage(s)*

WEDNESDAY

BREAKFAST
Chilled Pineapple Juice
Assorted Cold Cereals
or
Oatmeal, with Cream
Hot Rolls (40)
Butter or Margarine
Jelly
Beverage(s)

DINNER
Chicken, oven
fried
Baked Potato
Creamed Peas and
Carrots
Wilted Lettuce
Salad/Bacon
dressing (241)
Rolls (46)
Butter or Margarine
Chocolate Fudge
Cake /Icing
Beverage(s)

SUPPER
Navy Bean Soup (262)
Brown Bread and
Cream Cheese
Sandwiches
Jellied Fruit Salad/
dressing (231)
Baked Rice Custard
Beverage(s)

8:30 P.M.
Beverage(s)*

THURSDAY

BREAKFAST
Grapefruit Sections,
  Grenadine
♨ Poached Egg on
  Buttered Toast (19)
Apple Danish Roll
Butter or Margarine
Beverage(s)

DINNER
♨ Spareribs and Sauer-
  kraut (86)
Boiled Potatoes
Buttered Carrots
♨ Jellied Fruit Salad (231)
Wholewheat Bread
Butter or Margarine
Chilled Pears
Beverage(s)

SUPPER
♨ Split Pea Soup (264)
  and Crackers
♨ Potato Pancakes (197)
♨ Mixed Vegetable
  Garden Salad/
  dressing (222)
Peach Halves, chilled
♨♨ Vanilla Cookies (70)
Beverage(s)

8:30 P.M.
Beverage(s)*

FRIDAY

BREAKFAST
Chilled Prune Juice
Old Fashioned Waffles
Honey Butter
Warm Maple Syrup
Beverage(s)

DINNER
Creamed Tunafish over
♨♨   Buttered Baking
  Powder Biscuit (3)
Green Beans with
  Pimiento Strips
♨ Summer Green Salad/
  dressing (218)
Butterscotch Pudding
Beverage(s)

SUPPER
♨ Manhattan Clam
  Chowder (273)
Toasted Cheese Sand-
  wich
Buttered Green Peas
♨ Jellied Fruit Salad (231)
♨♨ Cream Puff (67)
Beverage(s)

8:30 P.M.
Beverage(s)*

SATURDAY

BREAKFAST
  Chilled Fresh Melon
    Slice
  Assorted Cold Cereals
    or
  Cream of Wheat,
    warm milk
  Cinnamon Raisin Pecan
    Roll
  Butter or Margarine
  Beverage(s)

DINNER
  ♨Italian Spaghetti with
    Meat Sauce (291)
  ♨Tossed Green Salad (221)
  ♨♨Hard Rolls, poppy seed
    (48)
  Butter or Margarine
  Baked Cherry Pudding/
    Topping
  Beverage(s)

SUPPER
  ♨Beef Broth and
    Crackers (256)
  Chicken Salad Sandwiches
  Potato Chips
  Assorted Pickles and
    Relishes
  ♨♨Coconut Custard Cup (58)
  Beverage(s)

8:30 P.M.
  Beverage(s)

NOTES
(Special Events,
Residents'
Birthdays, etc.)

28th Week

SUNDAY	MONDAY

BREAKFAST
Chilled Melon
🎩 Scrambled Eggs (19)
Hickory Smoked
   Bacon
Cinnamon Toast
Butter or Margarine
Beverage(s)

BREAKFAST
Assorted Fruit
Selected Cold Cereals
   or
Oatmeal, with Cream
🎩🎩 Raised Doughnut (41)
Beverage(s)

DINNER
🎩 Roast Turkey (117),
   stuffing (118)
🎩 Giblet Gravy (122)
Mashed Potatoes
Parsnips, browned
Peas
🎩 Waldorf Salad (226)
🎩🎩 Raisin Bread (7)
Butter or Margarine
🎩🎩 Strawberry Pie (65)
Beverage(s)

DINNER
🎩 Meat Loaf, gravy (65)
Fried Potatoes
Spiced Hot Beets
Escalloped Onions
🎩🎩 Rolls (47)
Butter or Margarine
Chilled Melon
Beverage(s)

SUPPER
🎩 Cream of Asparagus
   Soup (268)
Turkey Salad
Assorted Relishes—
   Pickles—Olives
Potato Chips
🎩🎩 Bread, raisin and whole-
   wheat (7)
Butter or Margarine
Whipped Fruit Gelatin
Beverage(s)

SUPPER
🎩 Potato Soup with
   Chives (265)
Sliced Corned Beef
   Sandwiches
Pickles—Relishes—
   Cole Slaw
Applesauce
Beverage(s)

8:30 P.M.
   Beverage(s)*

8:30 P.M.
   Beverage(s)*

TUESDAY

BREAKFAST
  Orange Sections
  Poached Egg on
    Buttered Toast (19)
  Hot Rolls (45)
  Butter or Margarine
  Jam
  Beverage(s)

DINNER
  Veal Stew (41)
  Hard Crusty Rolls (48)
  Butter or Margarine—
    Jelly
  Cabbage and Pineapple
    Salad (223)
  Orange Ice
  Beverage(s)

SUPPER
  Barley Tomato Soup
  Assorted Cold Meats
    and Cheese
  Potato Salad (225)
  Succotash (185)
  Bread, white and dark
  Butter or Margarine
  Jelly Roll (17)
  Beverage(s)

8:30 P.M.
  Beverage(s)*

WEDNESDAY

BREAKFAST
  Bananas with Cream
  Golden French Toast
  Maple Syrup or Honey
  Canadian Bacon
  Beverage(s)

DINNER
  Fricassee of Lamb,
    Buttered Rice
  Corn Bread (44)
  Butter or Margarine
  Spiced Beets
  Prune and Carrot
    Salad (229)
  Chilled Apricots
  Beverage(s)

SUPPER
  Chicken and Rice
    Soup (256)
  Frankfurters on Hot
    Rolls
  French Fried Potatoes
  Relishes—Catsup
  Apple and Celery
    Salad (226)
  Fluffy White Cake
    with Chocolate
    Frosting (29)
  Beverage(s)

8:30 P.M.
  Beverage(s)*

THURSDAY	FRIDAY

BREAKFAST

Assorted Juices
Selected Cold Cereal
or
Wheatena, with Cream
🎩🎩Corn Muffins (44)
Butter or Margarine
Jelly
Beverage(s)

BREAKFAST

Grapefruit Half
Fried Egg
Plantation Sausage
Toast
Butter or Margarine
Jam
Beverage(s)

DINNER

🎩Cubed Liver with
Onion Gravy (36)
🎩Potatoes au Gratin (196)
Broccoli with Lemon
Butter
Jellied Apple and Grape
Salad
Bread, white and dark
Butter or Margarine
Coconut Cream Pudding
Beverage(s)

DINNER

🎩Fried Scallops (167)
with Tartar
🎩   Sauce (287)
Baked Potato
Fresh Spinach with
Hard Cooked Egg
Garnish
🎩Tomato and Lettuce
Salad/dressing (218)
Lime Snow
Beverage(s)

SUPPER

Cream of Corn Soup
Grilled Hamburger
on Bun, with slice
of onion served
separately
Catsup
🎩Baked Tomato (187)
Butter or Margarine
🎩🎩Apple Crisp (76)
Beverage(s)

SUPPER

Fisherman's Soup
🎩Tunafish Salad (221)
Potato Chips
🎩Cabbage-Apple-Pine-
apple Salad (223)
Olives—Pickles
Banana Cream Pie
Beverage(s)

8:30 P.M.
Beverage(s)*

8:30 P.M.
Beverage(s)*

SATURDAY

BREAKFAST
  Assorted Juices
  Buttermilk Pancakes
  Honey Butter
  Warm Maple Syrup
  Grilled Ham
  Beverage(s)

DINNER
  V-8 Juice
  Baked Manicotti
  Buttered Green Beans
  Bread, white and dark
  Butter or Margarine
  ✏️Tossed Green Salad/
    dressing (218)
  Chilled Watermelon
  Beverage(s)

SUPPER
  ✏️Cream of Peanut Butter
    Soup (260)
  Cheese Sandwich on
    Whole Wheat Bread
  ✏️Shredded Lettuce with
    dressing (221)
  Apple Turnover
  Beverage(s)

8:30 P.M.
  Beverage(s)*

29th Week

SUNDAY	MONDAY

BREAKFAST
Chilled Orange Juice
Country Fresh Egg
Grilled Sausages
👨‍🍳👨‍🍳 Honey Dip Dough-
    nuts (41)
Beverage(s)

BREAKFAST
Fruit in Season
Old Fashioned Waffles
Crisp Bacon
Honey or Maple Syrup
Soft Butter
Beverage(s)

DINNER
👨‍🍳 Pork Loin Roast,
    gravy (87)
Baked Sweet Potato
Tomato and Celery
    Sauce
Spiced Apple Rings
👨‍🍳 Banana and Ground
    Nut Salad/dressing
    (230)
👨‍🍳👨‍🍳 Rolls (45)
Butter or Margarine
Lemon Sherbet
Beverage(s)

DINNER
Veal Parmigiana
Baked Potato
Buttered Brussel
    Sprouts
👨‍🍳👨‍🍳 Rolls (46)
Butter or Margarine
👨‍🍳 Green Salad/dressing
    (218)
Cherry Pudding
Beverage(s)

SUPPER
👨‍🍳 Cream of Mushroom
    Soup (268)
Ham and Cheese Sand-
    wich on whole
    wheat bread
👨‍🍳 Tossed Green Salad/
    dressing (221)
👨‍🍳👨‍🍳 Custard Pie (58)
Beverage(s)

SUPPER
Beef Soup with Rice
👨‍🍳 Baked Hash (61)
Marinated Bean Salad
Bread, white and dark
Butter or Margarine
Mixed Fruit, Upside
    Down Cake
Beverage(s)

8:30 P.M.
Beverage(s)*

8:30 P.M.
Beverage(s)*

TUESDAY

BREAKFAST
Assorted Juices
🍳Poached Egg on
  Buttered Toast (19)
Orange Pineapple Danish
  Roll
Butter or Margarine
Beverage(s)

DINNER
🍳Hungarian Goulash (41)
  Buttered Noodles
  Julienne Green Beans
  Black Bread
  Butter or Margarine
🍳Sections of Orange and
  Grapefruit on Lettuce/
  dressing (230)
🍳🍳Chocolate Cake (29)
  Beverage(s)

SUPPER
Pineapple Juice
Creamed Egg and
  Crumbled Bacon
  on Toast
🍳Tossed Green Salad
  (239)
Lemon Refrigerator
  Dessert
Beverage(s)

8:30 P.M.
  Beverage(s)*

WEDNESDAY

BREAKFAST
Half Grapefruit
Selected Cold Cereals
  or
Cream of Wheat,
  with cream
Golden Toast
Butter or Margarine
Jelly
Beverage(s)

DINNER
🍳Hamburger Steak (57)
  Fried Potatoes
  Creamed Onions
  with Pimiento
🍳Summer Squash (189)
🍳🍳Rolls (45)
  Butter or Margarine
  Chilled Peaches
  Beverage(s)

SUPPER
🍳Vegetable Soup (261)
🍳 Meat Croquettes (89)
  with Horseradish
  Sauce (287)
  Buttered Chopped
  Spinach
  Bread, white and dark
  Butter or Margarine
  Cup Custard
  Beverage(s)

8:30 P.M.
  Beverage(s)*

THURSDAY	FRIDAY

THURSDAY

BREAKFAST
  Chilled Fruit Juice
  Buttermilk Pancakes
  Soft Butter
  Warm Maple Syrup
    or Honey
  Beverage(s)

DINNER
  Baked Thuringer
    Sausage with
    Sauerkraut
  Boiled Potatoes
  Lima Beans
  🍳Tomato and Lettuce
    Salad/dressing (221)
  Bread, wholewheat
  Butter or Margarine
  Orange and Grapefruit
    Sections
  Beverage(s)

SUPPER
  🍳Potato and Leek
    Soup (264)
  Ham Salad Sandwiches
  🍳Jellied Fruit Salad/
    dressing (231)
  👨‍🍳🍳Orange Squares (3)
  Beverage(s)

8:30 P.M.
  Beverage(s)*

FRIDAY

BREAKFAST
  Orange Slices
  🍳Scrambled Eggs (19)
  Crisp Bacon
  Toast
  Butter or Margarine
  Jelly
  Beverage(s)

DINNER
  Oven Fried Fish
    Patties,
  🍳 Tartar Sauce (287)
  Buttered Parsley
    Potatoes
  Fresh Carrots
  🍳Cole Slaw (223)
  👨‍🍳🍳Rolls (46)
  Butter or Margarine
  👨‍🍳🍳Hot Bread Pudding
    with Raisins and
    Vanilla Sauce (76)
  Beverage(s)

SUPPER
  🍳Clam Chowder (252)
  🍳Macaroni and Cheese
    Loaf (191) with
  🍳 Tomato Sauce (282)
  🍳Stuffed Celery (222)
  Rolls, wholewheat
  Butter or Margarine
  👨‍🍳🍳Fruit Bavarian (314)
  Beverage(s)

8:30 P.M.
  Beverage(s)*

SATURDAY

BREAKFAST
Stewed Prunes,
  Lemon Slices
Assorted Cold Cereals
  or
Oatmeal, with cream
Jelly Doughnuts
Beverage(s)

DINNER
American Chop Suey
  with Steamed Rice
☕ Baked Squash, (use
  brown sugar) (188)
Pickled Sliced Beets
☕ ☕ Rolls (45)
Butter or Margarine
☕ ☕ Date Bar (71)
Beverage(s)

SUPPER
☕ Scotch Broth with
  Barley and Crackers
  (257)
Hamburger Pie with
  Potato Fluff
Bread
Butter or Margarine
☕ Fruited Gelatin /
  topping (232)
Beverage(s)

8:30 P.M.
Beverage(s)*

NOTES
(Special Events,
Residents'
Birthdays, etc.)

30th Week

SUNDAY

BREAKFAST
Grapefruit and
    Orange Sections
🍽️ Bacon Omelet (20)
Golden Toast
Butter or Margarine
Jam or Marmalade
Beverage(s)

DINNER
🍽️ Roast Beef, Gravy (53)
Boiled Potatoes
Scalloped Corn
Buttered Small Beets
👨‍🍳🍽️ Roll (45)
Butter or Margarine
👨‍🍳🍽️ Strawberry Shortcake/
    Topping (37)
Beverage(s)

SUPPER
Turkey Noodle Soup
Assorted Cold Sand-
    wiches
Catsup and Mustard
Pickles and Olives
🍽️ Raw Carrot and
    Raisin Salad (229)
Peach Custard
Beverage(s)

8:30 P.M.
Beverage(s)*

MONDAY

BREAKFAST
Chilled Fruit Juice
Assorted Cold Cereals
    or
Wheatena, with cream
Apricot Danish Roll
Butter or Margarine
Beverage(s)

DINNER
Barbecued Pork Chops
Baked Rice
Buttered Green Peas
🍽️ Tossed Green Salad/
    dressing (218)
👨‍🍳🍽️ Corn Muffins (44)
Butter or Margarine
Whipped Fruit Gelatin
Beverage(s)

SUPPER
🍽️ Cream of Asparagus
    Soup (268)
🍽️ Deviled Egg Sand-
    wiches (224)
🍽️ Cole Slaw (223)
Olives
👨‍🍳🍽️ Jam Crunchies (74)
Beverage(s)

8:30 P.M.
Beverage(s)*

TUESDAY

BREAKFAST
Stewed Apricots
Fried Egg
Hickory Smoked
  Bacon
Golden Toast
Butter or Margarine
Jam
Beverage(s)

DINNER
☕ Roast Turkey (118),
  Stuffing (117)
☕ Giblet Gravy (122)
Mashed Potatoes
Julienne String Beans
Cranberry Sauce
Cherrynut Bread
Butter or Margarine
Chilled Pear Halves
Beverage(s)

SUPPER
☕ Vegetable Soup (261)
Ham Salad Sandwich
  on wholewheat bread
☕ Glazed Carrots (184)
☕ Jellied Waldorf Salad
  (Apple gelatin) (226)
☕☕ Peanut Butter
  Cookies (71)
Beverage(s)

8:30 P.M.
Beverage(s)*

WEDNESDAY

BREAKFAST
Chilled Pineapple Juice
Assorted Cold Cereals
  or
Oatmeal, with cream
☕☕ Hot Rolls (40)
Butter or Margarine—
  Jelly
Beverage(s)

DINNER
☕ Braised Calves
  Liver (36)
Parsley Buttered
  Potatoes
☕ Stewed Tomato with
  Bread Crumb
  Topping (187)
Spiced Peach Salad
☕☕ Rolls (48)
Butter or Margarine
☕☕ Yellow Sponge Cake
  (22)
Beverage(s)

SUPPER
☕ Cream of Chicken
  Soup (269)
Tamale Pie
Spinach
☕ Jellied Bing
  Cherry Salad (231)
Blueberry Tarts
Beverage(s)

8:30 P.M.
Beverage(s)*

THURSDAY

BREAKFAST
Grapefruit Sections,
Grenadine
🍳 Poached Egg on
Buttered Toast (19)
Apple Danish Roll
Butter or Margarine
Beverage(s)

DINNER
Veal Roast
Buttered Rice
Creamed Spinach
🍳 Tomato Aspic (234)
🍳🍳 Rolls (47)
Butter or Margarine
Pineapple-Graham
Cracker Refrigerator
Pudding
Beverage(s)

SUPPER
🍳 Beef Bouillon (256)
Stuffed Green Peppers
Buttered Brussel
Sprouts
Bread, white and dark
Butter or Margarine
Chilled Peaches
Beverage(s)

8:30 P.M.
Beverage(s)*

FRIDAY

BREAKFAST
Chilled Prune Juice
Old Fashioned Waffles
Honey Butter
Warm Maple Syrup
Beverage(s)

DINNER
🍳 Baked Fish Fillet (139)
Buttered Parsley
Potatoes
Creamed Spinach
🍳 Molded Carrot and
Pineapple Salad (233)
🍳🍳 Corn Muffins (44)
Butter or Margarine—
Apple Butter
Chilled Queen Anne
Cherries
Beverage(s)

SUPPER
🍳 Cream of Tomato
Soup (252)
🍳 Macaroni and Cheese
Casserole (191)
Buttered Green Beans
🍳 Shredded Cabbage
Salad (223)
🍳🍳 Roll (45)
Butter or Margarine
🍳🍳 Gingerbread with
Lemon Sauce (19)
Beverage(s)

8:30 P.M.
Beverage(s)*

SATURDAY

BREAKFAST
  Chilled Fresh Melon
    Slice
  Assorted Cold Cereals
    or
  Cream of Wheat,
    warm milk
  Cinnamon Raisin
    Pecan Roll
  Butter or Margarine
  Beverage(s)

DINNER
  ☙Roast Lamb
    Shoulder (84)
  ☙Candied Sweet
    Potatoes (177)
  Buttered Broccoli
  ☙Mixed Vegetable Salad
    (221)
  ☙☙Poppy Seed Roll
    (small) (46)
  Butter or Margarine
  Norwegian Prune Pudding
  Beverage(s)

SUPPER
  Spanish Rice with Meat
  Frenched Green Beans
  Bread, white and dark
  Butter or Margarine
  ☙ ☙Banana Cake with
    Icing (22)
  Beverage(s)

NOTES
(Special Events,
Residents'
Birthdays, etc.)

8:30 P.M.
  Beverage(s)*

31st Week

SUNDAY

BREAKFAST
   Chilled Melon
   ♙ Scrambled Eggs (19)
   Hickory Smoked
      Bacon
   ♙♙Strawberry Filled
      Doughnuts (41)
   Beverage(s)

DINNER
   Virginian Baked
      Chicken
   Mashed Potatoes and
      Gravy
   Jellied Cranberry and
      Orange Salad
   June Peas
   ♙♙Rolls (45)
   Butter or Margarine
   Raspberry Sherbet—
   ♙ Cookies (317)
   Beverage(s)

SUPPER
   ♙Vegetable Soup (261)
   Assorted Sandwiches
   Sauteed New Carrots
   ♙♙Peach Shortcake (37)
   Beverage(s)

8:30 P.M.
   Beverage(s)*

MONDAY

BREAKFAST
   Assorted Fruit Juices
   Selected Cold Cereals
      or
   Oatmeal, with cream
   Toast, Buttered
   Jelly
   Beverage(s)

DINNER
   Barbecued Beef Hash
      (potatoes included)
   Creamed Celery
   Buttered Spinach
   Bread, white and dark
   Butter or Margarine
   ♙♙Angel Food Cake—
      Icing (31)
   Beverage(s)

SUPPER
   ♙Split Pea Soup (264)
   Cold Cuts of Meat
      and Deviled Eggs
   ♙ Garden Salad/
      dressing (221)
   Bread, white and dark
   Butter or Margarine
   Chilled Pineapple
   Beverage(s)

8:30 P.M.
   Beverage(s)*

TUESDAY

BREAKFAST
Orange Sections
🍳 Poached Egg on
 Buttered Toast (19)
👨‍🍳🍳 Hot Rolls (46)
 Butter or Margarine—
 Jam
Beverage(s)

DINNER
Veal Shoulder,
 Bread Stuffing
Gravy
Mashed Potatoes
🍳 Carrot and Raisin
 Salad (229)
Buttered Cauliflower
👨‍🍳🍳 Rolls (45)
 Butter or Margarine
👨‍🍳🍳 Blueberry Pie (62)
Beverage(s)

SUPPER
Apple Cider
Grilled Cheese
 Sandwich
Carrot and Pineapple
 Salad
Olives and Pickles
👨‍🍳🍳 Peach Pudding (77)
Cookies
Beverage(s)

8:30 P.M.
 Beverage(s)*

WEDNESDAY

BREAKFAST
Bananas with Cream
Golden French Toast
Maple Syrup or Honey
Canadian Bacon
Beverage(s)

DINNER
🍳 Leg of Lamb, brown
 gravy (80)
Mint Jelly
🍳 Escalloped Potatoes
 (197)
Buttered Green Beans,
 French Style
Sliced Pineapple and
 Grated Cheese Salad
Bread, white and dark
Butter or Margarine
👨‍🍳🍳 Vanilla Cookies (70)
Beverage(s)

SUPPER
Beef Noodle Soup
Bacon, Tomato and
 Lettuce Sandwich
 on Toast
🍳 Fresh Summer Fruit
 Salad (227)
👨‍🍳🍳 Custard Pie (58)
Beverage(s)

8:30 P.M.
 Beverage(s)*

THURSDAY	FRIDAY
BREAKFAST	**BREAKFAST**

THURSDAY

BREAKFAST
 Assorted Juices
 Selected Cold Cereal
  or
 Wheatena, with cream
🍳🍳Corn Muffins (44)
 Butter or Margarine
 Jelly
 Beverage(s)

DINNER
 Braised Short Ribs
  with Buttered
  Noodles
🍳Southern Zucchini
  Squash (190)
 Snap Green Beans
🍳🍳Rolls (47)
 Butter or Margarine
🍳🍳Cherry Pie (62)
 Beverage(s)

SUPPER
🍳Cream of Potato
  Soup (265)
 Roast Frankfurters
  (stuffed with cheese
  and wrapped in bacon)
🍳Chilled Cole Slaw (223)
 Hot Weiner Buns
 Butter or Margarine
 Corn Syrup Brownies
 Beverage(s)

8:30 P.M.
 Beverage(s)*

FRIDAY

BREAKFAST
 Grapefruit Half
 Fried Egg
 Plantation Sausage
 Toast
 Butter or Margarine—
  Jam
 Beverage(s)

DINNER
🍳Breaded Fish Fillets
  (132)
 Tartar Sauce (287)
🍳Oven Browned
  Potatoes (192)
🍳Cole Slaw (223)
 Green Beans,
  French Style
 Rolls, graham
 Butter or Margarine
 Apple Souffle
 Beverage(s)

SUPPER
🍳Cream of Asparagus
  Soup (268)
🍳Peach and Cottage
  Cheese Salad
  (main dish) (229)
 Toasted Raisin Bread
🍳🍳Strawberry Shortcake
  (37)
 Beverage(s)

8:30 P.M.
 Beverage(s)*

SATURDAY

BREAKFAST
Assorted Juices
Buttermilk Pancakes
Honey Butter
Warm Maple Syrup
Grilled Ham
Beverage(s)

DINNER
Baked Shoulder
Lamb Chops
Parsley Potatoes
Tomato and Celery Sauce
Tossed Green Salad/
dressing (221)
Rolls (48)
Butter or Margarine
Cup Custard
Beverage(s)

SUPPER
Cream of Mushroom
Soup (268)
Pork Sausage Patties
Hot Potato Salad (225)
Bread, white or dark
Butter or Margarine
Devils Food Cake (29)
Beverage(s)

8:30 P.M.
Beverage(s)*

32nd Week

SUNDAY

BREAKFAST
   Chilled Orange Juice
   Country Fresh Egg
   Grilled Sausages
  Almond Nut Dough-
     nuts (41)
   Butter or Margarine
   Beverage(s)

DINNER
  Southern Fried Chicken
     and Gravy (97)
   Mashed Potatoes
   Buttered Asparagus
  Jellied Fruit Salad (231)
  Hot Rolls (46)
   Butter or Margarine
   Chocolate Cream Pie
   Beverage(s)

SUPPER
   Beef Noodle Soup
   Cold Meat Plate
  Sliced Tomato on
     Watercress/dress-
     ing (218)
   Bread, white and dark
   Butter or Margarine
   Potato Chips
   Vanilla Ice Cream
   Beverage(s)

8:30 P.M.
   Beverage(s)*

MONDAY

BREAKFAST
   Fruit in Season
   Old Fashioned Waffles
   Crisp Bacon
   Honey or Maple Syrup
   Soft Butter
   Beverage(s)

DINNER
  Roast Beef, Natural
     Gravy (53)
  Oven Browned
     Potatoes (192)
   Cauliflower, buttered
  Tossed Green Salad
     (218)
   Bread, white and dark
   Butter or Margarine
   Chilled Pears
   Beverage(s)

SUPPER
  Spaghetti with Tomato
     Meat Sauce (291)
   Buttered Lima Beans
   Italian Bread
   Butter or Margarine
   Chocolate Cream Pie
   Beverage(s)

8:30 P.M.
   Beverage(s)*

TUESDAY	**WEDNESDAY**

BREAKFAST
Assorted Juices
☙Poached Egg on
Buttered Toast (19)
Orange Pineapple Danish
Roll
Butter or Margarine,
Jelly
Beverage(s)

BREAKFAST
Half Grapefruit
Selected Cold Cereal
or
Cream of Wheat,
with cream
Golden Toast
Butter or Margarine,
Jelly
Beverage(s)

DINNER
☙Braised Calves Liver
and Onions (36)
Parsley Buttered
Potatoes
Breaded Tomatoes
Stuffed Celery
Rolls, graham
Fruit Whip
Beverage(s)

DINNER
American Chop Suey
with Chinese Noodles
Buttered Rice
Peas and Carrots
☙Pink Grapefruit Salad
on Lettuce/dressing
(230)
☙☙Rolls (48)
Butter or Margarine
Burnt Almond
Sponge Cake
Beverage(s)

SUPPER
☙Minestrone Soup (249)
Holland Style
Bologna
Sour Black Bread
Catsup and Horse-
radish Mustard
Butter or Margarine
Jellied Pineapple and
Carrot Salad (233)
Coconut Macaroons
Beverage(s)

SUPPER
☙Vegetable Beef Soup
(256)
☙Chicken Shortcake (99)
☙Jellied Fruit Salad (231)
☙☙Oatmeal Drop
Cookies (75)
Beverage(s)

8:30 P.M.
Beverage(s)*

8:30 P.M.
Beverage(s)*

THURSDAY

BREAKFAST
Chilled Fruit Juice
Buttermilk Pancakes
Soft Butter
Warm Maple Syrup
  or Honey
Beverage(s)

DINNER
Baked Swiss Steak
Baked Potato with
  Butter or Sour
  Cream (Commercial)
♧ Cauliflower Polonaise,
  Parsley Topping (184)
♧ Crisp Green Salad
  Bowl (239)
Cranberries, jellied
♧♧ Rolls (46)
Butter or Margarine
♧ Peach Melba (299)
Beverage(s)

SUPPER
Apple Juice
Pork Sausage Patties
Spinach with crumbled
  Bacon Sauce
♧ Tomato Slices on
  Lettuce Leaf/
  dressing (218)
Watermelon
Beverage(s)

8:30 P.M.
Beverage(s)*

FRIDAY

BREAKFAST
Orange Slices
♧ Scrambled Eggs (19)
Crisp Bacon
Toast
Butter or Margarine—
  Jelly
Beverage(s)

DINNER
♧ Broiled Halibut (136)
Lemon Wedges
French Fried Potatoes
♧ Glazed Carrot Rings
  (184)
♧ Coleslaw (223)
♧♧ Sesame Seed Rolls (44)
Butter or Margarine
Red Cherry Torte
Beverage(s)

SUPPER
Tuna Fish a la King
  on Toast surrounded
  with Peas
♧ Molded Spiced Fruit
  Salad (232)
Chilled Apricots
♧♧ Peanut Butter
  Cookies (71)
Beverage(s)

8:30 P.M.
Beverage(s)*

SATURDAY

**NOTES
(Special Events,
Residents'
Birthdays, etc.)**

BREAKFAST
   Stewed Prunes,
      Lemon Slices
   Assorted Cold Cereals
      or
   Oatmeal, with Cream
   Blueberry Streusel
      Danish
   Butter or Margarine
   Beverage(s)

DINNER
☕Meat Loaf, Gravy (65)
☕Scalloped Potatoes (197)
   Buttered Spinach and
      Bacon
☕Waldorf Salad (226)
   Rolls, wholewheat
   Butter or Margarine
   Pumpkin Cookies
   Beverage(s)

SUPPER
☕Chicken Soup with
      Noodles (208)
   Hot Frankfurter on
      Bun
☕Potato Salad (225)
   Buttered Carrots
   Pickles, Mustard,
      Catsup
   Baked Rice Custard
   Beverage(s)

8:30 P.M.
   Beverage(s)*

33rd Week

SUNDAY

BREAKFAST
  Grapefruit and
    Orange Sections
  🍴Bacon Omelet (20)
  Golden Toast
  Butter or Margarine
  Jam or Marmalade
  Beverage(s)

DINNER
  🍴Old Fashioned
    Baked Ham (85)
  Buttered Parsley
    Potatoes
  Lima Beans in
    Tomato Sauce
  Red Apple, Banana
    and Peanut Salad
  Rolls, graham
  Butter or Margarine
  Cherry Tapioca Pudding
  Beverage(s)

SUPPER
  🍴Consomme (255)
  🍴Tomato Stuffed with
    Shrimp Salad (229)
  Sesame Seed Rolls
  Butter or Margarine
  Coconut Cream Pie
  Beverage(s)

8:30 P.M.
  Beverage(s)*

MONDAY

BREAKFAST
  Chilled Fruit Juice
  Assorted Cold Cereals
    or
  Wheatena, with Cream
  Cheese Danish Roll
  Butter or Margarine
  Beverage(s)

DINNER
  🍴Panned Liver and
    Onions (36)
  Mashed Potatoes
  Whole Kernel Corn
  Sliced Harvard Beets
  Bread, white and dark
  Butter or Margarine
  🍴🍴Baked Apple/topping
    (37)
  Beverage(s)

SUPPER
  🍴Vegetable Soup (261)
  Cold Corned Beef Slices
  🍴Potato Salad (225)
  Wholewheat Bread
  Butter or Margarine
  Relishes—Olives—Pickles
  Assortment of Fresh
    Fruit
  Beverage(s)

8:30 P.M.
  Beverage(s)*

TUESDAY

BREAKFAST
   Stewed Apricots
   Fried Egg
   Hickory Smoked
      Bacon
   Golden Toast
   Butter or Margarine,
      Jam
   Beverage(s)

DINNER
   Grilled Frankfurter
      on Toasted Roll
   Boston Baked Beans
   🍳German Style
      Sauerkraut (187)
   Applesauce–Cookies
   Beverage(s)

SUPPER
   🍳Cream of Asparagus
      Soup (268)
   🍳Cheese Omelet (20)
   🍳Mixed Green Salad/
      dressing (221)
   Bread, wholewheat
   Butter or Margarine
   🍳 🍳Angel Food Cake (31)
   Beverage(s)

8:30 P.M.
   Beverage(s)*

WEDNESDAY

BREAKFAST
   Chilled Pineapple Juice
   Assorted Cold Cereals
      or
   Oatmeal, with Cream
   🍳 🍳Hot Rolls (45)
   Butter or Margarine
   Jelly
   Beverage(s)

DINNER
   🍳Beef Rump Roast (63)
   Browned Potatoes
   Buttered Green Peas
   🍳Hearts of Lettuce Salad/
      dressing (237)
   Bread
   Butter or Margarine
   Walnut Chiffon Cake
      (grind the nuts)
   Beverage(s)

SUPPER
   🍳Baked Macaroni and
      Cheese and Tomatoes
      (191)
   Bread, white and dark
   Butter or Margarine
   🍳Mixed Vegetable Salad/
      dressing (239)
   🍳 🍳Cheese Cake (35)
   Beverage(s)

8:30 P.M.
   Beverage(s)*

THURSDAY

BREAKFAST
  Grapefruit Sections,
    Grenadine
  ᗤ Poached Egg on
    Buttered Toast (19)
  Prune Danish Roll
  Butter or Margarine
  Beverage(s)

DINNER
  Breaded Pork
    Tenderloin
  ᗤ Scalloped Potatoes
    (197)
  Buttered Asparagus
  Cranberry, Jellied
  ᗤᗤ Rolls (46)
  Butter or Margarine
  Chocolate Chip Cookies
  Beverage(s)

SUPPER
  ᗤ Tomato Bouillon (256)
  Corned Beef Hash Patty
  Home Fried Potatoes
  ᗤᗤ Heated Rolls (45)
  Butter or Margarine
  ᗤ Cabbage and Apple
    Salad (223)
  Chilled Pineapple
    Chunks
  Beverage(s)

8:30 P.M.
  Beverage(s)*

FRIDAY

BREAKFAST
  Chilled Prune Juice
  Old Fashioned Waffles
  Honey Butter
  Warm Maple Syrup
  Beverage(s)

DINNER
  Baked Pike Fillets
  ᗤ Lyonnaise Potatoes (194)
  Buttered Mixed
    Vegetables
  Pimiento Cheese Stuffed
    Celery
  ᗤᗤ Rolls (46)
  Butter or Margarine
  Chilled Pears
  Beverage(s)

SUPPER
  ᗤ Creamy Potato
    Soup (265)
  Salmon Salad
  ᗤ Lettuce Wedges/
    Russian Dressing
    (221)
  Bread, wholewheat
  Butter or Margarine
  ᗤᗤ Apple Brown Betty (76)/
    Orange Sauce
  Beverage(s)

8:30 P.M.
  Beverage(s)*

SATURDAY

BREAKFAST
Chilled Fresh
Melon Slice
Assorted Cold Cereals
or
Cream of Wheat,
warm milk
Blueberry Muffin (43)
Butter or Margarine
Beverage(s)

DINNER
Salisbury Steak, with
brown sauce
Mashed Potatoes
Baked Corn and Tomatoes
Wilted Lettuce and Bacon
Salad (241)
Rolls (47)
Butter or Margarine
Fruit Cup (15)
Beverage(s)

SUPPER
Celery Soup (268)
Hot Bologna-Holland
Style
Old Fashioned Sour
Black Bread
Butter or Margarine
Green Beans
Mustard—Horseradish
Cream Puffs (67)
Beverage(s)

8:30 P.M.
Beverage(s)*

NOTES
(Special Events,
Residents'
Birthdays, etc.)

34th Week

SUNDAY	MONDAY

BREAKFAST
Chilled Melon
🍳Scrambled Eggs (19)
Hickory Smoked
  Bacon
Raisin Toast
Butter or Margarine
Beverage(s)

BREAKFAST
Assorted Fruit Juices
Selected Cold Cereals
  or
Oatmeal, with cream
Toast, buttered
Jelly
Beverage(s)

DINNER
🍳Roast Tom Turkey (118)
  and Dressing (117)
🍳Giblet Gravy (122)
Mashed Potatoes
Buttered Brussel
  Sprouts
🍳Fruit Salad, garnished
  with mint sprig (227)
🍳🍳Rolls (46)
Butter or Margarine
🍳🍳Baked Meringue with
  strawberries and
  topping (33)
Beverage(s)

DINNER
🍳Cubed Steak (57)
🍳Egg Plant, oven fried
  (185)
Buttered Green Peas
🍳Shredded Lettuce
  with dressing (239)
Bread, white and dark
Butter or Margarine
Spice Cake/Topping
Beverage(s)

SUPPER
V-8 Juice
Ham and Cheese
  Sandwiches
🍳Sliced Tomato and
  Lettuce Salad (218)
🍳🍳Chocolate Cookies, (74)
Ice Cream
Beverage(s)

SUPPER
Swedish Soup
Creamed Eggs and
  Cheese on Toasted
  English Muffins
🍳Orange and Apple
  Salad (230)
Extra Muffins with
  Butter or Margarine
Fresh Fruit (Apples,
  Bananas, Grapes)
Beverage(s)

8:30 P.M.
Beverage(s)*

8:30 P.M.
Beverage(s)*

TUESDAY

BREAKFAST
  Orange Sections
  Poached Egg on
    Buttered Toast (19)
  Hot Rolls (45)
  Butter or Margarine
  Jam
  Beverage(s)

DINNER
  Corned Beef and
    Cabbage (62)
  Boiled Potatoes
  Buttered coin sized
    Carrots
  Rye Bread, White
    Bread
  Butter or Margarine
  Gingerbread with
    Topping (19)
  Beverage(s)

SUPPER
  Minestrone Soup
    (249)
  Spaghetti with Tomato
    Meat Sauce (291)
  Buttered Green Beans
  Tossed Green Salad/
    Dressing (218)
  Canned Plums
  Jam Crunchies
    (cookies) (74)
  Beverage(s)

8:30 P.M.
  Beverage(s)*

WEDNESDAY

BREAKFAST
  Bananas with Cream
  Golden French Toast
  Maple Syrup or Honey
  Canadian Bacon
  Beverage(s)

DINNER
  Oven Fried Calves
    Liver with Bacon
    (36)
  Buttered Parsley
    Potatoes
  Stewed Tomatoes and
    Celery
  Bread, white and dark
  Butter or Margarine
  Frosted Yellow Cake
    Squares (29, 32)
  Beverage(s)

SUPPER
  Corn Chowder (273)
  Grilled Frankfurter on
    Hot Bun
  Baked Beans
  Cabbage-Apple-Celery
    Salad
  Chilled Pears
  Beverage(s)

8:30 P.M.
  Beverage(s)*

THURSDAY	FRIDAY

BREAKFAST
Assorted Juices
Selected Cold Cereal
or
Wheatena, with Cream
🍳🍳 Plain Doughnuts (41)
Butter or Margarine
Beverage(s)

DINNER
🍳 Meat Patties (Beef, (57)
Lamb, (84), Veal)
🍳 Hashed Brown
Potatoes (194)
Buttered Cauliflower
🍳 Hearts of Lettuce
with Dressing (221)
🍳🍳 Rolls, cloverleaf (46)
Butter or Margarine
Home-made Cottage
Pudding
Beverage(s)

SUPPER
🍳 Cream of Tomato
Soup (252)
Creamed Chipped Beef
🍳🍳 Hot Cornbread Squares
(44)
🍳 Jellied Peach Salad (232)
🍳🍳 White Cake with Boiled
Chocolate Frosting
(29)
Beverage(s)

8:30 P.M.
Beverage(s)*

BREAKFAST
Grapefruit Half
Fried Egg
Plantation Sausage
Toast
Butter or Margarine,
Jam
Beverage(s)

DINNER
Apricot Nectar
🍳 Deep Fried Scallops
(167)
🍳 Potatoes au Gratin
(196)
Buttered Lima Beans
🍳 Tomato Aspic (234)
🍳🍳 Rolls (46)
Butter or Margarine
Vanilla Pudding
Beverage(s)

SUPPER
🍳 Clam Chowder with
Saltines (252)
Creamed Tuna with
Cheese on Hot
🍳🍳 Buttered Baking
Powder Biscuit (3)
Spinach with Butter
Sauce
🍳 Chilled Fruit Cup (15)
Beverage(s)

8:30 P.M.
Beverage(s)*

SATURDAY

BREAKFAST
  Assorted Juices
  Buttermilk Pancakes
  Honey Butter
  Warm Maple Syrup
  Grilled Ham
  Beverage(s)

DINNER
  ♕Turkey Croquettes (120),
    Cream Sauce (284)
  Steamed Buttered Rice
  Buttered Peas
  Apricot and Banana
    Salad
  ♕♕Hot Rolls (47)
  Butter or Margarine
  ♕♕Apple Sauce and
    Raisin Cake (18)
  Beverage(s)

SUPPER
  ♕Chicken Rice
    Soup (256)
  Sliced Corned Beef
    Sandwich on Whole
    Wheat Bread
  ♕Sliced Cucumber
    Salad (220)
  Dill Pickles
  Fruit Gelatin
  Beverage(s)

8:30 P.M.
  Beverage(s)*

NOTES
(Special Events,
Residents'
Birthdays, etc.)

35th Week

SUNDAY

BREAKFAST
Chilled Orange Juice
Country Fresh Egg
Grilled Sausages
Jelly Doughnuts
Beverage(s)

DINNER
🍳Beef Roast (54)
🍳Oven Browned
  Potatoes (192)
Mixed Vegetables
🍳Tomato and Lettuce
  Salad/dressing (221)
🍳🍳Rolls (48)
Butter or Margarine
🍳🍳Peach Shortcake/
  Topping (37)
Beverage(s)

SUPPER
🍳Chicken Rice
  Soup (256)
Virginia Ham Sandwich
Mustard and Catsup–
  Pickles
🍳Stuffed Celery (222)
Assorted Fresh Fruits
  (Apples, Grapes,
  Plums, Bananas)
Beverage(s)

8:30 P.M.
Beverage(s)*

MONDAY

BREAKFAST
Fruit in Season
Old Fashioned Waffles
Crisp Bacon
Honey or Maple Syrup
Soft Butter
Beverage(s)

DINNER
🍳Baked Meat Loaf (65)
  with Tomato Sauce
  (282,283)
Fluffy Mashed Potatoes
🍳Baked Squash with
  Brown Sugar (188)
🍳Jellied Carrot and
  Pineapple Salad (233)
🍳🍳Muffins (43)
Butter or Margarine
🍳🍳Lemon Chiffon Pie (59)
Beverage(s)

SUPPER
Boston Baked Beans
  with Pork
Grilled Weiners
Warm Weiner Rolls
Catsup–Mustard–
  Pickles
🍳🍳Ice Cream–Cookies (74)
Beverage(s)

8:30 P.M.
Beverage(s)*

TUESDAY

BREAKFAST
 Assorted Juices
🍴Poached Egg on
   Buttered Toast (19)
 Orange Danish Roll
 Butter or Margarine
 Jelly
 Beverage(s)

DINNER
🍴Broiled Ham Steak (78)
🍴Candied Sweet
   Potatoes (177)
 Buttered Cauliflower
 Bread, white and dark
 Butter or Margarine
 Malaga Grapes and
   Orange Salad
🍴🍴Lemon Bread Pudding
   (76)
 Beverage(s)

SUPPER
🍴Green Split Pea
   Soup (264)
 Veal Salad Sandwich
🍴Pear and Cottage
   Cheese Salad (229)
 Bread, white and dark
 Butter or Margarine
 Cantaloupe
 Beverage(s)

8:30 P.M.
 Beverage(s)*

WEDNESDAY

BREAKFAST
 Half Grapefruit
 Selected Cold Cereal
   or
 Cream of Wheat, with
   Cream
 Golden Toast
 Butter or Margarine
 Jelly
 Beverage(s)

DINNER
🍴Braised Calves Liver
   and Onions (36)
 Whipped Potatoes
 Buttered Peas
🍴Mixed Fruit Salad/
   dressing (227)
 Bread, white and dark
 Butter or Margarine
🍴🍴Vanilla Cookies (72)
 Beverage(s)

SUPPER
🍴Tomato Rice Soup
   (256)
🍴Baked Corned Beef
   Hash (61)
🍴Pineapple Cabbage
   Slaw (223)
 Bread
 Butter or Margarine
 Tapioca Pudding with
   Cherries
 Beverage(s)

8:30 P.M.
 Beverage(s)*

THURSDAY	FRIDAY

BREAKFAST
Chilled Fruit Juice
Buttermilk Pancakes
Soft Butter
Warm Maple Syrup
  or Honey
Beverage(s)

BREAKFAST
Orange Slices
👨‍🍳Scrambled Eggs (19)
Crisp Bacon
Toast
Butter or Margarine
Jelly
Beverage(s)

DINNER
👨‍🍳Roast Loin of
  Pork (87)
Fluffy Whipped Potatoes
👨‍🍳Sage Dressing (117)
Broccoli, with drawn
  butter
Applesauce
👨‍🍳👨‍🍳Rolls, small (45)
Butter or Margarine
Raspberry Sherbet
Beverage(s)

DINNER
Fried Fillet of Perch
👨‍🍳 with Tartar Sauce
  (287)
Parsley Buttered Potato
👨‍🍳Stewed Tomatoes (187)
👨‍🍳Cucumber Watercress
  Salad (220) with
  Sour Cream
  Dressing (237)
Bread, wholewheat
Butter or Margarine
👨‍🍳👨‍🍳Lemon Pie (57)
Beverage(s)

SUPPER
👨‍🍳Creamed Chicken
  and Pimiento on
  Toast (99)
Asparagus
Sliced Orange Salad/
  dressing
👨‍🍳Ginger Cookies,
  homemade (73)
Beverage(s)

SUPPER
👨‍🍳Cream of Celery
  Soup (268)
Grilled Cheese Sand-
  wich
👨‍🍳Cabbage and Green
  Pepper Salad (223)
👨‍🍳👨‍🍳Pound Cake (21)
Beverage(s)

8:30 P.M.
  Beverage(s)*

8:30 P.M.
  Beverage(s)*

SATURDAY

BREAKFAST
 Stewed Prunes,
  Lemon Slices
 Assorted Cold Cereals
  or
 Oatmeal, with cream
 Orange Danish Roll
 Butter or Margarine
 Beverage(s)

DINNER
 Baked Thuringer
  Sausages and
  Sauerkraut
 Parsley Buttered Potatoes
 Black Bread (old fashioned)
 Butter or Margarine
 ♨Jellied Fruit Salad (231)
 Baked Custard
 Beverage(s)

SUPPER
 ♨Cream of Spinach
  Soup (268)
 Tomato, Lettuce and
  Bacon Sandwich on
  wholewheat bread
 Chilled Strawberry Rhubarb
  Sauce
 ♨♨Cupcakes (29)
 Beverage(s)

8:30 P.M.
 Beverage(s)*

NOTES
(Special Events,
 Residents'
Birthdays, etc.)

36th Week

SUNDAY	MONDAY

BREAKFAST
  Grapefruit and
    Orange Sections
🍳 Bacon Omelet (20)
  Golden Toast
  Butter or Margarine
  Jam or Marmalade
  Beverage(s)

BREAKFAST
  Chilled Fruit Juice
  Assorted Cold Cereals
    or
  Wheatena, with cream
  Cheese Danish Roll
  Butter or Margarine
  Beverage(s)

DINNER
🍳 Roast Chicken (106)
  Dressing (117)
🍳 Giblet Gravy (122)
  Mashed Potatoes
🍳 Cauliflower with
    Cheese Sauce (282)
  Jellied Cranberry Salad
🍳🍳 Rolls (45)
  Butter or Margarine
🍳🍳 Meringue Shells (33)
    Ice Cream—Fresh
    Strawberries
  Beverage(s)

DINNER
🍳 Pot Roast and Gravy
    (53)
  Egg Noodles in
    Casserole
🍳 French Fried Onion
    Rings (109)
🍳 Grapefruit Sections
    on Lettuce/Poppy
    Seed dressing (230)
  Apricot Upside-Down
    Cake
  Beverage(s)

SUPPER
🍳 Vegetable Soup (161)
🍳 Chef's Salad Bowl
    (214)
  Potato Chips
  Sliced Tomatoes
  Pickles
  Bread, wholewheat
  Butter or Margarine
🍳🍳 Home-made Ginger
    Cookies (73)
  Beverage(s)

SUPPER
🍳 Hot Chicken a la King
    on Toast (99)
  Buttered Green Peas
🍳 Cole Slaw (223)
  Chilled Purple Plums,
    canned
  Beverage(s)

8:30 P.M.
  Beverage(s)*

8:30 P.M.
  Beverage(s)*

TUESDAY

BREAKFAST
Stewed Apricots
Fried Egg
Hickory Smoked Baocn
Golden Toast
Butter or Margarine
Jam
Beverage(s)

DINNER
Veal Roast
Duchess Potatoes (193)
Broccoli Spears
Pineapple-Cottage
Cheese-Cherry
Salad (229)
Rolls (46)
Butter or Margarine
Molasses Cookies (73)
Beverage(s)

SUPPER
French Onion
Soup (253)
Sliced Roast Beef
Sandwich
Catsup–Horseradish
Coin-Sized Buttered
Carrots
Chocolate Cake (29)
Beverage(s)

8:30 P.M.
Beverage(s)*

WEDNESDAY

BREAKFAST
Chilled Pineapple Juice
Assorted Cold Cereals
or
Oatmeal, with cream
Hot Rolls (46)
Butter or Margarine
Jelly
Beverage(s)

DINNER
Baked Breaded
Pork Chops
Baked Rice
Buttered Wax Beans
Bibb Lettuce Salad/
dressing (218)
Rolls (48)
Butter or Margarine
Apple Pie (56)
Beverage(s)

SUPPER
Tomato Bouillon
(256)
Peanut Butter and
Bacon on Toast
Jellied Cream Cheese
and Bing Cherry
Salad (231)
Bread Pudding with
Lemon Sauce (76)
Beverage(s)

8:30 P.M.
Beverage(s)*

THURSDAY	FRIDAY

BREAKFAST
Grapefruit Sections,
   Grenadine
♨ Poached Egg on
   Buttered Toast (19)
Apple Danish Roll
Butter or Margarine
Beverage(s)

BREAKFAST
Chilled Prune Juice
Old Fashioned Waffles
Honey Butter
Warm Maple Syrup
Beverage(s)

DINNER
♨ Italian Spaghetti with
   Meat Sauce (291)
Parmesan Cheese
♨ Tossed Green Salad/
   Italian dressing (218)
French Bread
Garlic Butter or
   Butter or Margarine
Ice Cream
Beverage(s)

DINNER
♨ Codfish Balls (138),
   Cream Sauce (284)
Buttered Parsley Potatoes
Harvard Beets
♨ Carrots and Cabbage
   Slaw (223)
♨♨ Rolls (46)
Butter or Margarine
♨♨ Applesauce Cake (18)
Beverage(s)

SUPPER
♨ Corn Chowder and
   Saltines (271)
Hamburgers on Rolls
Buttered Green Beans
Potato Chips
Sweet Relish–Catsup
♨♨ Caramel Cake (32)
Beverage(s)

SUPPER
♨ Manhattan Clam
   Chowder (273)
♨ Macaroni and Cheese
   (191)
Buttered Asparagus
Bread, white and dark
Butter or Margarine
♨ Fruit Cup (15)
Beverage(s)

8:30 P.M.
Beverage(s)*

8:30 P.M.
Beverage(s)*

SATURDAY

BREAKFAST
Chilled Fresh Melon Slice
Assorted Cold Cereals
or
Cream of Wheat,
   warm milk
Cinnamon Raisin
   Pecan Roll
Butter or Margarine
Beverage(s)

DINNER
♕ Broiled Calves Liver (36)
♕ Potatoes, Scalloped (197)
♕ Shredded Cabbage
   Salad (221)
Buttered Broccoli
♕♕ Rolls (48)
Butter or Margarine
Egg Nog Chiffon Pie
Beverage(s)

SUPPER
Baked Chicken Legs
♕ Country Fried Potatoes
   (194)
♕ Glazed Carrots (184)
Bread, wholewheat
Butter or Margarine
Applesauce
Beverage(s)

8:30 P.M.
Beverage(s)*

NOTES
(Special Events
Residents'
Birthdays, etc.)

37th Week

SUNDAY

BREAKFAST
Chilled Melon
♥ Scrambled Eggs (19)
Hickory Smoked
Bacon
♟♥ Plain Doughnut (41)
Beverage(s)

DINNER
Apple Juice
Roast Leg of Veal
with Dressing
♥ Squash, brown
sugar sauce (188)
Three-Bean Salad
♟♥ Rolls (46)
Butter or Margarine
♟♥ Apricot Pie (60)
Beverage(s)

SUPPER
Chicken Noodle Soup
♥ Jellied Waldorf Salad
(226)/Honey Fruited
Dressing
♟♥ Hot Pan Rolls (45)
Butter or Margarine
♟♥ Baked Custard (58)
Beverage(s)

8:30 P.M.
Beverage(s)*

MONDAY

BREAKFAST
Assorted Fruit Juices
Selected Cold Cereals
or
Oatmeal, with cream
Toast, Buttered
Jelly
Beverage(s)

DINNER
♥ Baked Meat Loaf,
Mushroom Gravy
(65)
♥ Country Fried
Potatoes (194)
♥ Glazed Whole Carrots
(184)
Wholewheat Rolls
Butter or Margarine
♟♥ White Cake with
Chocolate Frost-
ing (29)
Beverage(s)

SUPPER
Barbecued Hamburgers
on Toasted Buns
♥ Coleslaw (223)
Relishes–Pickles
Blueberry Cobbler
Beverage(s)

8:30 P.M.
Beverage(s)*

TUESDAY	WEDNESDAY

BREAKFAST
Orange Sections
☕ Poached Egg on
    Buttered Toast (19)
☕☕ Hot Rolls (46)
    Butter or Margarine
    Jam
    Beverage(s)

BREAKFAST
Bananas with Cream
Golden French Toast
Maple Syrup or Honey
Canadian Bacon
Beverage(s)

DINNER
☕ Breaded Veal Cutlet (37)
    Baked Potato
    Buttered Spinach
☕ Fruit Salad with
    Stuffed Prunes/
    dressing (227)
Bread—Butter or Margarine
☕☕ Butterscotch Cookies (36)
    Beverage(s)

DINNER
☕ Beef Stroganoff (53)
☕ Oven Browned
    Potatoes (192)
    Green Beans, French
    Style
☕ Cabbage Salad (223)
☕☕ Rolls (48)
    Butter or Margarine
    Chilled Apricots
    Beverage(s)

SUPPER
☕ Chicken Broth (256)
☕ Individual Beef Pies (59)
☕ Jellied Peach and
    Cottage Cheese
    Salad (229)
☕☕ Rolls (45)
    Butter or Margarine
    Floating Island Pudding
    Beverage(s)

SUPPER
Chicken Noodle Soup
Creamed Tuna-Egg
    Casserole
☕ Cherry Red Fruit
    Gelatin
☕☕ Jiffy Sponge Cake (22)
    Beverage(s)

8:30 P.M.
    Beverage(s)*

8:30 P.M.
    Beverage(s)*

THURSDAY

BREAKFAST
  Assorted Juices
  Selected Cold Cereal
    or
  Wheatena, with cream
🐝🐝 Corn Muffins (44)
  Butter or Margarine
  Jelly
  Beverage(s)

DINNER
  Pork Chops in Sour
    Cream
  Baked Sweet Potatoes
🐝 Buttered Corn and
    Green Peppers,
    sauteed (185)
🐝 Orange and Grapefruit
    Salad (230)
  Currant Muffins
  Butter or Margarine
🐝🐝 Baked Apple/Topping
    (37)
  Beverage(s)

SUPPER
  Cream of Lima Bean
    Soup
🐝 Sliced Tongue (63)
    Sandwiches
    (wholewheat)
  Catsup—Horseradish
  French Fried Egg
    Plant (Cubed)
🐝 Jellied Fruit Salad
    (232)
  Vanilla Pinwheel
    Cookies
  Beverage(s)

8:30 P.M.
  Beverage(s)*

FRIDAY

BREAKFAST
  Grapefruit Half
  Fried Egg
  Plantation Sausage
  Toast
  Butter or Margarine
  Jam
  Beverage(s)

DINNER
  Baked Salmon Steak
🐝   with Tartar Sauce
    (287)
🐝 Potatoes au Gratin (196)
🐝 Sliced Tomato and
    Lettuce Salad (218)
  Parsley Buttered Celery
    and Carrots
🐝🐝 Rolls (45)
  Butter or Margarine
🐝🐝 Oatmeal Cookies (75)
  Beverage(s)

SUPPER
🐝 New England Clam
    Chowder (270)
  Grilled Cheese
    Sandwich
  Jellied Pineapple and
    Carrot Salad
🐝🐝 Escalloped Apples
    (76)
  Beverage(s)

8:30 P.M.
  Beverage(s)*

SATURDAY

BREAKFAST
Assorted Juices
Buttermilk Pancakes
Honey Butter
Warm Maple Syrup
Grilled Ham
Beverage(s)

DINNER
Barbecued Pork Chops
Baked Rice
Creamed Cabbage
Spring Garden Salad
(221)
Rolls (46)
Butter or Margarine
Strawberry Pie (65)
Beverage(s)

SUPPER
Beef Broth with
Barley (256)
Bologna, Holland Style
Wholewheat Bread
Butter or Margarine
Mustard—Catsup—
Horse·adish
Perfection Salad
Squares (234)
Pineapple Upside Down
Cake (19)
Beverage(s)

8:30 P.M.
Beverage(s)*

38th Week

SUNDAY	MONDAY

BREAKFAST
Chilled Orange Juice
Country Fresh Egg
Grilled Sausages
🧑‍🍳🧑‍🍳 Coconut Doughnuts
    (41)
Butter or Margarine
Beverage(s)

BREAKFAST
Fruit in Season
Old Fashioned Waffles
Crisp Bacon
Honey or Maple Syrup
Soft Butter
Beverage(s)

DINNER
🧑‍🍳 Roast Chicken (106)
    Giblet Gravy (122)
🧑‍🍳 Bread Stuffing (117)
Cranberry Sauce
Buttered Asparagus
🧑‍🍳🧑‍🍳 Rolls, Hot Parker
    House (46)
Butter or Margarine
Ice Cream with
    Chocolate Sauce
Beverage(s)

DINNER
Salisbury Steak with
    Mushroom Sauce
Baked Potato
Whole Kernel Corn
🧑‍🍳 Tomato and Lettuce
    Salad (221)
Bread, white and dark
Butter or Margarine
Whipped Fruit Gelatin
Beverage(s)

SUPPER
🧑‍🍳 Cream of Mushroom
    Soup (268)
Cold Plate—Sliced Ham,
    Cheese
🧑‍🍳 Potato Salad (225),
    Pickled Beets
Bread, wholewheat
Butter or Margarine
🧑‍🍳🧑‍🍳 Banana Cake (22)
Beverage(s)

SUPPER
🧑‍🍳 Split Pea Soup (264)
Ham Sandwich on
    Wholewheat Bread
Pickles and Olives
🧑‍🍳 Cottage Cheese-Pine-
    apple Salad (229)
🧑‍🍳🧑‍🍳 Refrigerator Cookies
    (71)
Beverage(s)

8:30 P.M.
Beverage(s)*

8:30 P.M.
Beverage(s)*

TUESDAY	WEDNESDAY

TUESDAY

BREAKFAST
  Assorted Juices
  🍳 Poached Egg on
    Buttered Toast (19)
  Pineapple Danish Roll
  Butter or Margarine
  Beverage(s)

DINNER
  🍳 Meat Loaf with
    Spanish Sauce (66)
  🍳 Oven Browned
    Potatoes (192)
  Peas, buttered
  Carrot, Prune and
    Celery Salad
  Peach Cobbler
  Beverage(s)

SUPPER
  🍳 Cream of Celery
    Soup (268)
  Rice and Cheese
    Casserole
  Buttered Broccoli
  Deviled Egg Salad
  Vanilla Cream Pudding
    with Grated Orange
    Rind
  Beverage(s)

8:30 P.M.
  Beverage(s)*

WEDNESDAY

BREAKFAST
  Half Grapefruit
  Selected Cold Cereal
    or
  Cream of Wheat, with
    Cream
  Golden Toast
  Butter or Margarine
  Jelly
  Beverage(s)

DINNER
  Vegetable Juice
  Chop Suey with Rice
  Baked Tomato with
    Crumb Topping
  Three-Bean Salad
  🍳🍳 Rolls (48)
  Butter or Margarine
  Graham Cracker Date
    Roll/Topping
  Beverage(s)

SUPPER
  Beef Noodle Soup
  Pork Link Sausages
    with Apple Rings
  🍳 Hashed Brown
    Potatoes (194)
  Creamed Carrots
  Blue Plums, canned
  Beverage(s)

8:30 P.M.
  Beverage(s)*

THURSDAY

BREAKFAST
    Chilled Fruit Juice
    Buttermilk Pancakes
    Soft Butter
    Warm Maple Syrup
       or Honey
    Beverage(s)

DINNER
    🍳Italian Spaghetti
       with Meat Sauce
       (291)
    Parmesan Cheese
    Apple Gelatin with
       Crushed Pineapple
       Salad
    🍳🍳Rolls (48)
    Butter or Margarine
    🍳🍳Lemon Chiffon Pie (59)
    Beverage(s)

SUPPER
    V-8 Juice
    Toasted Chicken
       Salad Sandwiches
    Celery Sticks
    Carrot Sticks
    🍳🍳Chocolate Cake with
       White Frosting
       (squares) (29)
    Beverage(s)

8:30 P.M.
    Beverage(s)*

FRIDAY

BREAKFAST
    Orange Slices
    🍳Scrambled Eggs (19)
    Crisp Bacon
    Toast
    Butter or Margarine
    Jelly
    Beverage(s)

DINNER
    🍳Fried Fillet of Haddock,
       Lemon Wedges (136)
    Baked Potato
    🍳Stewed Tomatoes with
       Onion (187)
    🍳🍳Corn Muffin (44)
    Butter or Margarine—
       Apple Butter
    Baked Custard
    Beverage(s)

SUPPER
    🍳Cream of Celery
       Soup (268)
    Baked Salmon Loaf
    Buttered Frenched
       Green Beans
    🍳Waldorf Salad (226)
    Bread
    Butter or Margarine
    Chilled Butterscotch
       Pudding
    Beverage(s)

8:30 P.M.
    Beverage(s)*

SATURDAY

BREAKFAST
Stewed Prunes,
Lemon Slices
Assorted Cold Cereals
or
Oatmeal, with cream
Lemon Danish
Butter or Margarine
Beverage(s)

DINNER
Tomato Juice
Pan Broiled Liver
and Gravy (36)
Mashed Potatoes
Asparagus Spears
with Lemon Butter
Pear Halves on Lettuce/
dressing (229)
Rolls, wholewheat
Butter or Margarine
Molasses Bars
(cookies) (73)
Beverage(s)

SUPPER
Beef Broth and Rice
Knockwurst—Catsup
and Horseradish
Baked Beans
Coleslaw (223)
Bread, white and dark
Butter or Margarine
Chocolate Chiffon
Cake (10)
Beverage(s)

8:30 P.M.
Beverage(s)*

39th Week

SUNDAY	MONDAY
BREAKFAST	**BREAKFAST**
Grapefruit and	Chilled Fruit Juice
Orange Sections	Assorted Cold Cereals
✿Bacon Omelet (20)	or
Golden Toast	Wheatena, with cream
Butter or Margarine	✿✿Blueberry Muffin (43)
Jam or Marmalade	Butter or Margarine
Beverage(s)	Beverage(s)
DINNER	**DINNER**
✿Baked Ham (85)	✿Roast Shoulder of
Buttered Parsley	Rolled Lamb, Mint
Potatoes	Jelly (82, 83)
Buttered Brussel	✿Lyonnaise Potatoes
Sprouts	(194)
✿Fruit Salad/	Fritter Fried Egg Plant
dressing (227)	✿✿Rolls (46)
Bread, wholewheat	Butter or Margarine
Butter or Margarine	Carrots and Pineapple
✿✿Coconut Custard Pie	Salad
(58)	Vanilla Cream Pudding
Beverage(s)	Beverage(s)
SUPPER	**SUPPER**
✿Turkey Soup with	✿Cream of Celery Soup
Rice (259)	(268)
Veal Salad Plate	Frankfurter on Toasted
Potato Chips	Bun, buttered
Olives, Pickles and	Catsup—Relish—Mustard
Celery Curls	✿Cabbage Salad (223)
✿✿Rolls (45)	✿✿Orange Gelatin
Butter or Margarine	Cubes—Cookies (75)
Vanilla Ice Cream	Beverage(s)
with Chocolate	
Topping	
Beverage(s)	
8:30 P.M.	8:30 P.M.
Beverage(s)*	Beverage(s)*

TUESDAY

BREAKFAST
  Stewed Apricots
  Fried Egg
  Hickory Smoked
    Bacon
  Golden Toast
  Butter or Margarine
  Jam
  Beverage(s)

DINNER
  🍳 Veal Cutlets with
    Brown Gravy (288)
  Mashed Potatoes
  🍳 Cucumber Salad (220)
  Fried Parsnips
  Rolls, wholewheat
  Butter or Margarine—
    Jelly
  Cherry Upside Down
    Cake
  Beverage(s)

SUPPER
  Shepherd's Pie (cubed
    Lamb, Onions,
    Tomatoes, Parsley,
    Potatoes)
  🍳 Jellied Lime and Pear
    Salad (233)
  Bread, white and dark
  Butter or Margarine
  Apricot Tapioca
  Beverage(s)

8:30 P.M.
  Beverage(s)*

WEDNESDAY

BREAKFAST
  Chilled Pineapple Juice
  Assorted Cold Cereals
      or
  Oatmeal, with cream
  🍳🍳 Hot Rolls (40)
  Butter or Margarine
  Jelly
  Beverage(s)

DINNER
  🍳 Spareribs and Sauer-
    kraut (86)
  Boiled Potatoes
  Beet and Cucumber
    Salad
  🍳🍳 Corn Bread Muffins
    (44)
  Butter or Margarine—
    Apple Butter
  Caramel Custard
  Beverage(s)

SUPPER
  Beef Noodle Soup
  🍳 Baked Hash (61)
  Creamed Corn
  🍳 Cabbage and Apple
    Salad (223)
  🍳🍳 Angel Food Cake
    (31)
  Beverage(s)

8:30 P.M.
  Beverage(s)*

THURSDAY

BREAKFAST
Grapefruit Sections,
    Grenadine
♨ Poached Egg on
    Buttered Toast (19)
Cranberry Nut Muffin
Butter or Margarine
Beverage(s)

DINNER
♨ Beef Stew (Onions,
    Potatoes, Carrots,
    Celery) (69)
Jellied Citrus Fruit
    Salad
Bread, white and dark
Butter or Margarine—
    Jelly
Banana Cream Pie
Beverage(s)

SUPPER
♨ Navy Bean Soup
    (262)
Boiled Ham Slices
♨ Hashed Brown
    Potatoes (194)
♨ Tossed Salad (219)
♨♨ Rolls, homemade (46)
Butter or Margarine
Chilled Pears
Beverage(s)

8:30 P.M.
Beverage(s)*

FRIDAY

BREAKFAST
Chilled Prune Juice
Old Fashioned Waffles
Honey Butter
Warm Maple Syrup
Beverage(s)

DINNER
♨ Shrimp Creole (150)
Buttered Rice
Buttered Mixed
    Vegetables
Blushing Pear Salad
    with Peanut Butter
    Filling
♨♨ Frosted Devils Food
    Cake (29)
Beverage(s)

SUPPER
V-8 Juice
Canned Salmon Rice
    Loaf
♨ Stewed Tomatoes
    (187)
♨ Tossed Green Salad
    (219)
♨♨ Corn Muffins (44)
Butter or Margarine—
    Apple Butter
♨♨ Prune Whip (77)
Beverage(s)

8:30 P.M.
Beverage(s)*

SATURDAY

BREAKFAST
Chilled Fresh
   Melon Slice
Assorted Cold Cereals
   or
Cream of Wheat,
   warm milk
Pecan Roll
Butter or Margarine
Beverage(s)

DINNER
Grilled Hamburger
☕Cheese-Potato Casse-
   role (196)
Buttered Cauliflower
☕Spiced Beet Salad/
   Sliced Eggs (216)
Rolled Wheat Muffin
Butter or Margarine
Cherry Gelatin/
   whipped Topping
Beverage(s)

SUPPER
Grapefruit Juice
Pork Chop Suey with
   Chinese Noodles
☕☕Rolls (45)
Butter or Margarine
☕Cabbage-Pineapple
   Salad (223)
Chilled Plums
Beverage(s)

8:30 P.M.
Beverage(s)*

NOTES
(Special Events,
Residents'
Birthdays, etc.)

40th Week

SUNDAY	MONDAY

BREAKFAST
  Chilled Melon
  Scrambled Eggs (19)
  Hickory Smoked
    Bacon
  Cinnamon Toast
  Butter or Margarine
  Beverage(s)

BREAKFAST
  Assorted Fruit Juices
  Selected Cold Cereals
    or
  Oatmeal, with cream
  Toast, Buttered
  Jelly
  Beverage(s)

DINNER
  Roast Veal and Gravy
  Fluffy Mashed Potatoes
  Buttered Broccoli
  Perfection Salad/
    Dressing (234)
  Rolls, small (45)
  Pineapple Cream Pie
  Beverage(s)

DINNER
  Baked Beans with
    1½ in. squares of
    Ham
  Hot Potato Salad (225)
  Carrot Sticks—Olives
  Boston Brown Bread
  Butter or Margarine
  Chilled Pears
  Beverage(s)

SUPPER
  Cream of Corn Soup
    (273)
  Chicken Salad Sand-
    wich (wholewheat
    bread)
  Catsup—Mustard
  Potato Chips
  Relish—Pickles
  Ice Cream
  Beverage(s)

SUPPER
  Tomato Juice
  Beef Pot Pie,
    Flaky Crust (59)
  Peach and Cottage
    Cheese Salad (229)
  Hot Parker House Rolls,
    homemade (46)
  Butter or Margarine
  Cornflake Macaroons
    (70)
  Beverage(s)

8:30 P.M.
  Beverage(s)*

8:30 P.M.
  Beverage(s)*

TUESDAY

BREAKFAST
Orange Sections
🍳 Poached Egg on
   Buttered Toast (19)
👨‍🍳🍳 Hot Rolls (40)
Butter or Margarine—
   Jam
Beverage(s)

DINNER
🍳 Hamburger Steaks (57)
🍳   with Tomato
   Sauce (282)
Buttered Parsley Potatoes
🍳 Apple and Celery Salad
   (226)
Scalloped Sweet Corn
Bread, wholewheat
Butter or Margarine
Snow Pudding Dessert
Beverage(s)

SUPPER
Apple Juice
🍳 Turkey a la king on
   Toast (99)
🍳 Tossed Salad/
   dressing (219)
Whipped Fruit
   Gelatin/Topping
Beverage(s)

WEDNESDAY

BREAKFAST
Bananas with Cream
Golden French Toast
Maple Syrup or Honey
Canadian Bacon
Beverage(s)

DINNER
🍳 Corned Beef and
   Cabbage (62)
Boiled Potatoes,
   Buttered
🍳 Grated Carrot and
   Raisin Salad (229)
Bread, wholewheat
Butter or Margarine
Chilled Slices of
   Pineapple
👨‍🍳🍳 Old Fashioned Molasses
   Cookie (73)
Beverage(s)

SUPPER
🍳 Vegetable Soup (261)
Creamed Beef and
   Peas on Toast
Three Bean Salad
Applesauce
Beverage(s)

8:30 P.M.
   Beverage(s)*

8:30 P.M.
   Beverage(s)*

THURSDAY

BREAKFAST
Assorted Juices
Selected Cold Cereal
or
Wheatena, with cream
👨‍🍳👨‍🍳 Corn Muffins (44)
Butter or Margarine—
Jelly
Beverage(s)

DINNER
👨‍🍳 Beef Roast and
Gravy (53)
👨‍🍳 O'Brien Potatoes
(194)
👨‍🍳 Glazed Whole Carrots
(184)
👨‍🍳 Mixed Salad Greens/
Dressing (218)
👨‍🍳👨‍🍳 Rolls—Butter or
Margarine (46)
👨‍🍳👨‍🍳 Apple Pie with Streusel
Topping (56)
Beverage(s)

SUPPER
👨‍🍳 Tomato Rice Soup
(256)
Mock Drum Sticks
(Veal and Pork)
Spinach with Bacon
Dressing
Bread—Butter or
Margarine
Chilled Queen Anne
Cherries
Beverage(s)

8:30 P.M.
Beverage(s)*

FRIDAY

BREAKFAST
Grapefruit Half
Fried Egg
Plantation Sausage
Toast
Butter or Margarine—
Jam
Beverage(s)

DINNER
V-8 Juice
Baked Pike Fillets
French Fried Potatoes
👨‍🍳 Scalloped Celery and
Tomatoes (187)
👨‍🍳 Creamy Cole Slaw
(223)
Rolls, wholewheat
Butter or Margarine
Chilled Purple Plums
Beverage(s)

SUPPER
Cream of Pea Soup,
Saltines
Individual Casseroles
of Cheese Fondue
Buttered Peas
Toasted Bread Squares
Butter or Margarine
Blueberry Cottage
Pudding, Lemon
Sauce
Beverage(s)

8:30 P.M.
Beverage(s)*

SATURDAY

BREAKFAST
   Assorted Juices
   Buttermilk Pancakes
   Honey Butter
   Warm Maple Syrup
   Grilled Ham
   Beverage(s)

DINNER
   Swedish Meat Balls
🍳Potatoes au Gratin
    (196)
   Whole Kernel Corn
🍳Yankee Slaw (cabbage,
    carrots, green
    peppers) (223)
   Bread, wholewheat
   Butter or Margarine
   Whipped Fruit
    Gelatin/Topping
   Beverage(s)

SUPPER
🍳Chicken Rice Soup
    (256)
   Assorted Sandwiches
🍳Fruit Salad/Honey Fruit
    Dressing (227)
   Chocolate Icebox Cake
   Beverage(s)

8:30 P.M.
   Beverage(s)*

NOTES
(Special Events
Residents'
Birthdays, etc.)

41st Week

SUNDAY	MONDAY

BREAKFAST
    Chilled Orange Juice
    Country Fresh Egg
    Grilled Sausages
🍳🍳Cinnamon Doughnuts
    (41)
    Butter or Margarine
    Beverage(s)

BREAKFAST
    Fruit in Season
    Old Fashioned Waffles
    Crisp Bacon
    Honey or Maple Syrup
    Soft Butter
    Beverage(s)

DINNER
    Apple Juice
🍳Young Roast Turkey
    (118), Giblet Gravy
    (122)
🍳New England Bread
    Stuffing (117)
    Buttered Peas
    Cranberry Sauce
🍳Fruit Salad (227)
🍳🍳Parker House Rolls
    (46)
    Butter or Margarine
    Pineapple Sherbet
    Beverage(s)

DINNER
    Tomato Juice
🍳Baked Hash (including
    potatoes) (61)
    Creamed Style Corn
    Cottage Cheese with
    Chopped Chives
🍳🍳Rolls (46)
    Butter or Margarine
🍳🍳Apple Dumpling (37)
    Beverage(s)

SUPPER
    Macaroni-Ham-Cheese
    Casserole
🍳Crisp Vegetable
    Salad (218)
    Pickles—Olives
    Stuffed Celery
🍳🍳Red Cherry Tarts (65)
    Beverage(s)

SUPPER
🍳Swiss Steak (58)
    Buttered Broccoli Cuts
🍳Hashed Brown
    Potatoes (194)
    Bread
    Butter or Margarine
    Grilled Tomatoes
🍳Caramel Bavarian (314)
    Beverage(s)

8:30 P.M.
    Beverage(s)*

8:30 P.M.
    Beverage(s)*

TUESDAY

BREAKFAST
Assorted Juice
♥Poached Egg on
    Buttered Toast (19)
Prune Danish Roll
Butter or Margarine
Jelly
Beverage(s)

DINNER
♥Roast Pork (87)
♥Glazed Sweet
    Potatoes (177)
Green Beans, french style
Fried Parsnips
Graham Rolls
Butter or Margarine
Lemon Bread Pudding
Beverage(s)

SUPPER
♥Cream of Asparagus
    Soup (268)
♥Corn Fritters (166)
Maple Syrup (warm)
♥Peach and Cottage
    Cheese Salad (229)
Orange Sherbet
Beverage(s)

8:30 P.M.
Beverage(s)*

WEDNESDAY

BREAKFAST
Half Grapefruit
Selected Cold Cereal
    or
Cream of Wheat,
    with cream
Golden Toast
Butter or Margarine—
Jelly
Beverage(s)

DINNER
Veal Roast
Buttered Rice
♥Asparagus (182),
    Hollandaise (285)
♥Molded Spiced Fruit
    Salad (232)
Orange Rolls
Butter or Margarine
♥♥Cherry Pie (63)
Beverage(s)

SUPPER
♥Cream of Chicken
    Soup (269)
Stuffed Green Peppers
Parsleyed Carrots
♥♥Rolls (46)
Butter or Margarine
Steamed Fig Pudding
Beverage(s)

8:30 P.M.
Beverage(s)*

THURSDAY

BREAKFAST
Chilled Fruit Juice
Buttermilk Pancakes
Soft Butter
Warm Maple Syrup
  or Honey
Beverage(s)

DINNER
🍳Ham Loaf (89)
🍳 with Horseradish
    Sauce (87)
Buttered Potatoes
Southern Style Green
  Beans
🍳Head Lettuce (218)
    Rouquefort Cheese
    Dressing (239)
🍳🍳Rolls, homemade (46)
Butter or Margarine
🍳🍳Apricot Pie (60)
Beverage(s)

SUPPER
🍳Beef Bouillon (255)
🍳Grilled Liver and
    Bacon (calves
    liver) (36)
🍳Stewed Whole
    Tomatoes (187)
🍳Shoestring Potatoes
    (194)
Butter or Margarine
Chocolate Marsh-
  mallow Squares
Beverage(s)

8:30 P.M.
Beverage(s)*

FRIDAY

BREAKFAST
Orange Slices
🍳Scrambled Eggs (19)
Crisp Bacon
Toast
Butter or Margarine
Jelly
Beverage(s)

DINNER
🍳Baked Salmon Steak
    with Tartar Sauce
    (287)
🍳Oven Browned Potatoes
    (192)
Parsley Buttered Carrots
🍳Jellied Vegetable Salad
    (234)
🍳🍳Corn Meal Muffins (44)
Butter or Margarine
  or Apple Butter
Baked Winesap Apple/
  Topping
Beverage(s)

SUPPER
🍳Cream of Celery Soup
    (268)
🍳Egg Salad Sandwiches
    (224)
🍳Mixed Green Salad/
    French dressing
    (218)
🍳🍳Pineapple Cheese
    Cake (34)
Beverage(s)

8:30 P.M.
Beverage(s)*

SATURDAY

BREAKFAST
  Stewed Prunes,
    Lemon Slices
  Assorted Cold Cereals
    or
  Oatmeal, with cream
  Cherry Danish
  Butter or Margarine
  Beverage(s)

DINNER
  Baked Pork Chops
  Applesauce
  ⑫Cottage Fried
    Potatoes (194)
  Cabbage au Gratin
  ⑫ Sliced Tomato on
    Lettuce Salad/
    dressing (218)
  ⑫⑫ Rolls, homemade (45)
  Butter or Margarine
  Whipped Orange
    Gelatin
  Beverage(s)

SUPPER
  ⑫ Cream of Spinach
    Soup (268)
  Corned Beef Sand-
    wiches on Rye
    Bread
  Potato Chips
  Celery and Carrot
    Sticks
  Dill Pickles
  ⑫⑫ Peach Crumble
    Dessert (76)
  Beverage(s)

8:30 P.M.
  Beverage(s)*

NOTES
(Special Events,
Residents'
Birthdays, etc.)

42nd Week

SUNDAY	MONDAY

BREAKFAST
Grapefruit and
    Orange Sections
🍳 Bacon Omelet (20)
Golden Toast
Butter or Margarine
Jam or Marmalade
Beverage(s)

BREAKFAST
Chilled Fruit Juice
Assorted Cold Cereals
    or
Wheatena, with cream
Cheese Danish Roll
Butter or Margarine
Beverage(s)

DINNER
🍳 Roast Leg of Lamb,
    Mint Jelly (80)
Mashed Sweet Potatoes
Buttered Broccoli Spears
🍳🍳 Rolls, homemade (46)
Butter or Margarine
🍳 Sliced Radishes and
    Lettuce/dressing (218)
Chocolate Souffle
    (baked in individual
    molds)
Beverage(s)

DINNER
V-8 Juice
🍳 Creamed Chunks of
    Chicken (99)
Mashed Potatoes
Asparagus
Grapefruit–Malaga
    Grapes Salad/
    Honey Fruit
    Dressing
🍳 Angel Food Cake/
    Topping (316)
Beverage(s)

SUPPER
Chicken Noodle Soup
Cold Plate (Boiled Ham,
    Swiss Cheese,
🍳   Potato Salad (225),
    Relishes–Green and
    Black Olives
Bread, wholewheat
Butter or Margarine
Fresh Fruits (Apples,
    oranges, grapes,
    bananas)
Beverage(s)

SUPPER
🍳 Split Pea Soup (264)
Oven Baked French
    Toast with Maple
    Syrup
Pork Sausage Links
🍳 Tossed Salad Greens/
    dressing (218)
Whipped Black Cherry
    Gelatin/topping
Beverage(s)

8:30 P.M.
    Beverage(s)*

8:30 P.M.
    Beverage(s)*

TUESDAY	WEDNESDAY

BREAKFAST
  Stewed Apricots
  Fried Egg
  Hickory Smoked
    Bacon
  Golden Toast
  Butter or Margarine
  Jam
  Beverage(s)

DINNER
  Spanish Rice with
    Chopped Meat
  Shredded Cabbage,
    Apple and Ground
    Nut Salad
  Graham Rolls
  Butter or Margarine
  Pineapple Cream
    Pudding
  Beverage(s)

SUPPER
  Beef Noodle Soup
  ♧Turkey Salad (221)
  Fried Parsnips
  ♧Sliced Tomato on
    Lettuce (219)
  ♧♧Corn Bread (44)
  Butter or Margarine—
    Plum Butter
  ♧♧Honey Bars (cookies)
    (70)
  Beverage(s)

8:30 P.M.
  Beverage(s)*

BREAKFAST
  Chilled Pineapple Juice
  Assorted Cold Cereals
    or
  Oatmeal, with cream
  ♧♧Hot Rolls (40)
  Butter or Margarine
  Jelly
  Beverage(s)

DINNER
  ♧Chicken Rice Soup
    (256)
  Beans and Sausage,
    Mexican Style
  ♧Tossed Vegetable
    Salad (219)
  Bread, black sour
    and white
  Butter or Margarine
  Chilled Purple Plums
  Beverage(s)

SUPPER
  Tomato Juice
  Salami and Liverwurst
    Sandwiches, with
    lettuce
  ♧Jellied Fruit Salad
    (231)
  Orange Bread Pudding,
    Orange Sauce
  Beverage(s)

8:30 P.M.
  Beverage(s)*

THURSDAY

BREAKFAST
Grapefruit Sections,
  Grenadine
🍳Poached Egg on
  Buttered Toast (19)
Apple Danish Roll
Butter or Margarine
Beverage(s)

DINNER
Barbecued Hamburger
  Steak
French Fried Potatoes
🍳Squash (188, 189)
Buttered Beets
🍳🍳Hot Baking Powder
  Biscuits (3)
Butter or Margarine
Catsup—Apple Butter
Custard
Beverage(s)

SUPPER
🍳Vegetable Soup (261)
Sliced Corned Beef
  Sandwiches
🍳Potato Salad (225)
🍳Jellied Vegetable
  Salad (234)
🍳🍳Homemade Roll (48)
🍳🍳Boston Cream Pie (17)
Beverage(s)

8:30 P.M.
Beverage(s)*

FRIDAY

BREAKFAST
Chilled Prune Juice
Old Fashioned Waffles
Honey Butter
Warm Maple Syrup
Beverage(s)

DINNER
🍳Creamed Codfish and
  Hard-Cooked Eggs
  on Boiled Potato (132)
Buttered Green Peas
🍳Head Lettuce/Thous-
  and Island Dressing
  (219)
🍳🍳Rolls (46)
Butter or Margarine
Chilled Peaches
Beverage(s)

SUPPER
Tuna Noodle Casserole
Buttered Asparagus
  Spears
Bread, white and dark
Butter or Margarine
Whipped Fruit Gelatin
Beverage(s)

8:30 P.M.
Beverage(s)*

SATURDAY

BREAKFAST
Chilled Fresh Melon Slice
Assorted Cold Cereals
or
Cream of Wheat, warm
milk
Pineapple Muffins
Butter or Margarine
Beverage(s)

DINNER
Pork Roast (87)
Mashed Squash (188)
Creamed Cauliflower
with Pimiento Strips
Grapefruit and Orange
Sections on Curly
Endive/French
Dressing (230)
Rolls (46)
Butter or Margarine
Applesauce Cake (18)
Beverage(s)

SUPPER
V-8 Juice
Knockwurst and
Sauerkraut
Buttered Peas
Bread, white and dark
Butter or Margarine
Grape Gelatin Squares
Beverage(s)

8:30 P.M.
Beverage(s)*

NOTES
(Special Events,
Residents'
Birthdays, etc.)

43rd Week

SUNDAY	MONDAY

BREAKFAST
Chilled Melon
♕ Scrambled Eggs (19)
Hickory Smoked
  Bacon
Cinnamon Raisin
  Pecan Rolls
Beverage(s)

DINNER
♕ Southern Fried
  Chicken (97)
♕ Cream Gravy (284)
Mashed Potatoes
Buttered Peas and
  Carrots
Cranberry and
  Orange Salad
♕♕ Rolls (46)
Butter or Margarine
Raspberry Sherbet
Beverage(s)

SUPPER
♕ Tomato Bouillon (256)
♕ Cheeseburger (57)
Potato Chips
♕ Sliced Tomato on
  Lettuce Leaf (218)
Chocolate Custard Pie
Beverage(s)

8:30 P.M.
  Beverage(s)*

BREAKFAST
Assorted Fruit Juices
Selected Cold Cereals
  or
Oatmeal, with cream
Toast, buttered
Jelly
Beverage(s)

DINNER
♕ Irish Lamb Stew with
  Dumplings (83)
Buttered Frozen Peas
  with Mushrooms
Pineapple and Melon
  Salad/Celery Seed
  Fruit Dressing
Rolls, wholewheat
Butter or Margarine
♕♕ Cornflake Kisses (70)
Beverage(s)

SUPPER
♕ Consomme (255)
♕ Chicken Salad on
  Lettuce (221)
Bread, white and dark
Butter or Margarine
♕ Jellied Vegetables
  (Salad) (234)
Chocolate Tapioca
  Cream Pudding
Beverage(s)

8:30 P.M.
  Beverage(s)*

TUESDAY	WEDNESDAY

BREAKFAST
Orange Sections
🍽Poached Egg on
    Buttered Toast (19)
👨‍🍳🍽 Hot Rolls (40)
    Butter or Margarine
    Jam
    Beverage(s)

BREAKFAST
Bananas with Cream
Golden French Toast
Maple Syrup or Honey
Canadian Bacon
Beverage(s)

DINNER
Pork Noodle Casserole
Buttered Spinach with
    Bacon Bits
🍽Cabbage and Pineapple
    Salad (223)
Bread, white and dark
Butter or Margarine
White Grapes
Beverage(s)

DINNER
🍽Breaded Veal Cutlet
    (37)
Parsley Creamed
    Potatoes
Buttered Asparagus
🍽 Tossed Vegetable
    Salad (218)
👨‍🍳🍽Rolls, homemade (46)
    Butter or Margarine
    Mocha Almond
    Frozen Pie
    Beverage(s)

SUPPER
🍽Corn Chowder (271)
🍽 Sliced Corned Beef (63)
    Sandwich, (whole-
    wheat bread)
🍽 Baked Squash with
    brown sugar (188)
Snow Pudding, cut in
    squares and served
👨‍🍳🍽 with Custard Sauce (77)
Beverage(s)

SUPPER
🍽Vegetable Broth (261)
🍽Eggs Benedict (poached
    egg on ½ buttered
    english muffin with
    mock hollandaise
    sauce (284)
Buttered Green Peas
🍽Waldorf Salad (226)
👨‍🍳🍽Cupcakes (29)
Beverage(s)

8:30 P.M.
    Beverage(s)*

8:30 P.M.
    Beverage(s)*

THURSDAY

BREAKFAST
Assorted Juices
Selected Cold Cereal
  or
Wheatena, with Cream
🐱🐱 Corn Muffins (44)
Butter or Margarine
Jelly
Beverage(s)

DINNER
🐱 Meat Loaf,
  Gravy (65)
Buttered Boiled
  Potatoes
Scalloped Corn
🐱 Head Lettuce Wedges/
  dressing (219)
🐱🐱 Rolls (48)
Butter or Margarine
🐱🐱 Yellow Cake with
  Chocolate Icing (29)
Beverage(s)

SUPPER
🐱 Vegetable Soup (261)
Mock Chicken Legs
🐱 Hashed Brown
  Potatoes (194)
🐱 Glazed Carrots, coin
  sized (184)
Bread, white and dark
Butter or Margarine
Baked Custard
Beverage(s)

8:30 P.M.
Beverage(s)*

FRIDAY

BREAKFAST
Grapefruit Half
Fried Egg
Plantation Sausage
Toast
Butter or Margarine
Jam
Beverage(s)

DINNER
🐱 Fried Yellow Perch
  with Tartar Sauce
  (287)
Baked Potato
Broccoli Polonaise
🐱 Pear with Shredded
  Cheese on Lettuce
  Leaf/dressing (229)
Bran Rolls
Butter or Margarine
🐱🐱 Pineapple Cheese
  Cake (34)
Beverage(s)

SUPPER
🐱 Cream of Tomato
  Soup (252)
🐱 Tunafish Salad (221)
Bread, white and dark
Butter or Margarine
Potato Chips
Sliced Beet and Onion
  Salad (216)
🐱🐱 Apple Crisp (76)
Beverage(s)

8:30 P.M.
Beverage(s)*

SATURDAY

BREAKFAST
 Assorted Juices
 Buttermilk Pancakes
 Honey Butter
 Warm Maple Syrup
 Grilled Ham
 Beverage(s)

DINNER
 ♟Baked Meat Pie
  (including carrots,
  onions, potatoes)
  (59)
 ♟Jellied Fruit Salad (231)
♟♟Rolls, homemade (46)
 Vanilla Ice Cream
 Beverage(s)

SUPPER
 Chicken Noodle Soup
 Grilled Frankfurter on
  Hot Roll
 Mustard—Catsup—Relish
 Potato Salad
 Bread, white and dark
 Butter or Margarine
 Cottage Cheese and
  Chives Salad
♟♟Raisin Cake with
  Lemon Frosting (26)
 Beverage(s)

8:30 P.M.
 Beverage(s)*

NOTES
(Special Events
Residents'
Birthdays, etc.)

44th Week

SUNDAY	MONDAY

BREAKFAST
Chilled Orange Juice
Country Fresh Egg
Grilled Sausages
🍪🍪 Almond Nut
    Doughnuts (41)
Butter or Margarine
Beverage(s)

BREAKFAST
Fruit in Season
Old Fashioned Waffles
Crisp Bacon
Honey or Maple Syrup
Soft Butter
Beverage(s)

DINNER
🍪 Baked Ham with
    Honey Glaze (85)
Baked Sweet Potatoes
    with butter
Buttered Baby Lima
    Beans
Raspberry Ring Salad
Vienna Bread
Butter or Margarine
Vanilla Ice Cream
Beverage(s)

DINNER
🍪 Chunks of Chicken
    with Dumplings (99)
Buttered Julienne
    Green Beans
🍪 Chef's Salad/French
    Dressing (221)
Bread, white and dark
Butter or Margarine
Baked Coconut
    Custard
Beverage(s)

SUPPER
🍪 Tomato Rice Soup
    (256)
Ham Sandwiches (whole-
    wheat bread)
Celery Sticks
🍪🍪 Blond Brownies (36)
Beverage(s)

SUPPER
Split Pea Soup (264)
    Saltines
Baked Green Peppers
    (stuffed with ground
    meat, tomato sauce)
Fresh Fruit Salad (227)
Bread
Butter or Margarine
Blueberry Cupcake (43)
Beverage(s)

8:30 P.M.
    Beverage(s)*

8:30 P.M.
    Beverage(s)*

TUESDAY

BREAKFAST
Assorted Juices
♔Poached Egg on
Buttered Toast (19)
Prune Danish Roll
Butter or Margarine
Beverage(s)

DINNER
Stuffed Veal Shoulder
♔Bread Stuffing (117)
Natural Gravy
♔Hashed Brown
Potatoes (194)
Buttered Cauliflower
♔Sliced Pineapple and
Cream Cheese
Salad (229)
♔♔Rolls (46)
Butter or Margarine
♔♔Nut and Raisin
Cookies (70)
Beverage(s)

SUPPER
♔Scotch Broth and
Barley (257)
Boston Baked Beans
(with 1-in. chunks
of ham)
Brown Bread
Butter or Margarine
Chilled Pineapple
Beverage(s)

8:30 P.M.
Beverage(s)*

WEDNESDAY

BREAKFAST
Half Grapefruit
Selected Cold Cereal
or
Cream of Wheat,
with cream
Golden Toast
Butter or Margarine
Jelly
Beverage(s)

DINNER
Oven Baked Pork Chops
Brown Rice with
Mushroom Sauce
Buttered Green Peas
♔Jellied Carrot and
Pineapple Salad (233)
♔♔Rolls (46)
Butter or Margarine
♔♔Cocoa Cupcakes (79)
Beverage(s)

SUPPER
♔Beef Broth (256)
Cold Sliced Beef Tongue
Sandwich (wholewheat
bread)
French Fried Potatoes
♔Cole Slaw (223)
Wax Beans
♔♔Peanut Butter Cookies (71)
Beverage(s)

8:30 P.M.
Beverage(s)*

THURSDAY

BREAKFAST
  Chilled Fruit Juice
  Buttermilk Pancakes
  Soft Butter
  Warm Maple Syrup
    or Honey
  Beverage(s)

DINNER
  ☙Spareribs, barbecued
    (79)
  Boiled Potatoes
  Braised Celery
  ☙Shredded Lettuce
    Salad/dressing (218)
  Bread, wholewheat
  Butter or Margarine
  Lemon Pie
  Beverage(s)

SUPPER
  ☙Potato Soup (265)
  Frankfurter and
    Sauerkraut
  Dark Mustard—Catsup—
    Horseradish
  Fried Potatoes
  Hot Spiced Beets
  Bread, sour black and
    white
  Butter or Margarine
  ☙☙Chocolate Cake Squares
    with White Icing (29)
  Beverage(s)

8:30 P.M.
  Beverage(s)*

FRIDAY

BREAKFAST
  Orange Slices
  ☙Scrambled Eggs (19)
  Crisp Bacon
  Toast
  Butter or Margarine—
    Jelly
  Beverage(s)

DINNER
  ☙Scallops (167) with
    Tartar Sauce (287)
  Creamed Potatoes
    with Chives
  Buttered Green Beans
    with Pimiento
    Strips
  ☙Mixed Green Salad/
    dressing (219)
  ☙☙Rolls, homemade (46)
  Lemon Sherbet
  Beverage(s)

SUPPER
  V-8 Juice
  Tuna Noodle Casserole
  ☙Asparagus, buttered
    (182)
  Bread, white and dark
  Butter or Margarine
  ☙☙Date-Nut Squares (71)
  Beverage(s)

8:30 P.M.
  Beverage(s)*

SATURDAY

BREAKFAST
  Stewed Prunes, Lemon
    Slices
  Assorted Cold Cereals
    or
  Oatmeal, with cream
  Cinnamon Streusel
    Danish
  Butter or Margarine
  Beverage(s)

DINNER
  Braised Beef
    Minute Steak
  ☙Oven Browned Potatoes
    (192)
  Buttered Green Beans
  Assorted Relish Tray
    with Celery and
    Green Olives.
  ☙☙Rolls, homemade (46)
  Butter or Margarine
  ☙☙Home-Baked Fruit Pie
    (56, 65)
  Beverage(s)

SUPPER
  ☙Vegetable Soup (261)
  Pork Link Sausages
    with Apple Rings
  ☙Hashed Brown
    Potatoes (194)
  Spinach, buttered
  Bread, white and dark
  Butter or Margarine
  Purple Plums
  Beverage(s)

8:30 P.M.
  Beverage(s)*

NOTES
(Special Events,
  Residents'
Birthdays, etc.)

45th Week

| | SUNDAY | MONDAY |

SUNDAY

BREAKFAST
  Grapefruit and
    Orange Sections
  ♨ Bacon Omelet (20)
  Golden Toast
  Butter or Margarine
  Jam or Marmalade
  Beverage(s)

DINNER
  Country Fried Chicken,
    Cream Gravy
  Mashed Potatoes
  Spiced Peaches
  Whole Kernel Corn
  Pineapple-Melon-Apple
    Salad/Poppy Seed
    Fruit Dressing
  ♨♨ Rolls, homemade (46)
  Butter or Margarine
  Vanilla Ice Cream/
    Chocolate Sauce
  Beverage(s)

SUPPER
  ♨ Turkey Soup (259)
  Cold Plate (Ham Slices,
    Deviled Egg,
    Slice of Cheese)
  Bread, wholewheat and
    white
  Butter or Margarine
  Prune Spice Cake/
    Topping
  Beverage(s)

8:30 P.M.
  Beverage(s)*

MONDAY

BREAKFAST
  Chilled Fruit Juice
  Assorted Cold Cereals
    or
  Wheatena, with cream
  Cherry Danish Roll
  Butter or Margarine
  Beverage(s)

DINNER
  ♨ Old Fashioned Baked
    Ham (with bone)
    (85)
  ♨ Candied Sweet Potatoes
    (177)
  Steamed Cabbage
  ♨ Pear and Shredded
    Cheese Salad (229)
  Bread, white and dark
  Butter or Margarine
  Orange Tapioca Pudding
  Beverage(s)

SUPPER
  Grapefruit Juice
  Scrambled Eggs and
    Dried Beef
  Buttered Peas and
    Carrots
  Bread, white and dark
  Butter or Margarine
  ♨♨ Pineapple Upside
    Down Cake (19)
  Beverage(s)

8:30 P.M.
  Beverage(s)*

TUESDAY	WEDNESDAY
BREAKFAST	**BREAKFAST**

TUESDAY

BREAKFAST
Stewed Apricots
Fried Egg
Hickory Smoked
Bacon
Golden Toast
Butter or Margarine
Jam
Beverage(s)

DINNER
☕Beef Stew (59) and
Dumplings (258)
Jellied Citrus Salad/
Fruit Salad Dressing
Bread, wholewheat
and white
Butter or Margarine
Chilled Butterscotch
Pudding
Beverage(s)

SUPPER
☕ Cream of Mushroom
Soup (268)
Beef Patty on Ham-
burger Roll
☕Potato Salad (225)
Sliced Tomatoes
Onion and Pickle Slices
Strawberry Ice Cream
Beverage(s)

8:30 P.M.
Beverage(s)*

WEDNESDAY

BREAKFAST
Chilled Pineapple Juice
Assorted Cold Cereals
or
Oatmeal, with cream
☕☕ Hot Rolls, (40)
Butter or Margarine
Jelly
Beverage(s)

DINNER
☕ Braised Beef/Brown
Rice (53)
☕Cabbage Slaw—
Pimiento (223)
Buttered June Peas
Rolls, wholewheat
Butter or Margarine
Chilled Peaches
Beverage(s)

SUPPER
Apple Juice
Cheese Vegetable Rare-
bit on Toast, (includes
cheese, onion, green
peppers and celery)
Whole Kernel Corn
Prune Crunch/Topping
Beverage(s)

8:30 P.M.
Beverage(s)*

THURSDAY	FRIDAY

BREAKFAST
Grapefruit Sections,
   Grenadine
☭ Poached Egg on
   Buttered Toast (19)
Apple Danish Roll
Butter or Margarine
Beverage(s)

BREAKFAST
Chilled Prune Juice
Old Fashioned Waffles
Honey Butter
Warm Maple Syrup
Beverage(s)

DINNER
Liver Creole
Buttered Rice
Buttered Asparagus
☭☭ Raisin Bread (7)
Butter or Margarine
Pineapple Chunks
Beverage(s)

DINNER
Baked Perch Fillets
☭   with Fluffy Cheese
   Sauce (282)
Buttered Spinach
Boiled Parsley Potatoes
Bread
Butter or Margarine
☭☭ Raisin Bread Pudding
   (76)
Beverage(s)

SUPPER
Chili Con Carne
Apple-Cabbage-Carrot
   Slaw
Poppy Seed Hard Rolls
Butter or Margarine
☭☭ Pumpkin Pie (61)
Beverage(s)

SUPPER
☭ Cream of Tomato
   Soup (252)
☭ Tunafish Salad (221)
French Fried Potatoes
☭ Tossed Green Salad/
   dressing (219)
Bread, wholewheat,
   white
Butter or Margarine
☭☭ Yellow Cake with
   White Frosting
   (29,32)
Beverage(s)

8:30 P.M.
   Beverage(s)*

8:30 P.M.
   Beverage(s)*

SATURDAY

BREAKFAST
Chilled Fresh
Melon Slice
Assorted Cold Cereals
or
Cream of Wheat,
warm milk
Chocolate Coconut
Doughnut (41)
Beverage(s)

DINNER
Ground Beef and
Spaghetti (291)
Buttered Broccoli
Tossed Green Salad
(218)
French Bread
Butter or Margarine
Frosted Yellow Cup-
cake (29, 32)
Beverage(s)

SUPPER
Spinach Soup (268)
Ham Sandwich (whole-
wheat or white bread)
Confetti Cole Slaw
Relish Tray
Apple Raisin Cobbler
Beverage(s)

8:30 P.M.
Beverage(s)*

46th Week

SUNDAY	MONDAY

BREAKFAST
  Chilled Melon
  🧑‍🍳 Scrambled Eggs (19)
  Hickory Smoked
    Bacon
  Surprise Muffins
  Butter or Margarine
  Beverage(s)

BREAKFAST
  Assorted Fruit Juices
  Selected Cold Cereals
    or
  Oatmeal, with cream
  Toast, buttered
  Jelly
  Beverage(s)

DINNER
  🧑‍🍳 Roast Loin of
    Pork (87)
  Baked Potato, butter
    or sour cream
  Green Beans,
    French Style
  🧑‍🍳 Grapefruit and Orange
    Sections on Curly
    Endive/dressing (230)
  🧑‍🍳🧑‍🍳 Rolls, homemade (46)
  Butter or Margarine
  Chocolate Pie
  Beverage(s)

DINNER
  🧑‍🍳 Meat Loaf (65), Mush-
    room Gravy (288)
  Baked Potato
  Buttered Spinach
  🧑‍🍳 Cole Slaw (white and
    red cabbage) (223)
  🧑‍🍳🧑‍🍳 Biscuits, homemade (3)
  Butter or Margarine
  Chilled Apricots
  Beverage(s)

SUPPER
  🧑‍🍳 Tomato Bouillon with
    Rice (256)
  🧑‍🍳 Cold Plate—Ham, Cheese,
    Potato Salad (225),
    Pickles, Olives, (green
    and black)
  Bread—white and dark
  Fresh Fruit
  Beverage(s)

SUPPER
  Carrot and Celery Soup
  Assorted Sandwiches
  Deviled Egg and
    Tomato Salad
  Applesauce
  Cookies
  Beverage(s)

8:30 P.M.
  Beverage(s)*

8:30 P.M.
  Beverage(s)*

TUESDAY

BREAKFAST
Orange Sections
☕Poached Egg on
Buttered Toast (19)
☕☕ Hot Rolls (46)
Butter or Margarine
Jam
Beverage(s)

DINNER
☕Spareribs and
Sauerkraut (86)
Boiled Potatoes
☕ Waldorf Salad on
Lettuce (226)
Bread, white and dark
Butter or Margarine
☕ ☕ Coconut Cookies (73)
Beverage(s)

SUPPER
Tomato Juice
Shepherd's Pie
(includes onion,
carrot, celery
and potatoes)
☕ Pear in Lime Gelatin
(233)
Rolls, graham
Butter or Margarine
Maple Nut Chiffon
Cake
Beverage(s)

8:30 P.M.
Beverage(s)*

WEDNESDAY

BREAKFAST
Bananas with Cream
Golden French Toast
Maple Syrup or Honey
Canadian Bacon
Beverage(s)

DINNER
☕Lamb Roast, Mint
Jelly (80)
Mashed Sweet Potatoes
Buttered Turnips
☕☕Parkerhouse Rolls,
homemade (46)
Butter or Margarine
☕Pineapple and Carrot
Salad (233)
Baked Apple/Topping
Beverage(s)

SUPPER
Barbecued Beef on
Roll
Escalloped Corn
☕Cabbage and Green
Pepper Slaw (223)
Baked Custard
Beverage(s)

8:30 P.M.
Beverage(s)*

THURSDAY

BREAKFAST
Assorted Juices
Selected Cold Cereal
or
Wheatena, with cream
Corn Muffins (44)
Butter or Margarine
Jelly
Beverage(s)

DINNER
Creamed Chunks of
Chicken on Toast (99)
Asparagus Spears, buttered
Tomato and Shredded
Lettuce/dressing (218)
Coconut Cream Pie
Beverage(s)

SUPPER
Vegetable Soup (261)
Beef Chop Suey—
Steamed Rice
Bread, white and dark
Butter or Margarine
Chilled Pears
Beverage(s)

8:30 P.M.
Beverage(s)*

FRIDAY

BREAKFAST
Grapefruit Half
Fried Egg
Plantation Sausage
Toast
Butter or Margarine—
Jam
Beverage(s)

DINNER
Scallops (167)/
Tartar Sauce (287)
Buttered Parsley
Potatoes
Stewed Tomatoes/
croutons (187)
Shredded Lettuce
Salad/dressing (239)
Rolls (46)
Butter or Margarine
Cookies (71)
Beverage(s)

SUPPER
Puree of Pea Soup
(264)
Grilled Cheese Sand-
wich
Buttered Mixed Vege-
tables
Apple Pie (56)
Beverage(s)

8:30 P.M.
Beverage(s)*

SATURDAY

BREAKFAST
Assorted Juices
Buttermilk Pancakes
Honey Butter
Warm Maple Syrup
Grilled Ham
Beverage(s)

DINNER
� Oven Fried Calves
Liver (36)
Creamed New Potatoes
and Peas
Buttered Corn
Banana-Grapefruit-Grape
Salad/Honey Fruit
Dressing
� � Apricot Crisp (76)
Beverage(s)

SUPPER
Tomato and Celery Soup
Baked Beans/Sliced
Frankfurters
� Tossed Green Salad (238)
Brown Bread—with Cream
Cheese, if desired
Butter or Margarine
� Fruit Cup (15)
Beverage(s)

8:30 P.M.
Beverage(s)*

NOTES
(Special Events,
Residents'
Birthdays, etc.)

47th Week

SUNDAY	MONDAY

BREAKFAST
Chilled Orange Juice
Country Fresh Egg
Grilled Sausages
Jelly Doughnuts
Beverage(s)

BREAKFAST
Fruit in Season
Old Fashioned Waffles
Crisp Bacon
Honey or Maple Syrup
Soft Butter
Beverage(s)

DINNER
Broiled Ham Steak (78)
Scalloped Potatoes (197)
Buttered Baby Whole Beets
Chilled Molded Fruit Salad (231)
Rolls (46)
Butter or Margarine
Mincemeat Pie (homemade)
Beverage(s)

DINNER
Creamed Turkey Chunks, Pimiento (99)
Parsley Buttered Rice
Buttered Peas and Carrots
Jellied Cranberry and Orange Salad
Rolls, homemade (47)
Butter or Margarine—Jelly
Crispy Oatmeal Cookies (75)
Beverage(s)

SUPPER
Chili
Crackers
Corn Bread (44)
Butter or Margarine, Apple Butter
Chilled Peaches
Beverage(s)

SUPPER
Cream of Spinach Soup (268)
Cheese Omelet (20)
Green Beans, French Style
Bread, white and dark
Butter or Margarine
Cottage Pudding with Lemon Sauce
Beverage(s)

8:30 P.M.
Beverage(s)*

8:30 P.M.
Beverage(s)*

TUESDAY	WEDNESDAY

BREAKFAST
Assorted Juices
🍳 Poached Egg on
  Buttered Toast (19)
Orange Pineapple
  Danish Roll
Butter or Margarine—
  Jelly
Beverage(s)

BREAKFAST
Half Grapefruit
Selected Cold Cereal
  or
Cream of Wheat,
  with Cream
Golden Toast
Butter or Margarine
Beverage(s)

DINNER
Sauteed Chicken Livers
Creamed Potatoes
🍳 Stewed Tomatoes (187)
Cottage Cheese and
  Chives Salad
🍳 Fruit Cup (15)
Beverage(s)

DINNER
Minute Steaks
French Fried Potatoes
Broccoli, buttered
Carrot Sticks—Stuffed
  Celery
Bread, white and dark
Butter or Margarine
👨‍🍳🍳 Cherry Pie, homemade
  (62)
Beverage(s)

SUPPER
🍳 Corn Chowder (271)
Apple Fritters
Warm Maple Syrup
🍳 Romaine Lettuce—
  Grapefruit Sections
  with Sesame Seed
  Dressing (230)
👨‍🍳🍳 Fruit Cake—Hard Sauce
  (20)
Beverage(s)

SUPPER
🍳 Chicken Rice Soup (256)
Steamed Frankfurters
Mustard
Boston Baked Beans
Bread, white and dark
Butter or Margarine
🍳 Hearts of Lettuce (218)/
  Thousand Island
  Dressing (237)
👨‍🍳🍳 Jelly Roll, home baked (17)
Beverage(s)

8:30 P.M.
Beverage(s)*

8:30 P.M.
Beverage(s)*

THURSDAY

BREAKFAST
Chilled Fruit Juice
Buttermilk Pancakes
Soft Butter
Warm Maple Syrup
   or Honey
Beverage(s)

DINNER
♕ Spareribs and Sauer-
   kraut (86)
Boiled Potatoes
Rye Bread
Butter or Margarine—
   Plum Butter
Applesauce Cake
Beverage(s)

SUPPER
Cranberry Juice
♕ Baked Lamb Patties
   (84)
Baby Lima Beans
♕♕ Hot Corn Muffins (44)
Butter or Margarine—
   Syrup
Chilled Plums
Beverage(s)

8:30 P.M.
Beverage(s)*

FRIDAY

BREAKFAST
Orange Slices
♕ Scrambled Eggs (19)
Crisp Bacon
Toast
Butter or Margarine
Jelly
Beverage(s)

DINNER
V-8 Juice
♕ Salmon Croquettes
   with Cheese
   Sauce (282)
Buttered Green Peas
♕ Molded Fruit Salad
   (231)
Rolls, wholewheat
Butter or Margarine
♕♕ Devils Food Cake (29)
Beverage(s)

SUPPER
Cheese Souffle
♕ Tomato Sauce
   (282, 283)
Stuffed Celery, Ripe
   Olives
Chocolate Chip
   Oatmeal Cookies
Beverage(s)

8:30 P.M.
Beverage(s)*

SATURDAY

BREAKFAST
  Stewed Prunes,
    Lemon Slices
  Assorted Cold Cereals
    or
  Oatmeal, with Cream
  Lemon Danish
  Butter or Margarine
  Beverage(s)

DINNER
  ☙ Swiss Steak (68)
  Baked Potato
  Julienne Carrots
  ☙ Creamy Cole Slaw
    (223)
  ☙☙ Rolls (47)
  Butter or Margarine
  Chilled Pineapple Chunks
  Beverage(s)

SUPPER
  ☙ Cream of Asparagus
    Soup (268)
  Assorted Sandwiches
  Celery Sticks, Pickles
  ☙☙ Cinnamon Apple Cup
    Cakes with Lemon
    Sauce (18)
  Beverage(s)

8:30 P.M.
  Beverage(s)*

NOTES
(Special Events,
Residents'
Birthdays, etc.)

48th Week

SUNDAY

BREAKFAST
Grapefruit and
Orange Sections
🍳Bacon Omelet (19)
Golden Toast
Butter or Margarine
Jam or Marmalade
Beverage(s)

DINNER
🍳 Roast Lamb, Mint
Jelly (80)
Mashed Potatoes
🍳 Cauliflower with
Cheese Sauce (181)
🍳 Tossed Green Salad/
dressing (239)
🍳🍳 Rolls (45)
Butter or Margarine
Frozen Peach Short-
cake/Topping (37)
Beverage(s)

SUPPER
🍳Individual Beef
Pot Pie (68)
Cottage Cheese and
Chives Salad
🍳🍳 Rolls, homemade (46)
Butter or Margarine
🍳🍳Sponge Cake (22)
Beverage(s)

8:30 P.M.
Beverage(s)*

MONDAY

BREAKFAST
Chilled Fruit Juice
Assorted Cold Cereals
or
Wheatena, with Cream
Cheese Danish Roll
Butter or Margarine
Beverage(s)

DINNER
🍳 Braised Calves Liver
(36)
Parsley Buttered
Potatoes
🍳 Breaded Tomato and
Onions (187)
🍳🍳Rolls, homemade (48)
Butter or Margarine
Banana Bread Pudding
Beverage(s)

SUPPER
🍳Split Pea Soup (264)
Hot Roast Beef Sand-
wich with Gravy
Strawberry Gelatin with
Grapes
🍳🍳Chocolate Brownies
(36)
Beverage(s)

8:30 P.M.
Beverage(s)*

TUESDAY

BREAKFAST
Stewed Apricots
Fried Egg
Hickory Smoked
Bacon
Golden Toast
Butter or Margarine—
Jam
Beverage(s)

DINNER
🍳Beef Stew with
Vegetables (59)
🍳Tossed Salad,
French dressing (238)
🍳🍳Hot Pan Rolls (46)
Butter or Margarine
Fruit Cobbler—
Nutmeg Flavored/
Topping
Beverage(s)

SUPPER
Tomato Juice
🍳Swiss Steak (49)
🍳Hashed Brown
Potatoes (194)
🍳Cabbage Salad/
dressing (223)
Bread
Butter or Margarine
🍳🍳Dutch Apple Cake/
Chocolate Frost-
ing (18)
Beverage(s)

8:30 P.M.
Beverage(s)*

WEDNESDAY

BREAKFAST
Chilled Pineapple Juice
Assorted Cold Cereals
or
Oatmeal, with cream
🍳🍳Hot Rolls (45)
Butter or Margarine
Jelly
Beverage(s)

DINNER
🍳Baked Southern
Cured Ham (85)
🍳Glazed Sweet Potatoes
(177)
Buttered Green Peas
🍳Pear and Shredded
Cheese Salad/
dressing (229)
🍳🍳Hot Bran Muffins (43)
Butter or Margarine
🍳🍳Lemon Fluff (63)
Beverage(s)

SUPPER
Beef Noodle Soup
🍳Baked Lamb Patties
(84)
Creole Lima Beans
Bread
Butter or Margarine
Rice Bavarian/
Maple Sauce
Beverage(s)

8:30 P.M.
Beverage(s)*

THURSDAY	FRIDAY

BREAKFAST
    Grapefruit Sections,
      Grenadine
  ♧ Poached Egg on
      Buttered Toast (19)
    Apple Danish Roll
    Butter or Margarine
    Beverage(s)

BREAKFAST
    Chilled Prune Juice
    Old Fashioned Waffles
    Honey Butter
    Warm Maple Syrup
    Beverage(s)

DINNER
    American Chop Suey
    Fluffy Buttered Rice
    Carrot Sticks, Pickles,
      Green and Black
      Olives
 ♧♧ Rolls, homemade (48)
    Butter or Margarine
    Maple-Nut Mold/
      Custard Sauce
    Beverage(s)

DINNER
    Creamed Salmon
      and Peas on Hot
      Biscuits
  ♧ Asparagus Salad with
      Sliced Eggs/French
      Dressing (221)
 ♧♧ Biscuits (3)
    Butter or Margarine—
      Apple Butter
    Chilled Pears
    Beverage(s)

SUPPER
    Pineapple Juice
    Sliced Pork Sandwich
    Brown Gravy
  ♧ Beet and Onion
      Salad (216)
    Bread
    Butter or Margarine
    Chilled Butterscotch
      Pudding
    Beverage(s)

SUPPER
    Celery and Tomato
      Soup—Saltines
  ♧ Spanish Omelette (283)
    Buttered Green Peas
    Bread
    Butter or Margarine
    Homemade Applesauce
    Baked Rice Pudding/
      Topping
    Beverage(s)

8:30 P.M.
    Beverage(s)*

8:30 P.M.
    Beverage(s)*

SATURDAY

BREAKFAST
Chilled Fresh
  Melon Slice
Assorted Cold Cereals
    or
Cream of Wheat,
  warm milk
Cinnamon Nut Roll
Butter or Margarine
Beverage(s)

DINNER
🎩 Spaghetti and Meat
    Sauce (291)
Buttered Broccoli Cuts
🎩 Lettuce Wedges
  with Blue Cheese
  and Mayonnaise
  (239)
Sesame Rolls, homemade
Butter or Margarine
Spumoni (Ice Cream)
Beverage(s)

SUPPER
Apple Juice
Peanut Butter and
  Bacon Sandwich
🎩 Pear and Bing Cherry
  Salad (208) with
  Dressing and Ground
  Peanuts
Whipped Fruit Gelatin/
  Topping
Beverage(s)

8:30 P.M.
Beverage(s)*

Notes
(Special Events
Residents'
Birthdays, etc.)

49th Week

SUNDAY

BREAKFAST
Chilled Melon
Scrambled Eggs (19)
Hickory Smoked
   Bacon
Blueberry Muffin (43)
Butter or Margarine
Beverage(s)

DINNER
Roast Pork (87)
Glazed Sweet
   Potatoes (177)
Stewed Tomatoes
   (187)
Carrot and Raisin
   Salad (229)
Rolls, homemade (46)
Butter or Margarine
Ice Cream/Straw-
   berry Sauce
Beverage(s)

SUPPER
Beef Broth (256)
Spanish Rice (with
   chopped meat)
Rolls, graham
Butter or Margarine
Blueberry Puff
Beverage(s)

8:30 P.M.
Beverage(s)*

MONDAY

BREAKFAST
Assorted Fruit Juices
Selected Cold Cereals
   or
Oatmeal, with cream
Toast, Buttered
Jelly
Beverage(s)

DINNER
Corned Beef and
   Cabbage (62)
Boiled Potatoes
Jellied Vegetable
   Salad (234)
Rolls (45)
Butter or Margarine
Raisin Pudding
Beverage(s)

SUPPER
Chili Con Carne
Summer Squash (189)
Carrot Strips—Celery—
   Olives
Bread, wholewheat
Butter or Margarine
Whipped Fruit Gelatin
Beverage(s)

8:30 P.M.
Beverage(s)*

TUESDAY

BREAKFAST
Orange Sections
✿ Poached Egg on
Buttered Toast (19)
✿✿ Hot Rolls (40)
Butter or Margarine–
Jam
Beverage(s)

DINNER
✿ Baked Ham (85) with
Raisin Sauce (289)
Mashed Sweet Potatoes
Spinach, buttered
✿ Waldorf Salad (226)
✿✿ Rolls, homemade (46)
Butter or Margarine
Steamed Fig Pudding/
Topping
Beverage(s)

SUPPER
✿ Corn Chowder (273)
Fried Vienna Sausages
Buttered Broccoli
Spears
Bread, wholewheat
Butter or Margarine
✿ Beet and Onion
Salad (216)
✿ Angel Food Cake/
Frosted (316)
Beverage(s)

8:30 P.M.
Beverage(s)*

WEDNESDAY

BREAKFAST
Bananas with Cream
Golden French Toast
Maple Syrup or Honey
Canadian Bacon
Beverage(s)

DINNER
✿ Beef Stroganoff (53)
Buttered Noodles
✿ Pear Salad/dressing
(229)
Sesame Seed Rolls
Butter or Margarine
Cranberry and Raisin
Pie
Beverage(s)

SUPPER
✿ Veal Cutlet (37)
Tomato Sauce (282)
Buttered Whole Leaf
Spinach
✿ Vegetable Salad/
dressing (221)
Brownies (36)
Beverage(s)

8:30 P.M.
Beverage(s)*

THURSDAY

BREAKFAST
    Assorted Juices
    Selected Cold Cereal
    or
    Wheatena, with cream
👨‍🍳👨‍🍳Corn Muffins (44)
    Butter or Margarine—
    Jelly
    Beverage(s)

DINNER
👨‍🍳Fried Chicken and
    Gravy (97)
    Mashed Potatoes
    Fried Parsnips
    Buttered Green
    Peas
    Jellied Pineapple and
    Cucumber Salad
    Bread, white and dark
    Butter or Margarine
👨‍🍳👨‍🍳Jelly Roll (cake)
    (17, 22)
    Beverage(s)

SUPPER
👨‍🍳Beef Rice Soup (256)
    Green Peppers Stuffed
    (with ground meat
    and tomato sauce)
    Carrot Sticks
    Bread, white and dark
    Butter or Margarine
👨‍🍳👨‍🍳Apple Crisp (76)
    Beverage(s)

8:30 P.M.
    Beverage(s)*

FRIDAY

BREAKFAST
    Grapefruit Half
    Fried Egg
    Plantation Sausage
    Toast
    Butter or Margarine—
    Jam
    Beverage(s)

DINNER
    V-8 Juice
👨‍🍳Shrimp Creole (150)
    Steamed Buttered
    Rice
👨‍🍳Scalloped Egg Plant
    (185)
    French Bread
    Butter or Margarine
    Cherry Cobbler/
    Topping
    Beverage(s)

SUPPER
👨‍🍳👨‍🍳Crispy Corn Bread (44)
    Warm Maple Syrup
    Sliced American Cheese
👨‍🍳Country Fried Potatoes
    (194)
👨‍🍳Fruit Salad /dressing
    (227)
    Hot Lima Beans and
    Corn
    Chilled Chocolate
    Pudding
    Beverage(s)

8:30 P.M.
    Beverage(s)*

SATURDAY

BREAKFAST
  Assorted Juices
  Buttermilk Pancakes
  Honey Butter
  Warm Maple Syrup
  Grilled Ham
  Beverage(s)

DINNER
  🍳Beef Hash (including
     potatoes) (61)
  Green Beans, buttered
  Bread, white and dark
  Butter or Margarine
🍳🍳Hot Apple Pie (56)
  Beverage(s)

SUPPER
🍳Beef Bouillon (255)
🍳Chicken Chow Mein
    (100)
  Buttered Rice
🍳Jellied Vegetable
    Salad (234)
  Chilled Pears
  Beverage(s)

8:30 P.M.
  Beverage(s)*

NOTES
(Special Events,
Residents'
Birthdays, etc.)

50th Week

SUNDAY

BREAKFAST
   Chilled Orange Juice
   Country Fresh Egg
   Grilled Sausages
🍳🍳Almond Nut Dough-
      nuts (41)
   Butter or Margarine
   Beverage(s)

DINNER
🍳Roast Pork and
      Gravy (87)
   Whipped Yams
   Lima Beans
   Cottage Cheese Salad
🍳🍳Rolls (45)
   Butter or Margarine
🍳🍳Orange Chiffon Cake/
      Topping (10)
   Beverage(s)

SUPPER
🍳Cream of Corn
      Soup (273)
   Cold Cuts (including
      cheese and slice of
      Roast Pork)
   Catsup—Mustard—
      Pickles—Olives
   Bread, white and dark
   Butter or Margarine
   Oatmeal Crunch Cookies
   Beverage(s)

8:30 P.M.
   Beverage(s)*

MONDAY

BREAKFAST
   Fruit in Season
   Old Fashioned Waffles
   Crisp Bacon
   Honey or Maple Syrup
   Soft Butter
   Beverage(s)

DINNER
🍳Swiss Steak (60)
   Boiled Potatoes
   Buttered Broccoli
   Carrots and Celery
      Sticks
   Bread, white and dark
   Butter or Margarine
   Purple Plums
   Beverage(s)

SUPPER
🍳Potato and Onion
      Soup (265)
   Link Sausages with
      Apple Ring
   Creamed Carrots
🍳Head Lettuce (218)/
      Russian Dressing
   Bread, white and dark
   Butter or Margarine
   Hermits (cookies)
   Beverage(s)

8:30 P.M.
   Beverage(s)*

TUESDAY	WEDNESDAY

TUESDAY

BREAKFAST
  Assorted Juices
  ᰍ Poached Egg on
    Buttered Toast (19)
  Orange Pineapple
    Danish Roll
  Butter or Margarine
  Beverage(s)

DINNER
  ᰍ Lamb Stew (carrots,
    peas, celery)
  Graham Rolls
  Butter or Margarine
  ᰍ Gingerale Fruit Salad/
    dressing (217)
  Filled Cookies
  Beverage(s)

SUPPER
  ᰍ Beef Bouillon (255)
  Spiced Ham and
    Pimiento Loaf
    Sandwiches
  ᰍ Stewed Tomatoes
    (187)
  Butter or Margarine
  Creamy Tapioca
    Pudding
  Beverage(s)

8:30 P.M.
  Beverage(s)*

WEDNESDAY

BREAKFAST
  Half Grapefruit
  Selected Cold Cereal
    or
  Cream of Wheat,
    with cream
  Golden Toast
  Butter or Margarine–
    Jelly
  Beverage(s)

DINNER
  ᰍ Spaghetti and Meat
    Sauce (291)
  Buttered Leaf Spinach
  ᰍ Tossed Green Salad/
    Italian Dressing (221)
  French Bread
  Butter or Margarine
  Lemon Pie
  Beverage(s)

SUPPER
  ᰍ Cream of Spinach
    Soup (268)
  ᰍ Eggs a la King on an
    English Muffin,
    buttered (288)
  ᰍ Head Lettuce Salad
    (218)
  Cooked Apple Slices
    with Cinnamon
    Sauce
  Beverage(s)

8:30 P.M.
  Beverage(s)*

THURSDAY

BREAKFAST
  Chilled Fruit Juice
  Buttermilk Pancakes
  Soft Butter
  Warm Maple Syrup
    or Honey
  Beverage(s)

DINNER
  Baked Chicken,
    Gravy
  Whipped Potatoes
  Sliced Buttered Beets
  Apple-Date-Celery
    Salad/dressing
  ♕♕ Rolls, homemade (46)
  Butter or Margarine
  ♕ Individually Molded
    Coffee Bavarian
    (314)
  Beverage(s)

SUPPER
  ♕ French Onion
    Soup (253)
  Spanish Rice
  Orange and Green
    Pepper Salad/
    dressing
  ♕♕ Hard Rolls, sesame
    seed (48)
  Butter or Margarine
  Chilled Apricots
  Beverage(s)

8:30 P.M.
  Beverage(s)*

FRIDAY

BREAKFAST
  Orange Slices
  ♕ Scrambled Eggs (19)
  Crisp Bacon
  Toast
  Butter or Margarine
  Jelly
  Beverage(s)

DINNER
  Chilled Vegetable Juice
  ♕ Baked Stuffed Haddock
    (135)
  Creamy Mashed Potatoes
  ♕ Glazed Coin Sized
    Carrots (184)
  ♕♕ Rolls, petite size (45)
  Butter or Margarine
  ♕♕ Blueberry Pie, home
    baked (62)
  Beverage(s)

SUPPER
  ♕ Cream of Celery Soup
    (268), Saltines
  ♕ Spanish Omelette (283)
  ♕ Tomato Aspic Salad (234)
  ♕♕ Chocolate Cupcakes (79)
  Beverage(s)

8:30 P.M.
  Beverage(s)*

SATURDAY

BREAKFAST
Stewed Prunes,
Lemon Slices
Assorted Cold Cereals
or
Oatmeal, with cream
😋😋 Plain Doughnut (41)
Butter or Margarine
Beverage(s)

DINNER
Veal Roast
😋 Hashed Brown
Potatoes (194)
Peas and Onions
😋 Tomato and Cucumber
Salad (220)
😋😋 Baking Powder Biscuits
(3)
Butter or Margarine—
Plum Butter
😋😋 Coconut Frosted Cake
(29, 52)
Beverage(s)

SUPPER
Ham and Sweet Potato
Casserole
Buttered Green Beans
Bread, wholewheat
Butter or Margarine
😋😋 Applesauce and
Cookies (73)
Beverage(s)

8:30 P.M.
Beverage(s)*

51st Week

SUNDAY	**MONDAY**

BREAKFAST
  Grapefruit and
    Orange Sections
  🍳Bacon Omelet (20)
  Golden Toast
  Butter or Margarine
  Jam or Marmalade
  Beverage(s)

BREAKFAST
  Chilled Fruit Juice
  Assorted Cold Cereals
    or
  Wheatena, with cream
  Cheese Danish Roll
  Butter or Margarine
  Beverage(s)

DINNER
  🍳The First Ribs—
    Roast of Beef (54)
  🍳Yorkshire Pudding (54)
  Parsnips, buttered
  Creamed Carrots
  🍳🍳Hot Parkerhouse
    Rolls (46)
  Butter or Margarine
  Mincemeat Pie
  Beverage(s)

DINNER
  🍳Beef Hash (61)
  🍳Squash, (baked
    with brown sugar)
    (188)
  🍳Cole Slaw (223)
  Buttered Brussel
    Sprouts
  Bread, white and dark
  Butter or Margarine
  🍳🍳Bread Pudding, with
    Honey Sauce (76)
  Beverage(s)

SUPPER
  🍳Cream of Celery
    Soup (268)
  Cold Plate—Ham,
    Beef, Cheese
  🍳 Potato Salad (225)
  🍳🍳Rolls, petite (45)
  Butter or Margarine
  🍳🍳Baked Meringues
    with Apricot
    Sauce (33)
  Beverage(s)

SUPPER
  Tomato Juice
  Hot Pork Sandwich
  Mashed Turnips
  🍳🍳Sunshine Cake (32)
  Beverage(s)

8:30 P.M.
  Beverage(s)*

8:30 P.M.
  Beverage(s)*

TUESDAY

BREAKFAST
Stewed Apricots
Fried Egg
Hickory Smoked
Bacon
Golden Toast
Butter or Margarine—
Jam
Beverage(s)

DINNER
♨ Lamb Patties,
Mint Jelly (84)
♨ Lyonnaise Potatoes
(194)
♨ Buttered Cauliflower
(184)
♨ Tossed Salad/dressing
(218)
♨♨ Rolls, homemade (46)
Butter or Margarine
Oatmeal Molasses
Cookies
Beverage(s)

SUPPER
♨ Beef Stew with
Vegetables (59)
Steamed Rice
♨♨ Corn Bread (44)
Butter or Margarine—
Plum Butter
Chilled Apricots
Beverage(s)

8:30 P.M.
Beverage(s)*

WEDNESDAY

BREAKFAST
Chilled Pineapple Juice
Assorted Cold Cereals
or
Oatmeal, with cream
♨♨ Hot Rolls (40)
Butter or Margarine—
Jelly
Beverage(s)

DINNER
♨ Grilled Calves Liver
and Bacon (36)
Buttered Parsley
Potatoes
♨ Stewed Whole
Tomatoes (187)
♨♨ Rolls (48)
Butter or Margarine
♨ Shredded Cabbage and
Carrot Salad (223)
Chilled Peaches
Beverage(s)

SUPPER
♨ Chicken and Rice
Soup (256)
Broiled Meat Patty
Buttered Green Beans
Bread
Butter or Margarine
Whipped Fruit Gelatin
Beverage(s)

8:30 P.M.
Beverage(s)*

THURSDAY

BREAKFAST
 Grapefruit Sections,
  Grenadine
 Poached Egg on
  Buttered Toast (19)
 Apple Danish Roll
 Butter or Margarine
 Beverage(s)

DINNER
 Pizza Pie (50)
 Tossed Green Salad/
  dressing (218)
 Applesauce
 Molasses Drop
  Cookies (73)
 Beverage(s)

SUPPER
 Navy Bean Soup
  (262)
 Turkey Salad with
  Tomato Wedges
  (221)
 Rolls (47)
 Butter or Margarine
 Devils Food Cake
  Squares/Icing (29)
 Beverage(s)

8:30 P.M.
 Beverage(s)*

FRIDAY

BREAKFAST
 Chilled Prune Juice
 Old Fashioned Waffles
 Honey Butter
 Warm Maple Syrup
 Beverage(s)

DINNER
 Cheese Souffle
 Green Beans,
  French Style
 Baked Potato
 Spiced Pear
 Assorted Homemade
  Cookies
 Beverage(s)

SUPPER
 French Onion
  Soup (253)
 Tomato Stuffed with
  Tunafish Salad (221)
 Buttered Asparagus
 Corn Muffin, hot (44)
 Butter or Margarine—
  Apple Butter
 Banana Cream Pie
 Beverage(s)

8:30 P.M.
 Beverage(s)*

SATURDAY

BREAKFAST
Chilled Fresh
Melon Slice
Assorted Cold Cereals
or
Cream of Wheat,
warm milk
Cinnamon Raisin
Pecan Roll
Butter or Margarine
Beverage(s)

DINNER
Chili Con Carne
Buttered Rice
Celery Hearts and
Stuffed Olives
🍳🍳 Poppy Seed Hard
Rolls (48)
Butter or Margarine
Butterscotch Pudding
Beverage(s)

SUPPER
🍳 Vegetable Soup (261)
🍳 Chicken Pot Pie (104)
🍳 Pear and Cottage
Cheese Salad (229)
🍳🍳 Hot Parker House Rolls
(46)
Butter or Margarine
🍳🍳 Frosted Yellow Cake
Slice (29, 32)
Beverage(s)

8:30 P.M.
Beverage(s)*

52nd Week

	SUNDAY	MONDAY

SUNDAY

BREAKFAST
Chilled Melon
🍳 Scrambled Eggs (19)
Hickory Smoked
Bacon
🍳🍳 Sugar Doughnut (41)
Beverage(s)

DINNER
Pineapple Juice
Assorted Relish Tray
🍳 Baked Ham (85),
Raisin Sauce (289)
🍳 Candied Sweet Potato
(177)
Buttered Green Beans,
French Style
🍳🍳 Home-Baked Nut Bread
(8)
Butter or Margarine
Orange Sherbet and
Vanilla Cookies
Beverage(s)

SUPPER
🍳 Corn Chowder (271),
Saltines
Assorted Sandwiches
🍳 Mixed Green Salad/
dressing (218)
🍳🍳 Pineapple Cheese Cake
(35)
Beverage(s)

8:30 P.M.
Beverage(s)*

MONDAY

BREAKFAST
Assorted Fruit Juices
Selected Cold Cereals
or
Oatmeal, with cream
Toast, buttered
Beverage(s)

DINNER
🍳 Veal Stroganoff (53)
Buttered Rice
Buttered Broccoli
🍳 Perfection Salad (234)
Bread
Butter or Margarine
Caramel Custard
Beverage(s)

SUPPER
Baked Green Peppers
(stuffed with ground
meat, tomato sauce)
🍳 Jellied Fruit Salad (231)
🍳🍳 Raisin Bread (7)
Butter or Margarine
🍳🍳 Fruit Cake (20)
Beverage(s)

8:30 P.M.
Beverage(s)*

TUESDAY

BREAKFAST
Orange Sections
☕Poached Egg on
  Buttered Toast (19)
☕☕Hot Rolls (45)
Butter or Margarine–
  Jam
Beverage(s)

DINNER
☕ Lamb Stew with
  Dumplings (84, 258)
Buttered Green Peas
Buttered Carrot Rings
☕ Cole Slaw (223)
Bread
Butter or Margarine
☕☕ Pound Cake (21)
Beverage(s)

SUPPER
Chilled Tomato Juice
☕ Turkey Salad (221)
Cranberry Sauce
☕Stuffed Celery (222)
Rolls, sesame
Butter or Margarine
Mincemeat Cookies
Beverage(s)

8:30 P.M.
Beverage(s)*

WEDNESDAY

BREAKFAST
Bananas with Cream
Golden French Toast
Maple Syrup or Honey
Canadian Bacon
Beverage(s)

DINNER
☕Chicken and Vegetable
  Pie (104)
☕Candied Sweet Potatoes
  (177)
☕ Shredded Lettuce/
  dressing (239)
Bread
Butter or Margarine
Orange Date Nut Cake
Beverage(s)

SUPPER
☕ Puree Mongole (264)
Beef and Rice Balls
Wax Beans, Buttered
☕ Jellied Fruit Salad/
  dressing (231)
☕☕ Rolls (46)
Butter or Margarine
☕☕ Crisp Molasses Cookies
  (73)
Beverage(s)

8:30 P.M.
Beverage(s)*

THURSDAY	FRIDAY

BREAKFAST
  Assorted Juices
  Selected Cold Cereal
    or
  Wheatena, with cream
🍴🍴 Corn Muffins (44)
  Butter or Margarine
  Jelly
  Beverage(s)
	BREAKFAST
	  Grapefruit Half
	  Fried Egg
	  Plantation Sausage
	  Toast
	  Butter or Margarine—
	    Jam
	  Beverage(s)

DINNER
🍴 Meat Loaf (65)
  Boiled Potatoes
  Buttered Cut Green
    Beans
🍴 Fruited Gelatin (232)
  Bread
  Butter or Margarine
  Lemon Coconut Cake
  Beverage(s)
	DINNER
	  Salmon Loaf
	  Parsley Potatoes
	  Carrot Strips
	🍴 Braised Celery (186)
	  Bread
	  Butter or Margarine
	🍴🍴 Apple Crisp (76)
	  Beverage(s)

SUPPER
🍴 Navy Bean Soup (262)
  Weiners on Rolls
  Butter—Catsup—
    Mustard—Relish
🍴 Cole Slaw (223)
  Cottage Pudding with
    Fruit Sauce
  Beverage(s)
	SUPPER
	🍴 Washington Chowder,
	    Saltines (271)
	🍴 Creamed Eggs and
	    Mushrooms on
	    Toast (288)
	  Brown Sugar Crumb
	    Cake with Topping
	  Beverage(s)

8:30 P.M.
  Beverage(s)
	8:30 P.M.
	  Beverage(s)*

SATURDAY

BREAKFAST
Assorted Juices
Buttermilk Pancakes
Honey Butter
Warm Maple Syrup
Grilled Ham
Beverage(s)

DINNER
Spanish Rice with
Crumbled Bacon
Shredded Cabbage and
Apple and Nut
Salad/dressing (223)
Buttered Asparagus
Rolls (47)
Butter or Margarine
Baked Honey Custard
Beverage(s)

SUPPER
Cream of Tomato
Soup (252)
Grilled Cheese Sandwich
Jellied Fruit Salad (231)
Applesauce Cake, boiled
icing (18)
Beverage(s)

8:30 P.M.
Beverage(s)*

NOTES
(Special Events,
Residents'
Birthdays, etc.)

Extra Menu Days

"EXTRA" SUNDAY

BREAKFAST
  Chilled Orange Juice
  Country Fresh Eggs
  Grilled Sausages
  Jelly Doughnuts
  Beverage(s)

DINNER
  Fruit Cocktail
  ♕ Baked Chicken (106)
      and dressing (117)
  Mashed Potatoes
  Green Beans, buttered
  ♕♕ Parker House Roll (46)
  Butter or Margarine
  Vanilla Ice Cream
      with Pineapple Sauce
      and Whipped Cream
      Rosette
  Beverage(s)

SUPPER
  ♕ Beef Broth and
      Rice (256)
  Saltines
  Cold Plate—Ham,
      Cheese, Roast Beef
  Stuffed Celery—Olives
  Bread, wholewheat
  Butter or Margarine
  Mincemeat Fudge
      Squares
  Beverage(s)

8:30 P.M.
  Beverage(s)

"EXTRA" MONDAY

BREAKFAST
  Fruit in Season
  Old Fashioned Waffles
  Crisp Bacon
  Honey or Maple Syrup
  Soft Butter

DINNER
  ♕ Baked Roast Beef Hash
      (61) (onions and
      potatoes included in
      hash)
  Buttered Spinach
  ♕ Jellied Tomato Salad
      (234)
  Bread, white and dark
  Butter or Margarine
  Lemon Refrigerator
      Dessert
  Beverage(s)

SUPPER
  ♕ Corn Chowder (271)
  Apple Fritters
  Hot Maple Syrup
  ♕ Chopped Raw Salad
      (221)
  Chilled Queen Anne
      Cherries
  Beverage(s)

8:30 P.M.
  Beverage(s)*

"EXTRA" TUESDAY

BREAKFAST
Assorted Juices
🍳 Poached Egg on
    Buttered Toast (19)
Apricot Danish Roll
Butter or Margarine
Beverage(s)

DINNER
Liver Creole
Mashed Potatoes
Buttered Cauliflower
🍳 Jellied Pineapple and
    Carrot Salad (233)
Bread
Butter or Margarine
Baked Custard
Beverage(s)

SUPPER
Apple Juice
Spanish Rice
Molded Cottage
    Cheese Salad
🍳🍳 Rolls (48)
Butter or Margarine
Chilled Pears
Beverage(s)

8:30 P.M.
Beverage(s)*

"EXTRA" WEDNESDAY

BREAKFAST
Half Grapefruit
Selected Cold Cereal
    or
Cream of Wheat,
    with cream
Golden Toast
Butter or Margarine—
    Jelly
Beverage(s)

DINNER
🍳 Lamb Stew with
    Dumplings (79, 258)
Buttered Peas
Dark Bran Muffins
Chopped Spinach
    with Bacon
Butter or Margarine
🍳🍳 Golden Chiffon Cake
    (25)
Beverage(s)

SUPPER
🍳 Cream of Celery Soup
    (268)
🍳 Corned Beef Hash (61)
Bread, white and dark
Butter or Margarine
🍳 Fruited Gelatin (232)
Beverage(s)

8:30 P.M.
Beverage(s)*

"EXTRA" THURSDAY

BREAKFAST
Chilled Fruit Juice
Buttermilk Pancakes
Soft Butter
Warm Maple Syrup
   or Honey
Beverage(s)

DINNER
ⓅNew England Boiled
   Dinner (62)
   (includes potatoes,
   onions, etc.)
Buttered Peas
ⓅFruit Salad (227)
ⓅⓅRolls (46)
Butter or Margarine
Lemon Coconut Cake
Beverage(s)

SUPPER
Cold Cuts (Ham,
   Beef, and Cheese)
Bread, white and dark
Butter or Margarine
ⓅGreen Salad (218)
Raspberry Jumble
   Cookies
Beverage(s)

8:30 P.M.
Beverage(s)*

"EXTRA" FRIDAY

BREAKFAST
Orange Slices
ⓅScrambled Eggs (19)
Crisp Bacon
Toast
Butter or Margarine—
   Jelly
Beverage(s)

DINNER
ⓅFried Fish Fillets (132)
Parsley Buttered
   Potatoes
Baked Tomatoes
ⓅWaldorf Salad (226)
Bread
Butter or Margarine
Lemon-Filled Cupcake
Beverage(s)

SUPPER
ⓅPotato Chowder (270)
ⓅTunafish and Celery
   Salad (221)
Potato Chips
Pickles
ⓅⓅCustard Pie (58)
Beverage(s)

8:30 P.M.
Beverage(s)*

"EXTRA" SATURDAY

BREAKFAST
Stewed Prunes,
Lemon Slices
Assorted Cold Cereals
or
Oatmeal, with cream
Lemon Streusel Danish
Butter or Margarine
Beverage(s)

DINNER
Baked Ham (85) with
Raisin sauce (289)
Browned Potatoes
Green Beans
Jellied Pineapple and
Carrot Salad (233)
Bread, white and dark
Butter or Margarine
Maple Nut Cake
with Topping
Beverage(s)

SUPPER
Turkey Goulash
Lettuce and Tomato
Salad (218)
Rolls (46)
Butter or Margarine
Cream Cheese Apricot
Turnovers
Beverage(s)

8:30 P.M.
Beverage(s)*

Menus for the Holidays

New Year's Day
Leap Year, February 29th
St. Patrick's Day
Easter
July 4th
Labor Day
Thanksgiving
Christmas

NEW YEAR'S DAY

BREAKFAST
Chilled Orange Juice
Country Fresh Eggs
Grilled Sausages
🧑‍🍳🧑‍🍳 Almond Nut
    Doughnuts (41)
Butter or Margarine
Beverage(s)

DINNER
Wine
🧑‍🍳 Roast Duck
    Burgundy (117)
🧑‍🍳 Glazed Sweet Potato
    (177)
Buttered Asparagus
Jellied Cranberry
    Salad
🧑‍🍳🧑‍🍳 Rolls, Butter or
    Margarine (46)
🧑‍🍳🧑‍🍳 Fruit Cake with
    Hard Sauce (20)
Beverage(s)

SUPPER
Smorgasbord
Sliced Cold Turkey
    and Baked Ham
🧑‍🍳🧑‍🍳 Hot Rolls, butter or
    margarine (45)
Cranberry Sauce, un-
    strained
Cabbage, Almond,
    Marshmallow and
    Pineapple Salad
🧑‍🍳🧑‍🍳 Date Nut Bread (8)
Relishes
Fresh Fruits (a variety)
🧑‍🍳 Meringue Kisses
    (sprinkled with green
    and red sugar)
    (309, 311)
Chocolate Pinwheel Cookies
Beverage(s)

8:30 P.M.
    Beverage(s)*

302

IS IT LEAP YEAR?
IF SO, THIS IS FOR
FEBRUARY 29TH

BREAKFAST
 Grapefruit and Orange
  Sections
🍳 Bacon Omelet (20)
 Golden Toast
 Butter or Margarine
 Jam or Marmalade
 Beverage(s)

DINNER
🍳 Pork Loin Roast,
  Gravy (87)
 Mashed Potatoes
 Buttered Peas
🍳 Vegetable Salad/
  Dressing (221)
 Oatmeal Rolls
 Butter or Margarine
🍳🍳 Golden Chiffon Cake
  (25)
 Beverage(s)

SUPPER
🍳 Oyster Stew (259)
 Grilled Cheese Sandwich
🍳 Tomato Aspic (234)
🍳🍳 Cornflake Kisses (70)
 Beverage(s)

8:30 P.M.
 Beverage(s)*

ST. PATRICK'S DAY

BREAKFAST
 Chilled Melon
🍳 Scrambled Eggs (19)
 Hickory Smoked
  Bacon
 Cinnamon Raisin
  Pecan Rolls
 Beverage(s)

DINNER
 Wine
🍳 Roast Rolled Shoulder
  of Lamb, Boulangere
  (80)
   or
🍳 Corned Beef and
  Cabbage (62)
🍳🍳 Rolls (47)
 Butter or Margarine—
  Mint Jelly
🍳 Green Gelatin and Half
  Pear Salad/dressing
  (229)
 Peas, buttered
🍳🍳 Angel Food Cake/
  Topping (use green
  coloring) (31)
 Beverage(s)

SUPPER
🍳 Split Pea Soup (264)
 Ham and Egg Salad
🍳 Potato Salad (225)
🍳🍳 Rolls (46)
 Butter or Margarine
 Green Olives and Pickles
 Asparagus, buttered
 Ice Cream
 Beverage(s)

8:30 P.M.
 Beverage(s)*

EASTER SUNDAY

BREAKFAST
Chilled Orange Juice
Country Fresh Eggs
Grilled Sausages
🍳🍳Cinnamon Doughnuts
    (41)
Butter or Margarine
Beverage(s)

DINNER
🍳Lamb Roast, Pan
    Gravy (80)
Parsleyed Buttered
    Potatoes
Creamed Asparagus
    (or buttered)
🍳Fruit Salad (227)
🍳🍳Rolls (48)
Butter or Margarine
🍳🍳Golden Chiffon Cake
    with Topping (25)
Beverage(s)

SUPPER
🍳Cream of Celery
    Soup (268)
Cold Plate—Lamb,
    Beef, Ham, Cheese
Bread, white and dark
Butter or Margarine
Relishes
Ice Cream
Coconut Peanut
    Butter Stick
    Cookies
Beverage(s)

8:30 P.M.
    Beverage(s)*

JULY 4th

BREAKFAST
Orange Juice
Selected Cold Cereals
Crisp Bacon and
    Fried Eggs
Toast
Butter or Margarine—Jam
🍳🍳Glazed Doughnuts (41)
Beverage(s)

DINNER
Oven Fried Chicken
Mashed Potatoes
Green Beans
🍳Lettuce and Tomato
    Salad/dressing (218)
🍳🍳Rolls or Baking Powder
    Biscuits (45, 3)
Butter or Margarine
    and Honey
🍳🍳Strawberry Pie (65)
Beverage(s)

SUPPER
Picnic Supper
    (outdoors)
Beer and/or Lemonade
Sliced Ham
Weiners
Weiner Rolls
🍳Chopped Raw Slaw (223)
🍳German Potato Salad (225)
Fudge Loaf Cake
Ice Cream in Cups
Beverage(s)

8:30 P.M.
    Beverage(s)*

LABOR DAY	THANKSGIVING

BREAKFAST
    Orange, Tomato
        or Prune Juice
    Soft Cooked Eggs
    Toast
    Butter or Margarine
    Dutch Apple Coffee
        Cake with Topping
    Beverage(s)

BREAKFAST
    Chilled Melon
    🎓 Scrambled Eggs (19)
    Hickory Smoked
        Bacon
    Toast, Buttered
    Jelly
    Beverage(s)

DINNER
    Wine
    🎓 Roast Turkey (118),
        Dressing (117), and
        Giblet Gravy (122)
    Browned Parsnips
    Buttered Green Beans
    Mashed Potatoes
    🎓 Stuffed Celery Sticks (222)
    Oatmeal Rolls, Butter
        or Margarine
    Lemon Refrigerator
        Dessert
    Beverage(s)

DINNER
    Wine
    🎓 Roast Turkey (118)
        Dressing (117),
        Giblet Gravy (122)
    Buttered Parsnips
    Mashed Potatoes
    Buttered Peas
    🎓 Waldorf Salad with
        Honey Dressing (226)
    Radishes and Olives
        and Celery
    🎓🎓 Rolls (45)
    Butter or Margarine
    Pumpkin Pie
    Beverage(s)

SUPPER
    🎓 Celery Soup (268)
    Roast Beef Sandwiches
    Potato Chips
    🎓 Orange and Grapefruit
        Salad/dressing (230)
    🎓🎓 Cherry Pie (62)
    Beverage(s)

SUPPER
    Tomato Juice—Hors
        d'Oeuvres
    Assorted Cold Meats
        and Cheese
    Relish Tray including
        Pickled Pears and
        Peaches—Carrot
        and Celery Curls
    Bread, white and dark
    Butter or Margarine
    Fresh Fruit, (various
        kinds)
    Beverage(s)

8:30 P.M.
    Beverage(s)*

8:30 P.M.
    Beverage(s)*

CHRISTMAS

BREAKFAST
  Chilled Orange Juice
  Country Fresh Eggs
  Grilled Sausages
  Lemon-Filled Doughnuts
  Beverage(s)

DINNER
  Wine and/or Apple Juice
  ⌬Roast Turkey (118)
      Dressing (117), and
      Giblet Gravy (122)
  Whipped Potatoes
  Buttered Asparagus Spears
  Spiced Pears—Brandied
      Peaches
  Olives (green and black)—
      Celery
  ⌬Waldorf Salad (226)
  ⌬Raisin Bread (7), butter
      or margarine
  Mincemeat Pie—Apple Pie
  Beverage(s)

SUPPER
  Smorgasbord
  Cranberry Juice
  Sliced Baked Ham,
      Turkey, Assorted Cheeses
  ⌬Potato Salad (225)
  ⌬⌬Rolls, butter or
      margarine (46)
  Relishes
  Fresh Fruits (Grapes, etc.)
  Three Bean Salad
  Assortment of Homemade
      Christmas Cookies
  Ice Cream Cups
  Beverage(s)

8:30 P.M.
  Beverage(s)*

Special Menus and Diets for the Sick

The regular diet is used for persons who require no dietary restrictions. It is planned to meet all the requirements as established by the Food and Nutrition Board of the National Research Council, and to stimulate good food habits. The regular diet should include all the basic seven foods.

MILK: Two or more glasses daily for adults.
VEGETABLES: Two or more servings daily besides potato.
FRUITS: Two or more servings daily.
EGGS: Three to five a week, one daily preferred.
MEAT, CHEESE, FISH, FOWL: One or more servings daily.
CEREAL AND BREAD: Two or more servings daily.
BUTTER: Two or more tablespoons daily.

The Calorie Restricted or the Reducing Diet
The low calorie diet is a modification of the normal diet pattern in that the prescribed allowance has a caloric value below the total energy requirement for the day. The level of caloric intake prescribed for a moderate reduction program may range between 1,000 and 1,500 calories for women and between 1,500 and 2,000 calories for men. Excessive weight is due to the taking into the system of more food than it can use in daily living. This does not imply that one is eating exceptional quantities of food. It is merely a case of one's eating more than one needs of certain energy-producing foods.

Many unpleasant and sometimes fatal illnesses are associated with obesity. Some of these are: diabetes, heart disease, kidney disturbances, gall bladder trouble, backaches and sore feet.

The changing of food habits is a most important adjustment for a person to accept and learn to do. Changing easy-going ways is not easy, especially when one must relinquish sweets, rich gravies, and quantities of bread, etc., but a person can—if he or she honestly tries. The dieter should not become discouraged, however. Psychologists tell us that we expect far too much of ourselves, and when we fall short of our demands on ourselves we grow tense and discontented. The main purpose of a diet is not to try to prove to the world that the dieter is super-human. The person on a diet should be willing to accept a momentary lapse as an understandably human error—and keep trying!

By properly appraising height and the size of frame, the person wishing to diet can estimate how many pounds he (or she) must lose in order to arrive at the weight that is best.

SPECIAL DIET MENUS

Approx. 601 Calories
Steaming Bouillon—1 cup
Juicy Roast Leg of Lamb—
　4 oz.
Fresh Green Peas—½ cup
Cauliflower—½ cup
Tomato Aspic on Lettuce
　Leaf—½ cup
Rye Wafer (2)—Pat of
　Butter
Old Fashioned Ginger-
　bread—one small
　portion
Black Coffee

Approx. 608 Calories
Hot or Cold Consomme—
　1 cup
Sizzling Broiled Steak—
　3 oz., boneless
Broiled Mushroom Caps—
　2 large
Green Beans—½ cup
Crisp Garden Salad—½ cup
Lemon Juice Dressing—
　1 tbsp.
Sliced American Cheese—
　1 slice

Approx. 372 Calories
Shrimp Salad Supreme—
　8 shrimp
Lettuce Salad, Dressing
Rye Wafer
Fluffy Prune Whip—¾ cup
Skim Milk or Black Coffee

Approx. 588 Calories
Chilled Tomato Juice—½ cup
Broiled Halibut Steak,
　Lemon Wedge—4 oz.
Broccoli Spears—1 stalk,
　5 in. long
Fresh Steamed Carrots—
　½ cup
Cottage Cheese Salad
　with Chives—½ cup
Apricot Halves—Vanilla
　Wafer—4 halves, one
　cookie
Black Coffee

Approx. 386 Calories
Chilled Chicken Slices—
　3½ oz.
Low Calorie Dressing—1 tsp.
Hot Asparagus—4 med. stalks
Fresh Tomato Wedges—medium
Enriched Bread—1 slice
Cluster of Fresh Grapes
　(Tokay 20)
Skim Milk or Black Coffee

Approx. 455 Calories
Hearty Vegetable Soup—1 cup
Chopped Lean Beef Patty—
　4 oz.
Rosy Onion Rings—3
Savory Green Beans—2/3 cup
Chilled Cantaloupe—½
Skim Milk or Black Coffee—
　1 cup

The dieter should not be impatient or try to go too fast. A weight loss of 1½ pounds a week, or approximately 5 pounds a month, is as rapid as is usually advisable.

If this seems slow, it is well to remember that a gradual reduction of 5 pounds a month will, in a year, account for 60 unwanted pounds.

CALORIE CHART

Dairy Foods	Size of Portion	Calories
Milk, whole	1 glass (8 oz.)	170
Milk, skim or buttermilk	1 glass (8 oz.)	85
Milk, chocolate drink	1 glass (8 oz.)	185
Cheese, American or Swiss	1 in. cube or med. slice (1 oz.)	110
Cheese foods, Cheddar-type	2 tablespoons (1 oz.)	90
Cheese, Cottage, creamed	2 tablespoons (1 oz.)	30
Cheese, Cream	2x1x½ in. or 2 tbsp.	110
Butter	1 tablespoon (½ oz.)	100
Butter	teaspoon or small pat	35
Cream, light style	2 tablespoons	60
Cream, heavy, whipped	1 heaping tablespoon	50
Half-and-half	¼ cup	80
Ice cream, vanilla	¼ pint (½ cup)	150
Ice cream, as for a la mode	Medium scoop (1/5 pt.)	125
Sherbet	½ cup	120

Meat, Fish, Poultry, Eggs, Legumes

Meat, Fish, Poultry, lean to medium fat, averaged	1 serving (3 oz. cooked, weight without bones)	230
Liver	1 serving (3 oz. cooked)	180
Frankfurter	1 medium (1¾ oz.)	125
Luncheon Meat	2 medium slices (2 oz.)	165
Ham, boiled or baked	1 thin slice, 5x4 in.(1 oz.)	85
Tuna or Salmon, canned	1/3 cup (2 oz.)	105
Chicken, creamed	½ cup	210
Sausage, cooked	1 link, 3 in. long (2/3 oz.)	95
Bacon, crisp	2 long slices (½ oz.)	100
Eggs	1 medium	75
Eggs, scrambled	1 egg, tbsp. milk, tsp. butter	120
Dried Beans, split peas	¾ cup, cooked	150
Baked Beans with pork	¾ cup	245
Nuts, shelled, roasted	3 tbsp. chopped 30 peanuts	150

Other Popular Main Dishes

Meat and Vegetable Stew	¾ cup	190
Cheese Fondue	Med.serving, 1½x2x2½ in.	150
Macaroni and Cheese	¾ cup	350
Spaghetti, Italian style	Large serving with cheese	420
Chicken Pie, peas, potatoes	1 pie, 3¾ in. diameter	460
Soup, Navy Bean	1 cup	190
Soup, creamed style	1 cup	200

Fruits

FRESH,UNSWEETENED	1 med. serving, average	50-100
Citrus fruit	small orange, ½ grapefruit	50
Melon	½ medium cantaloupe	50
Peach	1 medium	50
Strawberries	1 cup	55
Grapes	small bunch	55
Blackberries, Raspberries	1 cup	75
Apple, Banana, Pear	1 medium	85
Avocado	¼ medium	140
COOKED, LIGHTLY SWEETENED	½ cup	100
Apple, baked, sweetened	1 large	210
Rhubarb sauce, sweetened	½ cup	190
DRIED	¼ cup raisins, or 4 large prunes or 2 small figs, or 3-4 dates	90
Fruit Juice	½ cup	50
Tomato Juice	½ cup	25

Vegetables and Salads

Green Beans	½ cup, cooked	15
Green leafy vegetables	½ cup, cooked	25
Carrots	½ cup, cooked	20
Root, others, as Beets, Onions	½ cup, cooked	35
Squash, winter	½ cup, cooked	50
Legumes; Green Peas	½ cup, cooked	65
Baby Lima Beans	½ cup, cooked	75
Starchy, as Corn	½ cup, cooked	70
Potatoes, white	1 small potato, cooked	80
Potatoes, mashed, french fried	½ cup or 6 med. pieces	120

Vegetables and Salads (cont.)	Size of Portion	Calories
Potatoes, sweet	½ med. potato, cooked	90
Raw Carrot, Tomato	1 small to medium	25
Lettuce	¼ medium head	10
Tossed Salad, Mixed Veg.	¾ cup, without dressing	30
Coleslaw	½ cup	50
Waldorf Salad	3 heap. tablespoons	140
Potato Salad	½ cup	185
Chicken and Celery Salad	3 heap. tablespoons	185

Breadstuffs and Cereals

Bread, whole-grain or enriched	1 medium slice (¾ oz.)	60
Bread, raisin, enriched	1 medium slice (¾ oz.)	65
Cereal, cooked, whole-grain or enriched	½ cup	70
Cereal, ready-to-eat, whole-grain or enriched	½ cup	50
Corn Grits, enriched	½ cup, cooked	60
Rice or Spaghetti	½ cup, cooked	105
Noodles	½ cup, cooked	55
Biscuit	1 small (1 oz.)	95
Corn Meal Muffin	1 med., 2¾ in. dia.	105
Rolls, plain, enriched	1 small (1 oz.)	85
Rolls, sweet	1 med. (2 oz.)	180
Waffle	1 med., 4½x5½x½ in.	215
Pancake	1 thin, 4 in. diameter	60
Crackers, plain or graham	2 medium	50
Rye Wafers	2 small	45
Gingerbread	1 piece, 2 in. square	180

Pastries and Puddings

Cookies, plain	2 small or 1 large	100
Cookies, oatmeal	2 small or 1 large	115
Wafers, as vanilla	2 small, thin	45
Cupcake, not iced	1 med. 1¾ in. dia.	80
Cupcake, iced	1 med., 1¾ in. dia.	130
Brownies	1 piece, 2x2x¾ in.	140
Cake, not iced	Med. piece, 2x3x1½ in.	175-300
Cake, layer, plain icing	Med. piece, 1/6 of 6-in. cake	250-400
Cake, angel food or sponge	Small piece, 2 in. sector	115
Doughnut	1 medium	135
Eclair, chocolate	1 average	250
Pie, fruit	1/7 med.-size pie	300-350

Pastries and Puddings (cont.)	Size of Portion	Calories
Pie, custard type	1/7 med.-size pie	250-300
Pudding, cornstarch, vanilla	½ cup	140
Pudding, rice with raisins	½ cup	165
Fruit Betty	½ cup	170
Prune Whip	½ cup	100
Custard	½ cup	140
Gelatin dessert with fruit	½ cup	85
Gingerbread	1 piece, 2 in. square	180

Sauces

Cream Sauce or Milk Gravy	2 tablespoons, med. thick	50
Cheese Sauce	2 tablespoons, med. thick	65
Hollandaise Sauce	1 tablespoon	90
Catsup, Chili, Tomato Sauce	1 tablespoon	20
Custard Sauce	2 tablespoons	40
Fruit Sauce	2 tablespoons	90
Chocolate Sauce	2 tablespoons	90
Hard Sauce	2 tablespoons	100
Butterscotch Sauce	2 tablespoons	200

Candy

Candy bar, milk chocolate	1 small bar (7/8 oz.)	125
Fondant mints or patties	1 average (40 to lb.)	40
Chocolate creams	1 average (35 to lb.)	50
Fudge, plain	1 piece, 1 in. square	100
Peanut Brittle	1 piece, 2½x2½x¼ in.	120
Gumdrops	1 large or 8 small	35
Marshmallows	1 average (60 to lb.)	25

Fountain Specialties

Milk Shake, chocolate	Fountain size (5 oz. milk, 2 small scoops ice cream, 2 tablespoons syrup)	400
Malted Milk Shake	Fountain size	500
Cocoa, all milk	1 table-size (6 oz. milk)	180
Sundaes	1 medium, 2 tbsp. topping	225-335
Sodas	Fountain Size	260
Eggnog	1 large glass (8 oz. milk)	290
Carbonated drinks	1 large glass (8 oz.)	110

Fountain Specialties (cont.)

	Size of Portion	Calories
Lemonade, slightly sweetened	1 large glass (10 oz.)	100
Ginger Ale	1 large glass (8 oz.)	80
Gingerflip	1 large glass (milk, gingerale, ice cream)	225
Mambo Shake	1 large glass (milk, banana, ice cream, lemon juice, sugar)	300
Mint Cow	1 large glass (milk, chocolate syrup, mint extract, ice cream)	320

Other Snacks

Pizza, quickly made type	1 med. serving 4-in. dia.	185
Hamburger, including bun	1 medium, lightly buttered bun	360
Hot Dog, including bun	1 medium	210
Potato Chips	10 med. or 7 large	110
Pickles	1 large dill or sweet pickle, or 4 slices cucumber pickle, or 1 tablespoon relish	15
Olives, green	2 med. olives	15
Pretzels	5 small sticks	20
Popcorn, lightly buttered	½ cup	75

Count These Too

Salad Dressing, cooked type	1 tablespoon	30
French dressing	1 tablespoon	60
mayonnaise	1 tablespoon	90
lemon juice or vinegar	1 tablespoon	3
Salad Oil	1 tablespoon	125
Jam, syrup, sugar	1 tablespoon	55

The Soft Diet

This diet represents the usual dietary step between the general liquid and regular diet. The soft diet is made up of simple, easily digested foods and contains no harsh fiber, no rich or highly seasoned foods. It is as adequate nutritionally as a normal diet.

A person on a soft diet may select foods from the regular or normal menu which offers a choice of all foods. This diet permits those foods which are mild in texture and consistency but are non-irritating to chew and digest.

SAMPLE MENU FOR THE SOFT DIET

BREAKFAST
Chilled California Grapefruit Juice
Hot Oatmeal with Cream
Scrambled Eggs
Buttered Toast with Jelly
Homogenized Milk
Coffee with Sugar and Cream

DINNER
Chilled Tomato Juice
Pot Roast of Beef
Creamy Mashed Potatoes
Buttered Carrots
Enriched Bread with Butter
Vanilla Ice Cream Slice
Homogenized Milk

SUPPER
Cream of Spinach Soup
Buttered Waxed Beans
Whipped Orange Gelatin
Tea, Sugar, Lemon

Diabetic Diets

The diabetic diet is individualized for each patient and so planned that it is physiologically correct. The physician calculates the prescription basing his allowances on:

1. The history of both the patient and his family.
2. Sex, age, weight, height and activity of the patient.
3. Type of diabetes—mild or severe.
4. Type of insulin, amount and when administered.
5. Nutritional requirements as based on the above data.

The right kind of food—in the right amount—at the right times is a most important rule for the diabetic.

Diabetes can be controlled by diet in some cases, or by diet plus insulin in others. Everyone has some sugar in his blood, but the person with diabetes has too much sugar in his blood. The diabetic does not make sufficient insulin to use the sugar from the food he eats. Almost every food he eats makes some sugar in the body. This food must be balanced with the insulin his body makes, or his doctor prescribes. Even the temporary or continued use of insulin does not mean that the diabetic can avoid constant attention to the proper diet. For a good reference to the diabetic diet, see Charles B. Knox Gelatine Company, Inc., NEW VARIETY IN MEAL PLANNING FOR THE DIABETIC, Jamestown, New York, 1958.

Sodium Restricted Diets

The sodium restricted diet is a modification of the normal diet except that the sodium content has been restricted to a prescribed level. Other nutrients remain as nearly as possible on a level satisfactory for nutritive efficiency. Restriction of sodium is indicated for treatment of diseases in which there is edema, such as cardiac diseases, kidney disease and hypertension. There are three levels of sodium restriction: mild, moderate and severe. A number of the so-called "strongly flavored vegetables" have been included in the planning of low sodium diets. Many persons can and do eat some or all of these vegetables without distress. Consequently, the person may choose any vegetable that he feels he is able to tolerate.

Low Sodium Diet—Mild Restriction

This diet is a modification of the regular diet. A salt substitute is served instead of table salt. With this diet, you should avoid: salt at table; salt preserved foods such as ham, bacon, dried beef, salted fish, olives, bologna or sausage, anchovies, sauerkraut, bouillon cubes and meat extracts; highly salted foods such as salted nuts, potato chips, crackers, relishes, such as catsup, pickles and prepared mustards, Worcestershire or meat sauces, celery salt, garlic salt, cheese unless specially prepared without salt, peanut butter unless specially prepared without salt.

SAMPLE MENU

BREAKFAST
Chilled Florida Orange Juice
Hot Oatmeal with Cream
Scrambled Eggs
Buttered Toast with Jelly
Coffee, Sugar, Cream

LUNCHEON
Chilled Tomato Juice
Pot Roast of Beef
Fluffy Mashed Potatoes
Buttered Sliced Carrots
Lettuce Wedge
Hot Parker House Rolls
    with Butter
Homogenized Milk

DINNER
Chicken Noodle
    Casserole
Buttered Green Beans
Sliced Tomatoes
Enriched Bread with
    Butter
Sliced Peaches
Milk, Tea with Sugar
    and Lemon

Low Sodium Diet—Moderate Restrictions

On this diet you should avoid: salt in any kind of cooking and all foods listed under Mild Restriction diet; canned vegetables, meat, fish or soups unless prepared without salt; frozen peas, lima beans, frozen fish fillet; foods prepared with benzoate of soda; shellfish, except oysters; salted fat, such as butter, margarine and bacon fat; ordinary bread; anything cooked with soda, baking powder, prepared flour mixes or prepared flour; instant coffee, instant tea and postum.

Foods allowed daily under this diet are:
1. Milk; fresh, canned or powdered, 1 pint.
2. Cheese; washed cottage cheese or low Na. cheese.
3. Meat; unsalted meat, fish or fowl, 4 to 6 oz. daily.
4. Eggs; 1 or 2 daily.
5. Vegetables; any kind, fresh canned or frozen without salt.
6. Fruits; any kind.
7. Bread or alternate; low sodium bread, potatoes, puffed rice, puffed wheat, macaroni, spaghetti, noodles, any unsalted cooked cereal.
8. Fats; unsalted butter, vegetable shortenings, corn oil, lard, olive oil.
9. Dessert: pudding made with low Na. milk or part of milk allowance. Sweets: Jams, jellies, sugar, honey and hard candy.
10. Beverages; coffee, tea, cocoa (except Dutch process).

SAMPLE MENU

BREAKFAST
Chilled Florida Orange Juice
Hot Salt-Free Oatmeal
Poached Egg on Salt-Free
  Toast
Coffee, Sugar, Cream

LUNCHEON
Chilled Salt-Free
  Tomato Juice
S.F.* Pot Poast of Beef
Fluffy S.F.* Mashed Potatoes
Buttered S.F.* Sliced Carrots
Lettuce Salad with S.F.*
  Salad Dressing
Homogenized Milk

DINNER
S.F.* Chicken Noodle
  Casserole
S.F.* Buttered Green
  Beans
Sliced Tomato S.F.*
  Dressing
S.F.* Bread with Butter
Chilled Sliced Peaches
Homogenized Milk
Tea—Sugar, Lemon

S.F.*—Salt Free

Low Sodium Diet—Severe Restriction

Foods to be avoided on this diet are: All foods listed on diet No. 2 plus: Beets, beetgreens, kale, spinach, celery, chard, dandelion greens, mustard, split peas; Instant tea and coffee unless they are the 100% pure product; Milk, except dialized or low Na. milk; Dutch process cocoa, malted milk, Ovaltine.

Foods allowed daily are:
1. Milk; low Na. milk (lonalac).
2. Meat or alternate: unsalted meat, fish or fowl 4 oz. daily.
3. Eggs: one a day only.
4. Bread: low Na. bread, potato, cooked cereals, rice, spaghetti, macaroni, noodles, puffed wheat, puffed rice, shredded wheat.
5. Vegetables: use fresh or canned or frozen without salt, asparagus, beans, brussel sprouts, cabbage, squash, corn, eggplant, carrots, lettuce, peas, radishes, onions, cucumbers, tomatoes, turnips, potatoes; omit frozen lima beans and peas.
6. Fruit, any kind.
7. Fat: unsalted butter, lard, salt-free cooking fats, home-made salt-free salad dressing.
8. Desserts and sweets: sugar, honey, jam, jellies, plain gelatin, puddings made with cornstarch and low Na. milk, un-salted nuts, hard sugar candies, low sodium cookies and cakes.
9. Beverages: water, tea and coffee, low Na. milk and cocoa except Dutch process.

SAMPLE MENU
BREAKFAST

Chilled Florida Orange Juice
S.F.* Hot Oatmeal
Scrambled Eggs

S.F.* Toast
S.F.* Butter
Coffee—Sugar, Cream

LUNCHEON
Chilled S.F.* Tomato Juice
S.F.* Pot Roast of Beef
Creamy S.F.* Mashed
    Potatoes
Buttered S.F.* Carrots
Lettuce Salad, S.F.*
    Salad Dressing
S.F.* Bread and Butter
Homogenized Milk
*Salt-Free

SUPPER
S.F.* Chicken and Noodle
    Casserole
S.F.* Green Beans
Sliced Tomatoes, S.F.*
    Dressing
S.F.* Hot Rolls with Butter
Chilled Sliced Fruit
Homogenized Milk, Tea—
    Sugar, Lemon

Recipe Favorites for Low Sodium Diets

LEMON POACHED FISH
Yield: 4 portions
Ingredients
Fresh Halibut (or fresh Cod, fresh Salmon,
   fresh Perch, fresh Bass), sliced   1 lb.
Fresh Lemon Juice   1 tbsp.
Method
   1. Cut fish into individual sized servings. Put enough water in a pan to barely cover fish, add lemon juice and bring to a boil.
   2. Place the fish in the water, cover and cook below boiling point for 8 to 10 minutes.
   3. Carefully remove fish from water and serve immediately with Thrifty Hollandaise Sauce.

THRIFTY HOLLANDAISE SAUCE
Yield: Approx. 1¼ cups sauce
Ingredients
Sweet Butter   2 tbsp.
Flour   2 tbsp.
Milk   1 cup
Black Pepper   1/8 tsp.
Egg Yolks, slightly beaten   2
Sweet Butter, melted   2 tbsp.
Fresh Lemon Juice   3 tbsp.
Method
   1. Melt 2 tbsp. butter over low heat. Blend in flour and cook, stirring constantly, until mixture is smooth and bubbly. Remove from heat. Add milk and mix thoroughly. Return to heat, beat in pepper and 2 egg yolks. Gradually beat in melted butter and lemon juice. Serve at once.

LEMON BAKED CHICKEN

Yield: 4 to 6 portions
Ingredients

Salad Oil	¼ cup
Fresh Lemon Juice	¼ cup
Garlic, crushed	1 clove
Medium Fryer (about 3 lb.) cut into individual serving pieces	1

Method

1. Thoroughly mix salad oil, lemon juice, and garlic. Arrange chicken in a casserole and brush each piece thoroughly with lemon-oil mixture.

2. Uncover casserole for last 20 minutes to allow chicken to brown. Chicken may be kept covered for full baking time, then browned under broiler.

3. Baste again with lemon-oil mixture before broiling. Sprinkle with chopped parsley and paprika.

TOMATO SALAD SOLO

Yield: 4 portions
Ingredients

Sugar	¼ cup
Fresh Lemon Juice	¼ cup
Tomatoes, medium, sliced	3 to 4

Method

1. Mix together sugar and lemon juice. Pour over tomato slices. Chill.

2. Serve on lettuce.

CUCUMBER HERB SALAD

Yield: 4 portions
Ingredients

Fresh Lemon Juice	¼ cup
Sugar	1 tbsp.
Grated Onion	½ tsp.
Marjoram or Thyme	1/8 tsp.
Cucumber, large	1

Method

1. Mix together lemon juice, sugar, onion and marjoram or thyme. Peel cucumber, if desired; slice and marinate in lemon mixture. Chill.

2. Serve with marinade, or drain and arrange on lettuce leaves. Good, also as a garnish for meats and salads.

BROILED BEEF PATTIES

Yield: 6 portions
Ingredients

Low-Sodium Bread Crumbs	¼ cup
Fresh Lemon Juice	2 tbsp.
Onion, small, finely chopped	1
Black Pepper	¼ tsp.
Ground Beef	1 lb.
Sweet Butter	Approx. 2 tbsp.

Method

1. Moisten low-sodium bread crumbs with lemon juice. Add crumbs, onion and pepper to ground beef and mix well.

2. Form into patties and brush with sweet butter before placing under broiler. Broil approx. 5 to 6 minutes.

3. Turn, brush with sweet butter and broil until done. Makes about 6 medium-sized patties.

BREAD

Yield: 2 loaves
Ingredients

Water	2 cups
Sugar	1 tsp.
Lard	1 tsp.
Dried Yeast	1½ pkg.
Lukewarm Water	½ cup
Sifted Flour	4-6 cups

Method

Put sugar, salt and fat into a bowl. Add boiling water and cool to lukewarm. Add yeast which has been dissolved in ½ cup lukewarm water.

Add about three cups of flour; stir free from lumps and beat well. Add flour to make stiff enough to handle. Turn out on a floured board and knead until soft, smooth and elastic. This thoroughly mixes the ingredients.

Put back into a bowl; moisten top; cover and let rise in a warm place until double in bulk. Knead again.

Shape into loaves and place in baking loaf tins. Cover and let rise until double its bulk.

Then bake in a moderate oven one hour. Too hot oven causes crusts to brown too quickly before the heat has reached the center and prevents further rising.

LEMON CAKE TOP PUDDING
Yield: 8 portions
Ingredients

Sweet Butter	3 tbsp.
Sugar	1 cup
Egg Yolks	4
Flour	3 tbsp.
Fresh Lemon Juice	1/3 cup
Lemon Peel, grated	2 tsp.
Milk	1 cup
Egg Whites	4

Method

1. Cream butter, add sugar gradually and cream together until light and fluffy. Add egg yolks and beat well.

2. Add flour, lemon juice, peel; mix well. Stir in milk.

3. Beat egg whites until stiff, fold into mixture. Pour into loaf baking dish, 9 by 5 in. Set in pan of hot water and bake in a slow oven (325°F.) 40 minutes.

4. Turn thermostat to 350°F. and bake about 10 minutes or until brown. Serve either warm or chilled.

LEMON NUT COOKIES
Yield: 2 doz.
Ingredients

Unsalted Vegetable Shortening	½ cup
Sugar	¼ cup
Egg Yolk, beaten	1
Vanilla	1 tsp.
Egg White	1
Fresh Lemon Juice	2 tbsp.
Lemon Peel, grated	2 tsp.
Orange Peel, grated	2 tsp.
Sifted Flour	1¼ cups
Chopped Nuts (unsalted)	½ cup

Method

1. Cream shortening and sugar until light and fluffy.

2. Add egg yolk, vanilla, lemon juice and grated peel. Mix well.

3. Add flour, mix thoroughly. Chill one hour.

4. In a flat dish, beat egg white slightly with a fork. Dip one side of a teaspoonful of dough in egg white, then in nuts.

5. Place nut side up, about 2 in. apart on greased cooky sheet.

6. Bake at 325°F. 20 to 25 min. until lightly browned.

High Carbohydrate, High Protein, Low Fat Diets

This diet is a modification of the normal diet with all other nutrients at a level suitable for nutritive efficiency but with fat content restricted. It contains easily digested foods and omits those high in roughage or which tend to cause distress. Because of the limitation on fat content, other foods high in vitamin A are served frequently. This diet is used for conditions in which impairment of an organ associated with fat digestion is involved, such as gall bladder diseases and some liver diseases where there is impairment of the flow of bile.

Foods allowed on this diet are:
Cereals, all cooked or prepared
Breads, whole wheat or enriched white (toasted or plain), crackers
Fruits, fresh, canned, dried or frozen, fruit juices
Vegetables, potatoes, boiled, baked or mashed, all others fresh, canned or frozen except the so-called "gas forming vegetables," cooked without butter or other fat
Meat, fish, poultry, lean beef, veal, lamb, chicken livers, non-fatty fish, roasted, boiled or broiled, but not fried
Milk, skimmed milk as desired
Cheese, farmer, pot or cottage cheese
Dessert, sherbet, ices, gelatin, angel food cake, fruit, fresh, canned or frozen
Beverages, tea, coffee, fruit juices
Sweets, sugar, honey, jams, jellies
Foods limited on this diet are:
Whole milk, 1 pt. daily; Eggs, one daily; Butter or Margarine, 3 tsp. a day
All fried foods
Pies, pastry, cake (except angel food)
Nuts, peanut butter, olives, avocados, potato chips
All meats high in fat, such as pork, ham, sausage, bologna, frankfurters and bacon, goose, duck, all fatty fish or fish canned in oil
Gravies and rich sauces
Salad dressings and salad oils
Pickles, spiced or highly seasoned foods, such as horseradish, dried beans, cucumbers, peppers, corn, unless their use causes no digestive discomfort

323

Bland Diet

This diet is used with much success in treating gastric disorders. Bland, as the term signifies, refers to the soothing, mildly-flavored foods that are easily handled by the digestive system. Such foods have the least tendency to cause further harm to an already damaged area in the stomach or intestines.

Foods allowed on this diet are:
Beverages: milk and milk drinks, tea, coffee, coffee substitute at the physician's discretion, not more than 1 cup a day.

Breads: rye bread without seeds, day-old white bread; melba toast; rusks; soda or oyster crackers; zwieback.

Cereal foods, refined and strained: cornflakes; cornmeal; farina; hominy grits; macaroni; noodles; pablum; puffed rice; rice; rice flakes; spaghetti; strained oatmeal, or whole wheat cereal.

Cheese: cream; cottage; mild cheddar when used in sauce.

Desserts: angel cake; sponge cake; arrowroot or sugar cookies; vanilla wafers; custard, plain ice cream; plain gelatin; junket; lady fingers; rice, bread, cornstarch or tapioca pudding; fruit whip.

Eggs; any way except fried.

Foods to avoid on this diet are:
Beverages: alcohol; soft drinks; tea and coffee except as indicated.

Breads: fresh bread and biscuits; wholegrain bread; graham crackers; pretzels; salted crackers; sweet rolls.

Cereals: bran, wholegrain cereals unless strained.

Cheese: strongly flavored.

Dessert: any containing fruit, nuts, or spices; doughnuts; gingerbread, pastries; pies, spice cake; tarts.

Egg, fried.

Foods easily digested are:
Meat: any tender or well-cooked, but not overcooked, meat, with the possible exception of pork. (Cooked by any method except frying.)

Bacon: broiled.
Vegetables: cooked vegetables.
Macaroni and Spaghetti: boiled or with cream sauce.
Bread: day old, or crisp toast.
Crackers
Milk or malted milk.
Butter, cream, olive oil.
Eggs: soft cooked by any method but frying.
Cereals.
Soups: bouillon, consomme, cream soups.
Fruit: stewed or canned. Fresh fruit; well chewed.
Puddings: custard, tapioca, gelatin, rice.
Cake: Plain, e. g. sponge, angel.
Cheese: cream, cottage cheese, ricotta.

Liquid Diets

FULL LIQUID DIET

The full liquid diet is made up of liquid foods and can include any food which becomes liquid at body temperature.

Foods allowed:

carbonated beverage, cereal beverage, tea, cocoa, coffee in moderation

refined or strained cooked cereals, farina, cream of rice cream of wheat, strained oatmeal

strained cream soups, broth, bouillion, consomme

plain ice cream, junket, gelatin, custard, sherbet, gelatin desserts

milk and milk beverages

eggnogs

strained fruit juices

pureed vegetables in soups

hard candy, sugar, honey

seasonings—salt, pepper, vanilla flavor, nutmeg in moderation

SAMPLE MENU—FULL LIQUID DIET

BREAKFAST	DINNER	SUPPER
Apple Juice	Cream of Tomato	Cream of Mushroom
Cream of Wheat	Soup	Soup
Cream	Pineapple Juice	Strained Orange
Tea	Baked Custard	Juice
	Milk	Junket
	Tea	Milk
		Tea

To Increase Protein Content: Use commercial protein supplement formulas or add gelatin to beverages.

To Decrease Fat Content: Omit butter, cream and margarine. Use skim milk. Limit eggs to one a day.

To Decrease Sodium Content: Omit salt in cooking. Use foods which have been processed and cooked without salt. Limit milk to one quart a day.

CLEAR LIQUID DIET

The clear liquid diet is made up of fluids which have little or no caloric value. It is used for patients post-operatively and in acute stages of many illnesses.

Foods allowed:
    carbonated beverages
    cereal beverages
    tea, coffee
    decaffeinated coffee
    plain gelatin
    clear fruit juices, strained fruit juices
    bouillion, broth, consomme
    sugar, honey, hard candy

SAMPLE MENU—CLEAR LIQUID DIET

BREAKFAST	DINNER	SUPPER
Apple Juice	Broth	Consomme
Tea	Gelatin	Gelatin
	Strained Pineapple Juice	Strained Grapefruit Juice
	Tea	Tea

Post Operative Fluids: Clear liquids are prescribed—fruit juices are omitted.

Low Sodium Diet Fluids: All broths and consommes are prepared without salt. Gelatin desserts are homemade. Commercial gelatin contains a sodium preservative.

Special Allergy Diets

The person with an allergy condition should receive medical guidance from his doctor and based on medical recommendations, a proper diet can be worked out. It is hoped that the information that follows will offer assistance in meal planning for those allergic to one or more of the staple foods: milk, eggs and wheat. Read the label carefully before using any type of prepared mix in order to determine if the product contains ingredients to be avoided on the allergy diet.

Flours

Standard recipes containing wheat flour may be altered to permit the use of other flours as follows:

Substitutes for 1 cup wheat flour: ½ cup barley flour; 1 cup corn flour; ¾ cup cornmeal (coarse); 1 scant cup cornmeal (fine); 5/8 cup potato flour; 7/8 cup rice flour; 1¼ cups rye flour; 1 cup rye meal; 1-1/3 cups ground rolled oats.

Combinations of flour to be substituted for 1 cup wheat flour:
(1) rye flour—½ cup; potato flour—½ cup
(2) rye flour—2/3 cup; potato flour—1/3 cup
(3) rice flour—5/8 cup (10 tbsp.); rye flour—1/3 cup
(4) soy flour—1 cup; potato starch flour—¾ cup

Products made with rice flour and cornmeal have rather grainy textures. In order to obtain a smoother texture, the rice flour may be mixed with liquid called for in the recipe, brought to a boil and then cooled before adding to other ingredients, or the cornmeal may be cooked.

Soy flour cannot be used as the only flour; it must be combined with another flour. A combination of flours should be thoroughly mixed with other dry ingredients.

Baked products made with flour other than wheat require long and slow baking, particularly when made without milk and eggs. Wheat flour should be sifted before measuring.

Coarse meals and flours require more leavening than wheat flour and 2½ tsp. of baking powder are recommended for each cup of coarse flour.

Batters of flours other than wheat often appear thicker or thinner than wheat flour batters.

Muffins and biscuits made of flours other than wheat often have a better texture when made in small sizes.

Cakes made with flours other than wheat are apt to be dry. Frosting and storing in a closed container tend to preserve their moisture.

Dry cereals such as rice flakes or corn flakes when crushed make an excellent breading for fowl, chops, or fish and meat patties.

Fat
Fat is the general term used in these recipes to indicate any cooking or table fat, liquid or solid. Fat, either vegetable or animal, may be used unless a particular flavor is desired.

Margarines and soy butter contain a small percentage of milk. Hydrogenated milk-free fat is available. Persons sensitive to milk can frequently tolerate butter.

Milk
Persons sensitive to cow's milk can often tolerate it in dried or evaporated form, or use milk other than cow's milk (examples: goat's milk, soy milk). It is wise to try these before eliminating milk from the diet.

Eggs
Baking powder should be increased 1 tsp. for each egg eliminated in the batter and dough recipes. Some baking powders also contain cornstarch. A leavening agent free from cornstarch and egg white may be prepared as follows: 1-1/8 tsp. cream of tartar plus ½ tsp. baking soda. This is equivalent to 1 tsp. of baking powder. This must be mixed as needed.

Wheat-, Milk- and Egg-Free Recipes

SPICE CAKE

Yield: 1 loaf cake
Ingredients

Brown Sugar	1 cup
Water	1¼ cup
Raisins, seedless	1 cup
Citron, cut fine	2 oz.
Fat	1/3 cup
Salt	½ tsp.
Nutmeg	1 tsp.
Cinnamon	1 tsp.
Baking Powder	4 tsp.
Cornmeal, fine	1 cup
Rye Flour	1 cup

Method

   1. Boil sugar, water, fruit, fat and salt together. When cool, add to sifted dry ingredients. Mix thoroughly.

   2. Bake in a greased loaf pan at 375°F. for about 45 min.

OAT FLOUR NUT MUFFINS

Yield: 6 muffins
Ingredients

Oat Flour	1 cup
Baking Powder	4 tsp.
Sugar	2 tsp.
Salt	¼ tsp.
Water	½ cup
Cottonseed Oil	1 tbsp.
Walnuts, chopped	½ cup

Method

   1. Sift dry ingredients together. Add water, oil and nuts. Mix.

   2. Fill muffin pans, greased with cottonseed oil, 2/3 full.

   3. Bake at 400°F. for about 30 minutes.

FRUIT PUDDING

Yield: 2 servings
Ingredients

Rye Wafers (such as Ry-Krisp)	10
Pineapple Juice	¾ cup
Lemon Juice	2 tsp.
Brown Sugar	2 tbsp.
Cloves	1/8 tsp.
Cinnamon	1/8 tsp.
Nutmeg	1/8 tsp.
Seedless Raisins	¼ cup

Method

1. Roll rye wafers into coarse crumbs or put through coarse blade of food grinder. Mix with other ingredients. Pour into greased dish.

2. Bake at 350°F. for about 1 hour.

3. Serve warm or cold with a sweet fruit sauce or a sugar sauce.

Variations: The pudding may be steamed for 90 min.

OAT PEANUT BUTTER COOKIES

Yield: 1 doz. cookies
Ingredients

Sugar	½ cup
Peanut Butter	1 tbsp.
Cottonseed Oil	2 tsp.
Water	¼ cup
Oat Flour	1½ cups
Baking Powder	2 tsp.

Method

1. Mix sugar, peanut butter and oil. Add water.

2. Add oat flour and baking powder; mix thoroughly.

3. Drop from a teaspoon on cookie sheet greased with cottonseed oil.

4. Press down each cookie with tines of fork. Bake at 400°F. until golden brown.

5. Remove from baking sheet as soon as taken from oven.

RICE PEANUT BUTTER MUFFINS

Yield: 6 muffins

Ingredients

Rice Flour	1 cup
Baking Powder	4 tsp.
Salt	¼ tsp.
Sugar	2 tbsp.
Cottonseed Oil	1 tbsp.
Water	½ cup
Peanut Butter	3 tsp.

Method

1. Sift dry ingredients together. Add oil, water and peanut butter. Mix.

2. Fill muffin pans, greased with cottonseed oil, 2/3 full.

3. Bake at 425°F. for about 20 minutes.

HAWAIIAN MEAT LOAF

Yield: 6 portions

Ingredients

Ground Veal	1 lb.
Ground Cooked Ham, firmly packed	1 cup
Minute Tapioca	2 tbsp.
Salt	1 tsp.
Crushed Pineapple, drained	½ cup
Pineapple Juice	½ cup
Brown Sugar	2 tbsp.

Method

1. Combine meats, tapioca, salt, pineapple and juice. Mix well.

2. Shape into loaf in shallow baking pan; sprinkle brown sugar over top.

3. Bake in moderate oven (350°F.) for about 1 hour.

4. Serve with gravy made from drippings and cornstarch, if desired.

FRUIT TAPIOCA

Yield: 4 to 6 servings
Ingredients

Diced Fruit (canned pineapple, fresh or canned peaches*)	1 cup
Powdered Sugar	2 tbsp.
Fruit Juice	2 cups
Sugar	¼ cup
Salt	¼ tsp.
Minute Tapioca	4 tbsp.
Lemon Juice	½ tsp.

Method

1. Mix fresh fruit with powdered sugar and allow to stand. Heat juice to boiling.
2. Mix sugar, salt and tapioca and add to boiling juice.
3. Boil until clear. Remove from fire and add lemon juice and fruit.
4. Chill and serve with sliced fruit.

*Apricots or red cherries may also be used.

STUFFED PEPPERS

Yield: 4 servings
Ingredients

Rye Wafers (such as Ry-Krisp), crushed	8
Green Peppers, medium sized	4
Fat	½ tbsp.
Ground Beef, lean	½ lb.
Onion, finely cut	¼ cup
Celery, finely cut	¼ cup
Canned Tomatoes, broken, drained	1/3 cup
Salt	¾ tsp.

Method

1. Wash green peppers; slice off tops; remove seeds. Put peppers in pan, cover with boiling water and boil gently 5 minutes. Drain.
2. Melt fat in skillet. Add beef and cook over moderate heat until brown, breaking with fork while cooking. Remove from heat.
3. Add rye wafer crumbs, onion, celery, tomatoes and salt. Mix well.
4. Fill peppers with meat mixture.
5. Stand peppers upright in baking dish. Add hot water to 1-in. depth. Cover and bake about 1 hour at 350°F.

APRICOT AND PINEAPPLE DELIGHT

Yield: 4 servings

Ingredients

Lemon Gelatin	4 tbsp.
Boiling Water	1 cup
Apricot Pulp (dried apricots)	4 tbsp.
Pineapple, diced	4 tbsp.

Method

    1. Dissolve lemon gelatin in boiling water.

    2. Chill until slightly thickened.

    3. Add apricot pulp and diced pineapple. Pour into mold and chill until firm.

    4. Garnish with nuts and cherries.

RYE BREAD

Yield: 2 loaves

Ingredients

Compressed Yeast	1 cake
OR	
Dry Yeast	1 envelope
Water, lukewarm	1-1/3 cups
Sugar	2 tbsp.
Salt	1½ tsp.
Shortening, melted	2 tbsp.
Light Rye Flour	Approx. 5 cups

Method

Crumble compressed yeast or empty envelope of dry yeast into large bowl. Add 1/3 cup of the lukewarm water and 1 teaspoon sugar. Stir and let stand 5 minutes.

Add remaining sugar, salt and shortening. Stir until well mixed. Stir in half the flour and beat until smooth.

Sprinkle about ½ cup of remaining flour on kneading board. Knead until smooth and elastic. Place in greased bowl, cover with a towel and let rise over hot water until double in bulk.

Divide into two parts and shape each on floured board, kneading until mixture can be shaped into a loaf. Place in greased bread pan and let rise until double.

Bake in a moderately hot oven (425°F.) until lightly browned (about 45 min.). Lower temperature to 350°F. and continue baking about 30 minutes more.

ROLLED OATS BISCUITS

Yield: 12 biscuits

Ingredients

Rolled Oats, finely ground	2 cups
Salt	1 tsp.
Baking Powder	3 tsp.
Shortening	3 tbsp.
Water	3/8 to 1/2 cup

Method

Mix ground rolled oats thoroughly with salt and baking powder. Cut in shortening until mixture is as fine as coarse cornmeal. Stir in enough water to make a stiff dough. Pat out and cut into rounds.

For a drop biscuit, add more water and drop by table-spoonsful on baking sheet.

Bake in hot oven (450°F.) from 10 to 12 minutes.

SCOTCH FINGERS

Yield: 24 2- by 1-in. sq.

Ingredients

Rolled Oats	1 cup
Salt	¼ tsp.
Baking Powder	1½ tsp.
Sugar	2 tbsp.
Warm Water	2 tbsp.
Molasses	2 tbsp.
Melted Shortening	1 tbsp.

Method

Mix ground oats, salt, baking powder and sugar. Stir in warm water, molasses and melted shortening; mix well.

Flour board with ground rolled oats. Roll out to a very thin sheet and cut into narrow strips.

Bake on a greased pan from 15 to 20 min. in a moderately hot oven (425°F.).

Wheat- and Egg-Free Recipes

ORANGE ICING

Ingredients

Orange Juice	3 tbsp.
Powdered Sugar	1 cup
Egg White, unbeaten	1
Salt	dash
Cream of Tartar	1/8 tsp.
Vanilla	½ tsp.

Method

1. Bring to boiling point only orange juice and powdered sugar.

2. Place egg white, cream of tartar and salt in small bowl of mixer. Add hot syrup and immediately beat all ingredients at top speed until the icing is of desired consistency to spread, about 3 or 4 min. Add vanilla while beating.

BROWN BETTY

Yield: 6 servings

Ingredients

Oatmeal, uncooked	1¼ cups
Brown Sugar	1 cup
Salt	½ tsp.
Cinnamon	¾ tsp.
Butter or Margarine, melted	2½ tbsp.
Lemon Juice	2 tsp.
Apples, diced	2 cups
Milk	1½ cups
Cornflakes, crumbled	½ cup

Method

1. Combine oatmeal, sugar, salt, cinnamon, shortening and lemon juice.

2. In greased 8- by 8- by 2-in. baking dish, arrange alternate layers of apples and oatmeal mixture, beginning with apples and ending with oatmeal mixture.

3. Add milk. Cover with crumbled cornflakes.

4. Bake at 350°F. for about 50 min.

LEMON SHERBET

Yield: 3 servings
Ingredients

Lemon Juice	¼ cup
Sugar	½ cup
Salt	dash
Milk	1 cup
Cream	1/3 cup

Method

1. Combine lemon juice, sugar and salt.
2. Combine milk and cream. Add lemon juice, sugar and salt slowly to milk and cream. Freeze in refrigerator tray.
3. When half frozen, beat until smooth but not melted. Freeze until firm.

MERINGUE COOKIES

Yield: 2 doz.
Ingredients

Rye Wafers (such as Ry-Krisp)	10
OR	
Rice Cereal (rice Chex)	1½ cups
Egg White	1
Brown Sugar	¼ cup
White Sugar	¼ cup
Salt	1/8 tsp.
Vanilla	½ tsp.

Method

1. Roll rye wafers into coarse crumbs. (Leave rice cereal whole.) Set aside.
2. Beat egg white until peaks are formed.
3. Fold in brown sugar a tablespoon at a time.
4. Fold in white sugar, salt and vanilla. Mix until all sugar is combined with egg white.
5. Drop from spoon on greased cookie sheet, spacing 2 in. apart. Bake at 300°F. 12 to 15 minutes, or until outside of cookie is dry and very light brown.
6. Remove from pan at once.

PECAN DROP COOKIES

Yield: 20 cookies
Ingredients

Shortening	¼ cup
Brown Sugar	½ cup
Egg	1
Rye Flour	2 tbsp.
Barley Flour	2 tbsp.
Chopped Pecans	¼ cup
Salt	1/8 tsp.
Maple Flavoring	1/8 tsp.
Soda	1/8 tsp.

Method

1. Cream shortening and sugar. Add egg. Sift dry ingredients together and add to creamed mixture, beating well. Add nuts and flavoring. Drop from teaspoon on greased cookie sheet. Bake at 325°F. for 10 to 12 minutes.

DATE BREAD

Yield: 1 loaf
Ingredients

Cornmeal, uncooked	1 cup
Barley Flour	2 cups
Baking Soda	½ tsp.
Baking Powder	2 tsp.
Salt	1 tsp.
Dates, Raisins, or Prunes, chopped	1 cup
Milk	1¼ cups
Molasses	¼ cup
Shortening, melted	2 tbsp.

Method

1. Sift dry ingredients together. Add fruit. Combine milk, molasses and shortening, and add to the first mixture.

2. Beat well and pour into well greased loaf pan. Let rise for 30 minutes.

3; Bake at 350°F. for about 1 hour and 20 minutes.

APPLE STRUDEL

Yield: 5 servings

Ingredients

Cornflakes or Rice Flakes, slightly crushed	3½ cups
Apples, sliced	2 cups
Granulated or Brown Sugar	½ cup
Cinnamon or Nutmeg	½ tsp.
Butter or Margarine	2 tbsp.

Method

1. Butter baking dish. Arrange crumbs and apples in layers, sprinkle the apples with sugar and spices and dot with butter.

2. Cover casserole dish. Bake at 375°F. for about 40 minutes or until apples are soft.

Note: Sprinkle few drops lemon juice on apples, if not tart.

PINEAPPLE RICE BAVARIAN CREAM

Yield: 5 portions

Ingredients

Plain Gelatin	1½ tsp.
Cold Water	¼ cup
Rice, cooked	½ cup
Sugar	2 tbsp.
Salt	1/8 tsp.
Vanilla	½ tsp.
Pineapple, shredded	½ cup
Whipping Cream	½ cup

Method

1. Soak gelatin in cold water five minutes. Dissolve soaked gelatin over boiling water. Add gelatin to rice, sugar and salt. Mix.

2. Cool mixture. Add pineapple and vanilla. Fold in whipped cream.

3. Pour into individual molds and chill.

SAVORY RICE AND BEEF SUPPER

Yield: 6 cups; 5 servings
Ingredients

Green Pepper, chopped	½ cup
Onion, chopped	½ cup
Butter or Margarine	¼ cup
Ground Beef	1 lb.
Tomatoes, No. 2 can	2¼ cups
Hot Water	1 cup
Minute Rice	1-1/3 cups (5 oz.)
Salt	2 tsp.
Pepper	¼ tsp.

Method

   1. Saute green pepper and onion in fat over medium heat until lightly browned; stir occasionally. Add beef and continue cooking 5 min. longer, stirring occasionally. Add tomatoes, water, rice, salt and pepper; mix just to moisten all rice.

   2. Cover and simmer slowly 15 minutes.

PLAIN CAKE

Yield: 1 layer cake or 6 cupcakes
Ingredients

Shortening	4 tbsp.
Sugar	½ cup
Milk	½ cup + 1 tbsp.
Barley Flour	1 cup
Baking Powder	3 tsp.
Salt	¼ tsp.
Vanilla	½ tsp.

Method

   1. Sift dry ingredients together. Cream shortening, add sugar, mix well.

   2. Add liquid, dry ingredients and vanilla.

   3. Bake in greased pan 9- by 9- by 2-in. or muffin pans at 375°F. for 25-30 minutes.

Variations: Barley, rye, rice or a combination of these flours may be used.

OVEN-FRIED CHICKEN
Yield: 3 to 4 portions
Ingredients

Frying Chicken, 2½ to 3½ lb.	1
Salad Oil	1/4-1/3 cup
Salt and Pepper	
Crushed Cornflakes (4 cups before crushing)	1 cup

Method

1. Cut chicken in serving pieces. Wash and dry well. Brush or dip pieces in oil; drain. Sprinkle each piece with salt and pepper, and roll in crushed cereal flakes.

2. Arrange in greased shallow baking dish leaving space between pieces.

3. Cover tightly, and bake in hot oven, 400°F. for 45-60 minutes, or until chicken is tender. Remove cover during last 20 minutes of baking to brown chicken.

PRUNE WHIP
Yield: 5 servings
Ingredients

Gelatin	1½ tsp.
Cold Water	2 tbsp.
Sugar	¼ cup
Prune Juice, hot	¼ cup
Lemon Juice	2 tbsp.
Whipping Cream	½ cup
Prune Puree	½ cup

Method

1. Soak gelatin in cold water until softened. Dissolve soaked gelatin in hot prune juice to which the sugar has been added.

2. Partly cool gelatin mixture and add lemon juice. Chill until cold and syrupy.

3. Whip mixture until fluffy and thick like whipped cream. Fold in cream, whipped only until thick, and continue beating until mixture is stiff enough to hold its shape.

4. Fold prune puree into gelatin and cream mixture. Turn into molds and chill until firm.

NUTBUTTER COOKIES

Yield: 4 doz.
Ingredients

Rye Wafers (such as Ry-Krisp)	22
Baking Powder	1 tsp.
Shortening	¼ cup
Peanut Butter	½ cup
Sweetened Condensed Milk (not evaporated milk)	1 can
Vanilla	1 tsp.

Method

1. Roll rye wafers into coarse crumbs. Stir in baking powder.

2. Melt shortening. Add peanut butter, milk, and vanilla. Mix until completely blended.

3. Add rye wafer crumb mixture to milk mixture. Stir well.

4. Drop from teaspoon on greased pan about 1½ in. apart. Bake at 350°F. for about 12 minutes. Remove from pan at once.

ORANGE BREAD

Yield: 1 loaf
Ingredients

Peel of 2 oranges	
Sugar	½ cup
Water	½ cup
Barley Flour	2 cups
Sugar	½ cup
Salt	½ tsp.
Baking Powder	3 tsp.
Eggs, beaten	2
Orange Juice	½ cup
Shortening, Melted Orange Mixture	3 tbsp.

Method

1. Cover orange peel with water; boil 10 minutes. Drain. Add more water; boil 10 minutes or until tender. Chop peel in food chopper. Add ½ cup water and sugar, cook orange mixture until thick. Sift dry ingredients together.

2. Add beaten eggs, orange juice, melted shortening and orange mixture. Combine well.

3. Pour into well greased bread pan. Bake at 350°F. for 60-70 minutes.

Wheat- and Milk- Free Recipes

BACON-BARLEY PUFFS

Yield: 6 servings
Ingredients

Bacon	6 slices
Pearl Barley, cooked	2 cups
Egg, beaten	1
Salt	¼ tsp.
Pepper	¼ tsp.
Minced Parsley	1 tbsp.

Method

1. Line muffin pans with strips of bacon.
2. Combine remaining ingredients; fill greased muffin pans 2/3 full.
3. Bake at 400°F. for about 30 minutes.

CRUMB CRUST

Yield: 1 8- or 9-in. pie shell
Ingredients

Rice Cereal (such as Rice Chex)	4½ cups
Sugar	¼ cup
Butter or Margarine	1/3 cup

Method

1. Roll rice cereal into fine crumbs or put through finest blade of food grinder.
2. Combine crumbs and sugar. Mix thoroughly.
3. Melt fat. Pour over crumb mixture. Mix until all crumbs are coated with fat. Pack evenly and firmly onto bottom and sides of greased pie pan.
4. Bake at 300°F. about 10 minutes. Cool before filling. OR, if you prefer, instead of baking crust, **refrigerate 1** hour before filling.

CORN AND OAT MUFFINS

Yield: 8 muffins
Ingredients

Cornmeal	¾ cup
Salt	1 tsp.
Baking Powder	3 tsp.
Sugar	3 tbsp.
Rolled Oats, finely ground	1 cup
Water	¾ cup
Melted Shortening	1 tbsp.
Egg, well beaten	1

Method

Mix and sift cornmeal, salt, baking powder and sugar. Add ground oats and mix well. Add water and melted shortening to beaten egg and stir into flour mixture.

Bake in small muffin pan in moderately hot oven (400° F.) about 25 minutes.

SCOTTISH FANCIES

Yield: 1 doz.
Ingredients

Rolled Oats	1 cup
Salt	½ tsp.
Baking Powder	1½ tsp.
Brown Sugar	½ cup
Egg, well beaten	1
Melted Shortening	1 tbsp.

Method

Mix ground rolled oats, salt, baking powder and sugar. Stir in egg and melted shortening; mix well. Drop from teaspoon on well greased baking sheet. Bake in a slow oven (325°F.) until delicately brown. Remove cakes from pan while hot.

Milk- and Egg-Free Recipes

WHITE BREAD

Yield: 2 loaves

Ingredients

Lukewarm Potato Water (water in which potatoes have been cooked)	2 cups
Shortening	2 tbsp.
Sugar	2 tbsp.
Salt	2 tsp.
Yeast	1 cake
Lukewarm Water	2 tbsp.
White Flour	Approx. 6 cups

Method

1. Combine lukewarm potato water, shortening, sugar and salt. Soften yeast in 2 tbsp. water; add to above mixture.

2. Add about 5 or 6 cups white flour, enough to make a stiff dough. Mix thoroughly.

3. Turn on floured board and knead about 10 minutes, until smooth and satiny.

4. Place dough in warm greased bowl, brush surface lightly with melted shortening, cover and let rise 2 hours.

5. Punch dough down thoroughly in bowl, cover and let rise about ½ hour, or until doubled in bulk.

6. Turn out on floured board. Divide in 2 equal parts.

7. Place in 2 greased loaf pans, brush top with melted shortening, cover and let rich dough rise 1 hour.

8. Bake in hot oven (400°F.) for 40-45 minutes.

CHICKEN AND RICE SUPPER

Yield: 6 servings
Ingredients

Minute Rice	2/3 cup
Salt	¼ tsp.
Boiling Water	¾ cup
Chicken Fat	¼ cup
Flour	¼ cup
Salt	1½ tsp.
Pepper	1/8 tsp.
Chicken Broth	2 cups
Cooked Chicken, diced	1/4-1/3 cup
Onion, chopped	2 cups
Lemon Juice	1 tsp.
Parsley, chopped	2 tbsp.

Method

1. Add rice and ¼ tsp. salt to boiling water. Mix only to moisten rice. Cover and remove from heat. Let stand about 15 minutes.

2. Melt chicken fat. Add flour, salt and pepper. Stir until blended.

3. Add chicken broth gradually, stirring constantly.

4. Cook and stir over medium heat til smooth, thick.

5. Add rice, chicken, onion, lemon juice and parsley to sauce, mixing carefully.

6. Heat thoroughly.

BATTER BREAD

Yield: 16 servings
Ingredients

Cornmeal, uncooked	2 cups
Baking Powder	5 tsp.
Salt	1½ tsp.
Rice, cooked	1 cup
Eggs, beaten	2
Shortening, melted	4 tbsp.
Milk	2¼ cups

Method

1. Sift together cornmeal, baking powder and salt. Mix with rice.

2. Combine eggs, shortening and milk. Add this to first mixture. Beat until smooth.

3. Turn mixture into two well-greased 8-in. square pans. Bake at 425°F. 30 minutes.

Wheat-Free Recipes

PLAIN BUTTER CAKE

Yield: 6 portions

Ingredients

Potato Flour	½ cup
Barley Flour	½ cup
Rye Flour	½ cup
Baking Powder	1 tsp.
Butter or Margarine	½ cup
Salt	dash
Sugar, granulated	1 cup
Egg Yolks, beaten	2
Milk	6 tbsp.
Flavoring	1 tsp.
Egg Whites, beaten	2

Method

1. Sift flour with baking powder and salt. Cream shortening and sugar.

2. Add beaten egg yolks and mix until creamy.

3. Alternately add milk and flour mixture. Beat well. Add flavoring.

4. Fold in stiffly beaten egg whites.

5. Pour into 8-in. square greased pan.

6. Bake in oven 350°F. for 25 to 30 minutes.

Variations

1. Cut in half and ice as 2-layer cake.

2. Add 1 square melted chocolate.

3. Add 1 tsp. mixed spices.

4. Add ¼ cup chopped nuts to batter or put on top of cake and omit icing.

REFRIGERATOR PINEAPPLE PIE

Yield: 1 pie
Ingredients

Soft Butter or Margarine	2 tbsp.
Shredded Coconut	1½ cups
Unflavored Gelatin	1 tbsp.
Cold Water	¼ cup
Eggs, separated	3
Crushed Pineapple, undrained	1 cup
Granulated Sugar	¼ cup
Lemon Rind, grated	1 tsp.
Lemon Juice	3 tbsp.
Salt	¼ tsp.
Sugar	6 tbsp.

Method

1. Spread fat evenly on bottom and sides of 9-in. pie pan. Add coconut and spread evenly over fat, pressing down firmly to form pie shell. Bake at 360°F. for 12-15 minutes or until golden brown. Cool.

2. In the meantime, mix gelatin and ¼ cup cold water. In double boiler, mix egg yolks with pineapple, sugar, lemon rind, juice and gelatin mixture.

3. Cook, stirring frequently, for 10-15 minutes or until smooth and thickened.

4. Remove from heat and cool slightly. Beat egg whites and salt until stiff, gradually adding 6 tbsp. sugar.

5. Fold in pineapple mixture. Put in coconut crust. Refrigerate.

SOUR CREAM COOKIES

Yield: 3 doz.
Ingredients

Rye Flour	2/3 cup
Rice Flour	½ cup
Cornstarch	½ cup
Baking Powder	1 tsp.
Salt	¼ tsp.
Butter or Margarine	1/3 cup
Sugar	2/3 cup
Egg, well beaten	1
Thick Sour Cream	1/3 cup
Sugar	1 tbsp.
Cinnamon	¼ tsp.

Method

1. Sift flour, cornstarch, baking powder and salt together. Cream fat, sugar together til light and fluffy. Add beaten egg.

2. Add flour mixture alternately with cream, beginning and ending with flour mixture. Beat until smooth after each addition. Drop by spoon on greased baking sheet.

3. Flatten slightly with bottom of glass which has been dipped in sugar.

4. Mix tablespoon of sugar with cinnamon and sprinkle small amount on top of each cookie. Bake at 357°F. for 15 minutes or until brown.

CORN SOUFFLE

Yield: 3 servings
Ingredients

Butter or Margarine	1 tbsp.
Rice Flour	1 tsp.
Cream	¼ cup
Egg yolk, beaten thick	1
Egg White, beaten stiff	1
Whole Kernel Corn	1/3 cup
Salt and Pepper	dash

Method

1. Melt shortening, add rice flour. Add cream and heat until thickened.

2. Add mixture slowly to egg yolk. Carefully fold in stiffly beaten egg white.

3. Add corn, salt and pepper. Put in ungreased cassero.

4. Bake at 350°F. for 15 minutes and then at 400°F. fo about 15 minutes.

DOUGHNUTS

Yield: 12 doughnuts
Ingredients

Eggs, beaten	2
Vanilla	1 tsp.
Sugar	½ cup
Milk	½ cup
Melted Shortening	1½ tbsp.
Rye Flour	2 cups
Baking Powder	3 tsp.
Salt	½ tsp.

Method

1. Beat eggs and vanilla together. Slowly add sugar, beating constantly.

2. Stir in milk and melted shortening. Add sifted dry ingredients. Mix.

3. Roll on a well-floured board to ½-in. thickness. Shape with cutter and deep fry at 380°F. until browned. Drain on unglazed paper.

CREAM PUFFS

Yield: 12
Ingredients

Butter	½ cup
Water	1 cup
Salt	½ tsp.
Wheat Flour*	1 cup
Eggs	4

Method

1. Heat fat, water and salt to boiling point. Add flour all at once to hot liquid, stirring constantly until mixture leaves sides of pan and clings to spoon.

2. Remove from heat. Cool slightly. Add unbeaten eggs one at a time. Beat to a smooth paste after each addition. Drop by spoon onto slightly greased cookie sheet 1½ in. apart. Bake at 410°F. for 10 min., then reduce heat gradually.

*If substitution for wheat flour is desired, see combinations of flours to be used in place of 1 cup wheat flour p. 328. For all flours, except when all rice flour is used, it is best to bake cream puffs at 410°F. for 10 minutes, 350°F. for next 15 or 20 minutes, and finish baking at 300°F. They should generally bake for an hour or slightly less.

RICE AND SALMON PATTIES
Yield: 4 servings
Ingredients

Minute Rice	2/3 cup
Boiling Water	¾ cup
Salmon, drained and flaked (1 lb. can)	2 cups
Mayonnaise	½ cup
Lemon Juice	1 tbsp.
Minced Onion	1 tsp.
Salt	¾ tsp.
Pepper	¼ tsp.
Cornflakes, finely crushed	½ cup

Method

1. Add rice to boiling water in saucepan. Mix just to moisten all rice. Cover and remove from heat. Let stand about 15 minutes.

2. To rice, add salmon, mayonnaise, lemon juice, salt and pepper. Mix well. Let stand 5 minutes. Shape into 8 patties and roll in crushed cereal. Store in refrigerator several hours. Place on greased baking sheet. Bake in hot oven (450° F.) for 15 minutes or until browned. Serve with chili sauce.

VIRGINIA SPOON BREAD
Yield: 6 servings
Ingredients

Milk	3 cups
Cornmeal	½ cup
Eggs, beaten	3
Butter or Margarine	2 tbsp.
Rice, cooked	1 cup
Salt	1¾ tsp.

Method

1. Scald 2½ cups milk, slowly stir in cornmeal mixed with ½ cup cold milk. Cook until moderately thick (about 5 minutes).

2. Remove from heat and add small amount to beaten eggs.

3. Combine eggs, fat, rice and salt with the rest of hot mixture.

4. Turn mixture into a greased baking dish and bake at 325°F. or at 400°F. in a pan of hot water, 45 min. to 1 hour.

WELSH RAREBIT

Yield: 1 serving
Ingredients

Butter or Margarine	1 tbsp.
Rice Flour	2 tsp.
Salt	1/8 tsp.
Milk	¼ cup
Cream	¼ cup
American Cheese, grated	2 tbsp.
Egg, well beaten	1
Paprika (if allowed)	1/8 tsp.

Method

1. Melt shortening, add flour and salt.
2. Slowly add milk and cream; stir until thickened.
3. Add grated cheese. Cook over boiling water until cheese is melted.
4. Stir small amount of hot mixture into beaten egg, then pour back into remaining mixture and cook until smooth.
5. Add paprika, if desired.
6. Serve on toasted rye wafers (such as Ry-Krisp).

OATMEAL COOKIES

Yield: 3 doz. 3-in. cookies
Ingredients

Rye Flour	1 cup
Baking Powder	½ tsp
Salt	½ tsp.
Cinnamon	¼ tsp.
Shortening	½ cup
Cloves	¼ tsp.
Brown Sugar, firmly packed	¾ cup
Egg, well beaten	1
Rolled Oats	¾ cup
Nut meats, chopped	½ cup
Seeded Raisins	½ cup
Sour Milk or Buttermilk	2 tbsp.

Method

Mix flour, soda, salt and spices. Cream shortening, add sugar slowly and cream until fluffy. Stir in well beaten egg, add rolled oats, nutmeats and raisins; mix well. Stir in dry ingredients alternately with sour milk or buttermilk. Drop by teaspoonfuls on greased baking sheet and let stand a few minutes. Flatten dough by stamping with a glass, covered with a damp cloth.

Bake in slow oven (325°F.) from 10 to 15 minutes.

Milk-Free Recipes

BANANA BREAD

Yield: 2 small loaves

Ingredients

Shortening	½ cup
Sugar	1 cup
Eggs	2
Cold Water	½ cup
Bananas	3
Flour	2½ cups
Baking Powder	1 tsp.
Soda	1 tsp.
Salt	¼ tsp.

Method

1. Cream shortening and sugar. Add eggs and cold water. Mix. Add mashed bananas.

2. Add sifted dry ingredients. Mix well.

3. Pour into 2 small greased loaf pans. Bake for about 60 minutes at 350°F.

SPONGE CAKE

Yield: 1 loaf cake

Ingredients

Cake Flour	1 cup
Salt	¼ tsp.
Egg Yolks, beaten	4
Sugar	1 cup
Lemon Juice	4 tsp.
Egg Whites, beaten	4

Method

1. Sift dry ingredients. Beat egg yolks until thick and lemon-colored. Add sugar gradually, beating constantly. Add lemon juice and mix.

2. Fold in flour, alternately with stiffly beaten egg whites. Do not beat.

3. Bake at once in a floured, ungreased loaf pan, about 8- by 4- by 3-in. deep.

4. Bake at 325°F. for 40-60 minutes.

Egg-Free Recipes

FUDGE CAKE

Yield: 8 servings
Ingredients

Brown Sugar	1 cup
Shortening	2 tbsp.
Flour	1½ cups
Soda	1 tsp.
Baking Powder	1 tsp.
Cocoa	2 tbsp.
Sour Milk	1 cup

Method

1. Cream shortening and sugar. Sift dry ingredients together. Add milk and flour mixture alternately.

2. Pour into greased and floured pans. Bake at 350°F. for 25-30 minutes.

3. Use any desired icing.

GRAHAM-CRACKER BROWNIES

Yield: 16 2-in. squares
Ingredients

Graham Crackers	24
Chocolate Bits	1 6-oz.pkg.
Sweetened Condensed Milk	1 15-oz.can

Method

1. Make graham cracker crumbs by crushing crackers in plastic bag, or between two sheets of wax paper, with rolling pin. Place in bowl.

2. Add chocolate bits and condensed milk. Mix.

3. Place in greased pan 8- by 8- by 1½-in., spreading batter into corners.

4. Bake in moderate oven, 425°F. for 20 to 25 min.

5. Cut into 2-in. squares and remove from pan while still warm.

Note: For chewy brownie, avoid overbaking.

EGGLESS MAYONNAISE

Yield: 1½ cups
Ingredients

Salt	1 tsp.
Paprika	½ tsp.
Sugar	1 tsp.
Dry Mustard	1-1/8 tsp.
Evaporated Milk, undiluted	1¼ cup
Salad Oil	1 cup
Lemon Juice	1 tbsp.
Vinegar	1 tbsp.

Method

1. Ingredients should be cold. While mixing, set the bowl in a pan of ice water.

2. Mix salt, paprika, sugar and dry mustard. Add evaporated milk.

3. Add 1/3 cup of the salad oil, a teaspoon at a time. Beat well after each addition.

4. Combine lemon juice and vinegar. Add a small amount at a time, alternating with remaining salad oil. Beat well after each addition.

5. Store in covered jar in refrigerator.

DATE PUDDING

Yield: 8 servings
Ingredients

Seeded Dates, cut fine	1 lb.
Soda	1 tsp.
Boiling Water	1 cup
Sugar	1 cup
Butter or Margarine	1 tbsp.
Flour	1½ cups
Vanilla	1 tsp.

Method

1. Mix dates, soda and boiling water. Stir well and cool.

2. Mix sugar, shortening and flour. Stir into date mixture. Add vanilla.

3. Pour into well greased baking dish. Bake about 45 minutes at 375°F.

4. Serve with a topping.

Note: This recipe can be doubled and served as a cake.

Bibliography

Barber, Edith M., Cooper, Lenna F., and Mitchell, Helen S. *Nutrition in Health and Disease,* Philadelphia: J. B. Lippincott Co., 1947.

Bryson, John. *Basic Techniques in Food Service Management.* Menomonie, Wisconsin: Stout State University.

Kotschevar, Lendal H. *Foodservice for the Extended Care Facility.* Boston: Cahners Publishing Co., 1973.

Kotschevar, Lendal H. *Quantity Food Production.* Berkeley, California: McCutcheon Publishing Co., 1964.

Kotschevar, Lendal H. *Quantity Food Purchasing.* New York: John Wiley and Sons, Inc., 1961.

New York State. Cooperative Extension Service Bulletins. Highlights on Food Service Management:
Sept. 1967–*Keeping Records*
Aug. 1970–*Feeding Aged Persons in an Institution*
Aug. 1971–*Planning Food Budget Expenditures*
Aug. 1971–*Keeping Records.*

U.S. Department of Agriculture. Home Garden Bulletins. Washington, D. C.: Government Printing Office.
Consumer and Marketing Service.
No. 144–*How to Buy Eggs by U.S.D.A. Grades and Classes Jan., 1968.*
No. 148–*Know Your Butter Grades. March, 1968.*
No. 166–*Meat for Your Freezer. December, 1969.*
No. 167–*Canned and Frozen Vegetables. April, 1969.*

West, Bessie B., Wood, LaVelle and Harger, Virginia. *Food Service in Institutions,* New York: John Wiley and Sons, 1966.

Index